SAUNDERS MATHEMATICS BOOKS

Consulting Editor

BERNARD R. GELBAUM, University of California

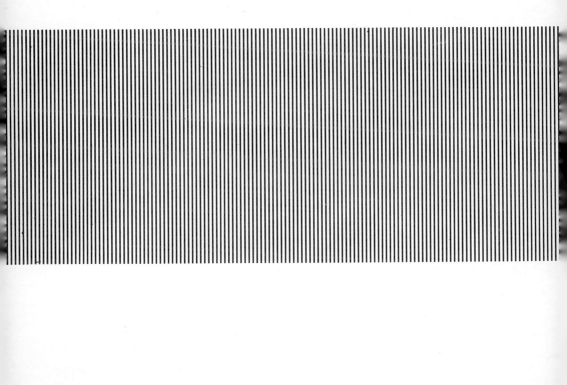

S. I. ZUKHOVITSKIY and L. I. AVDEYEVA
KIEV INSTITUTE

Translated by Scripta Technica, Inc.
Edited by Bernard R. Gelbaum

LINEAR AND CONVEX PROGRAMMING

W. B. SAUNDERS COMPANY · Philadelphia and London 1966

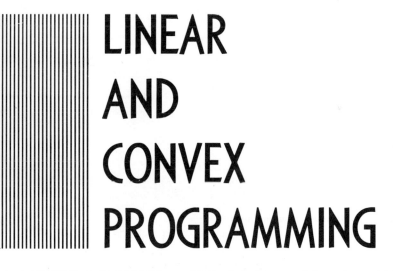

W. B. Saunders Company: West Washington Square
Philadelphia, Pa. 19105

12 Dyott Street
London, W.C.1

Linear and Convex Programming

Originally published in Moscow, 1964, by Izdatel'stvo NAUKA as LINEYNOYE I VYPUKLOYE PROGRAMMIROVANIYE SPRAVOCHNOYE RUKOVODSTVO

 Made in the United States of America. Press of W. B. Saunders Company. Library of Congress catalog card number 66-18824.

Foreword

This book provides a happy combination of mathematical rigor, patient exposition and a wide variety of illustrative material. The thrust of the book is to teach the most efficient and easily understood procedures in the field of linear and convex programming, and then to show by numerous and diverse examples how these procedures are applied in the solution of important problems. The writing is clear, patient, and to the point. A glance at the Table of Contents shows that standard topics are thoroughly covered and that there are, as well, extensive treatments of Chebyshev approximations and Convex (nonlinear) programming.

BERNARD R. GELBAUM

Contents

1

Jordan Elimination

1. ORDINARY JORDAN ELIMINATION

1. Definition

Consider a system

$$y_i = a_{i1}x_1 + a_{i2}x_2 + \dots + a_{in}x_n \qquad (i = 1, \dots, m) \tag{1.1}$$

of m linear forms in n unknowns x_1 $x_2, \dots, x_n$. This system can be written in the form of a table

$$\begin{array}{r|ccccc|}
 & x_1 & \dots & x_s & \dots & x_n \\
\hline
y_1 = & a_{11} & \dots & a_{1s} & \dots & a_{1n} \\
\dots & \dots & \dots & \dots & \dots & \dots \\
y_r = & a_{r1} & \dots & \boxed{a_{rs}} & \dots & a_{rn} \\
\dots & \dots & \dots & \dots & \dots & \dots \\
y_m = & a_{m1} & \dots & a_{ms} & \dots & a_{mn} \\
\hline
\end{array} . \tag{1.2}$$

Following E. Stiefel [35], we shall use the expression *ordinary Jordan elimination over Table (1.2) with resolvent element $a_{rs} \neq 0$, resolvent row r, and resolvent column s* to mean the operation of switching the roles of the dependent variable y_r and the independent variable x_s, i.e., the operation of solving the equation

$$y_r = a_{r1}x_1 + a_{r2}x_2 + \dots + a_{rs}x_s + \dots + a_{rn}x_n$$

for x_s, substituting the solution into all the remaining equations of system (1.1), and writing the system in the form of a new table analogous to (1.2). It is easy to see that the new table is of the form

$$\begin{array}{r|cccccc|l}
 & x_1 & x_2 & \dots & y_r & \dots & x_n & \\
\hline
y_1 = & b_{11} & b_{12} & \dots & a_{1s} & \dots & b_{1n} & \\
y_2 = & b_{21} & b_{22} & \dots & a_{2s} & \dots & b_{2n} & \\
\dots & \dots & \dots & \dots & \dots & \dots & \dots & : a_{rs}, \\
x_s = & -a_{r1} & -a_{r2} & \dots & \boxed{1} & \dots & -a_{rn} & \\
\dots & \dots & \dots & \dots & \dots & \dots & \dots & \\
y_m = & b_{m1} & b_{m2} & \dots & a_{ms} & \dots & b_{mn} & \\
\hline
\end{array} \tag{1.3}$$

where $b_{ij}=a_{ij}a_{rs}-a_{is}a_{rj}$ $(i \neq r,\ j \neq s)$ and all the entries in the table must be divided by a_{rs}.

Thus, ordinary Jordan elimination* with resolvent element a_{rs} transforms Table (1.2) into the new Table (1.3) by way of the following five rules:

1) the resolvent element is replaced by one;

2) the remaining columns in the resolvent column (the sth column) remain unchanged;

3) the remaining elements in the resolvent row (the rth row) change sign;

4) the "ordinary" elements b_{ij} $(i \neq r,\ j \neq s)$ (i.e., the elements that do not belong to either the resolvent row or column) are given by the formula

$$b_{ij}=a_{ij}a_{rs}-a_{is}a_{rj};$$

5) all the entries in the new table are divided by the resolvent element a_{rs} [which, in (1.3), is shown symbolically by division of the entire table by a_{rs}].

Example. For the table

	x_1	x_2	x_3
$y_1=$	1	−2	3
$y_2=$	−1	1	$\boxed{2}$
$y_3=$	2	−1	−1

one Jordan elimination with the second row and third column being the resolvents (i.e., having the roles of y_2 and x_3 exchanged) leads to the table

	x_1	x_2	y_2	
$y_1=$	5	−7	3	
$x_3=$	1	−1	1	:2
$y_3=$	3	−1	−1	

and, finally, to the table

	x_1	x_2	y_2
$y_1=$	$\frac{5}{2}$	$-\frac{7}{2}$	$\frac{3}{2}$
$x_3=$	$\frac{1}{2}$	$-\frac{1}{2}$	$\frac{1}{2}$
$y_3=$	$\frac{3}{2}$	$-\frac{1}{2}$	$-\frac{1}{2}$

.

*Here and henceforth we shall omit the word "ordinary."

2. Geometric Interpretation

We shall treat each set of values $x_1,\ldots,x_n$ as the coordinates of a point $x(x_1, \ldots, x_n)$ in Euclidean n-dimensional space R_n, while we shall treat the equations

$$y_i = a_{i1}x_1 + a_{i2}x_2 + \ldots + a_{in}x_n = 0 \qquad (i = 1, \ldots, m)$$

as the equations of [$(n-1)$-dimensional] planes passing through the coordinate origin. For each point $x'(x_1',\ldots,x_n')$ the quantity $y_i(x') = a_{i1}x_1' + \ldots + a_{in}x_n'$ denotes the signed weighted distance from the point x' to the plane $y_i = 0$, where the weighted distance is the distance multiplied by the quantity (weight)

$$\sqrt{\sum_{j=1}^{n} a_{ij}^2}.$$

We shall call $y_i(x')$ the *deviation* of the point x' from the plane (or equation) $y_i = 0$.

In the rectangular system defined by n orthogonal coordinate planes $x_1 = 0,\ldots,x_n = 0$, each point $x(x_1,\ldots,x_n)$ is given by its n deviations from all coordinate planes, i.e., by numbers $x_1,\ldots,x_n$ equal to the signed distances to the corresponding coordinate planes (with weights equal to one).

One Jordan elimination with resolvant element a_{rs} indicates replacement of the coordinate plane $x_s = 0$ by a new plane $y_r = 0$ that is generally not orthogonal to the remaining coordinate planes, so that in the set of coordinates (deviations) of each point in the space the deviation from the old coordinate plane $x_s = 0$ is replaced by the deviation from the new coordinate plane $y_r = 0$.

Thus, Jordan elimination makes it possible to pass from an arbitrary Cartesian system of coordinate planes to a new system in which the coordinates are the deviations from a system of planes that is of more interest for one problem or another, and in the new table of deviations all of the remaining planes of system (1.1) are expressed in terms of its deviations from the fundamental planes located at the top of the table.

This explains the important role played by Jordan elimination in all problems associated with deviations of points from planes, a class of problems including problems on Chebyshev approximation of linear systems of equations for inequalities and linear programming problems.

2. APPLICATION OF JORDAN ELIMINATION TO LINEAR ALGEBRA

1. Steinitz's Theorem

If all the linear forms of system (1.1) are linearly independent (so that $m \leqslant n$), then exactly m appropriately chosen Jordan *eliminations are required to convert all m dependent variables* $y_1, \ldots, y_m$ *into independent variables* (i.e., they can all be carried to the top of the table).

Indeed, if it were impossible to place some of the dependent variables at the top of the table, the rows corresponding to these variables would contain zeros under the independent variables x_i at the top of the table, i.e., the table would, for example, be of the form

$$\begin{array}{r|lll|}
 & y_1 \quad \ldots \; y_k & & x_{k+1} \; \ldots \; x_n \\
\hline
x_1 = & c_{11} \quad \ldots \; c_{1k} & & c_{1,k+1} \ldots c_{1n} \\
\ldots & \ldots\ldots\ldots & & \ldots\ldots\ldots \\
x_k = & c_{k1} \quad \ldots \; c_{kk} & & c_{k,k+1} \ldots c_{kn} \\
y_{k+1} = & c_{k+1,1} \ldots c_{k+1,k} & & 0 \quad \ldots 0 \\
\ldots & \ldots\ldots\ldots & & \ldots\ldots\ldots \\
y_m = & c_{m1} \quad \ldots \; c_{mk} & & 0 \quad \ldots 0 \\
\hline
\end{array}\;.$$

But then all the remaining dependent variables $y_{k+1}, \ldots, y_m$ would clearly be linear combinations of the variables $y_1, \ldots, y_k$ already carried to the top of the table, which would contradict the assumption that all the $y_1, \ldots, y_m$ are linearly independent.

2. Matrix Inversion

In system (1.1) let $m = n$ and assume that the matrix $A = \|a_{ij}\|$ of this system does not degenerate* in Table (1.2), so that all of the linear forms of system (1.1) are linearly independent. We execute n Jordan eliminations over Table (1.2) to convert all the dependent variables $y_1, \ldots, y_n$ into independent variables. After appropriate permutations, the final table will be of the form

$$\begin{array}{r|llll|}
 & y_1 & y_2 & \ldots & y_n \\
\hline
x_1 = & c_{11} & c_{12} & \ldots & c_{1n} \\
x_2 = & c_{21} & c_{22} & \ldots & c_{2n} \\
\ldots & \ldots & \ldots & \ldots & \ldots \\
x_n = & c_{n1} & c_{n2} & \ldots & c_{nn} \\
\hline
\end{array}\;,$$

and the matrix of this table, which we denote by A^{-1}, is the inverse of the matrix A.

Example. Assume that we are given the nondegenerate matrix

$$A = \begin{pmatrix} 1 & -2 & 3 \\ -1 & 1 & 2 \\ 2 & -1 & -1 \end{pmatrix}.$$

Consider the table

*That is, the determinant $\begin{vmatrix} a_{11} & \ldots & a_{1n} \\ \cdot & \cdot\;\cdot & \cdot \\ a_{n1} & \ldots & a_{nn} \end{vmatrix}$ is nonzero.

$$\begin{array}{r|ccc|l} & x_1 & x_2 & x_3 & \\ \hline y_1 = & \boxed{1} & -2 & 3 & \\ y_2 = & -1 & 1 & 2 & . \\ y_3 = & 2 & -1 & -1 & \\ \hline \end{array}$$

One Jordan elimination over the first row and column yields the table

$$\begin{array}{r|ccc|l} & y_1 & x_2 & x_3 & \\ \hline x_1 = & 1 & 2 & -3 & \\ y_2 = & -1 & \boxed{-1} & 5 & :1. \\ y_3 = & 2 & 3 & -7 & \\ \hline \end{array}$$

We now execute a Jordan elimination over the resolvent element —1 indicated by the box. This yields

$$\begin{array}{r|ccc|l} & y_1 & y_2 & x_3 & \\ \hline x_1 = & 1 & 2 & -7 & \\ x_2 = & 1 & 1 & -5 & :(-1), \\ y_3 = & 1 & 3 & -8 & \\ \hline \end{array}$$

and after division by —1, we find that

$$\begin{array}{r|ccc|l} & y_1 & y_2 & x_3 & \\ \hline x_1 = & -1 & -2 & 7 & \\ x_2 = & -1 & -1 & 5 & . \\ y_3 = & -1 & -3 & \boxed{8} & \\ \hline \end{array}$$

Finally, after exchanging x_3 and y_3 we obtain the table

$$\begin{array}{r|ccc|l} & y_1 & y_2 & y_3 & \\ \hline x_1 = & -1 & 5 & 7 & \\ x_2 = & -3 & 7 & 5 & :8 \\ x_3 = & 1 & 3 & 1 & \\ \hline \end{array}$$

and

$$\begin{array}{r|ccc|l} & y_1 & y_2 & y_3 & \\ \hline x_1 = & -\frac{1}{8} & \frac{5}{8} & \frac{7}{8} & \\ x_2 = & -\frac{3}{8} & \frac{7}{8} & \frac{5}{8} & . \\ x_3 = & \frac{1}{8} & \frac{3}{8} & \frac{1}{8} & \\ \hline \end{array}$$

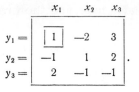

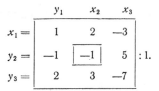

The computation concludes here and the inverse matrix is

$$A^{-1} = \begin{pmatrix} -\frac{1}{8} & \frac{5}{8} & \frac{7}{8} \\ -\frac{3}{8} & \frac{7}{8} & \frac{5}{8} \\ \frac{1}{8} & \frac{3}{8} & \frac{1}{8} \end{pmatrix}.$$

Usually, the final matrix requires rearrangement of some of the rows (columns) when some of the resolvent elements are not diagonal entries.

3. Computation of the Rank of a Matrix

It is desirable to use Jordan elimination to compute the rank of a rectangular matrix

$$A = \begin{pmatrix} a_{11} & a_{12} \dots a_{1n} \\ a_{21} & a_{22} \dots a_{2n} \\ \dots & \dots \\ a_{m1} & a_{m2} \dots a_{mn} \end{pmatrix}.$$

To do so, it is sufficient to consider the table

	$x_1 \dots x_n$
$y_1 =$	$a_{11} \dots a_{1n}$
$\dots$	$\dots\dots$
$y_m =$	$a_{m1} \dots a_{mn}$

and to use successive Jordan eliminations to carry dependent variables to the top of the table until the process cannot be continued, i.e., until a table of the following type is obtained:

	y_1	$\dots y_k$	x_{k+1}	$\dots x_n$
$x_1 =$	b_{11}	$\dots b_{1k}$	$b_{1,k+1}$	$\dots b_{1n}$
$\dots$	$\dots$	$\dots$	$\dots$	$\dots$
$x_k =$	b_{k1}	$\dots b_{kk}$	$b_{k,k+1}$	$\dots b_{kn}$
$y_{k+1} =$	$b_{k+1,1}$	$\dots b_{k+1,k}$	0	$\dots 0$
$\dots$	$\dots$	$\dots$	$\dots$	$\dots$
$y_m =$	b_{m1}	$\dots b_{mk}$	0	$\dots 0$

It is clear that the rank of the matrix A, as the maximum number of lineraly dependent rows, is equal to the number of y_j carried to the top of the table. Moreover, the table contains the coefficients of the linear relationship between the y_j remaining and the y_j carried to the top of the table.

Example. We shall determine the rank of the matrix

$$A = \begin{pmatrix} 2 & -1 & 3 & 4 \\ 1 & 0 & 2 & -3 \\ 5 & -2 & 8 & 5 \end{pmatrix}.$$

We have

	x_1	x_2	x_3	x_4
$y_1 =$	2	−1	3	4
$y_2 =$	**1**	0	2	−3
$y_3 =$	5	−2	8	5

After two Jordan eliminations—the first over the second row and first column, the second over the first row and second column—we obtain the table

	y_2	y_1	x_3	x_4
$x_2 =$	2	−1	1	10
$x_1 =$	1	0	−2	3
$y_3 =$	1	2	0	0

It is clearly impossible to carry y_3 to the top of the table. The maximum number of linearly independent rows is two, so the rank of the matrix A is two.

It is clear from the table that y_3 is a linear combination of y_2 and y_1, and that the coefficients of this combination are 1 and 2:

$$y_3 = y_2 + 2y_1.$$

4. Systems of n Linear Equations in n Unknowns

Various forms of Jordan eliminations exist for solution of systems of n linear equations in n unknowns

$$a_{i1}x_1 + a_{i2}x_2 + \ldots + a_{in}x_n = a_i \qquad (i = 1, \ldots, n), \tag{1.4}$$

where the rank of the matrix $\|a_{ij}\|$ is n.

1) *First method.* We write system (1.4) in the form

	x_1	x_2	$\ldots$	x_n
$a_1 =$	a_{11}	a_{12}	$\ldots$	a_{1n}
$\ldots$	$\ldots$	$\ldots$	$\ldots$	$\ldots$
$a_n =$	a_{n1}	a_{n2}	$\ldots$	a_{nn}

After n Jordan eliminations and appropriate rearrangement of rows and columns, we obtain

	a_1 a_2 ... a_n
$x_1 =$	
...	A^{-1}
$x_n =$	

.

2) *Second method.* We write system (1.4) in the form

	x_1	x_2 ... x_n	1
$0=$	a_{11}	a_{12} ... a_{1n}	$-a_1$
...	...	...	...
$0=$	a_{n1}	a_{n2} ... a_{nn}	$-a_n$

.

After n Jordan eliminations with resolvent columns *different from the column of slack terms*, and elimination of the columns (i.e., resolvent columns) of coefficients under zeros carried to the top of the table, we obtain a final solution in the form

	1
$x_1 =$	b_1
...	...
$x_n =$	b_n

.

Example. Consider the system

$$
\begin{aligned}
2x_1+2x_2-\ x_3+\ x_4-\ 4&=0,\\
4x_1+3x_2-\ x_3+2x_4-\ 6&=0,\\
8x_1+5x_2-3x_3+4x_4-12&=0,\\
3x_1+3x_2-2x_3+2x_4-\ 6&=0.
\end{aligned}
$$

We write it in the form

	x_1	x_2	x_3	x_4	1
$0=$	2	2	-1	$\boxed{1}$	-4
$0=$	4	3	-1	2	-6
$0=$	8	5	-3	4	-12
$0=$	3	3	-2	2	-6

.

One Jordan elimination over $a_{14} = 1$ and elimination of the resolvent (4-th) column yields the table

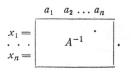

	x_1	x_2	x_3	1
$x_4 =$	−2	−2	1	4
$0 =$	0	−1	1	2
$0 =$	0	−3	1	4
$0 =$	−1	−1	0	2

.

We now execute a Jordan elimination over the second row and third column. After elimination of the resolvent column, we find that

	x_1	x_2	1
$x_4 =$	−2	−1	2
$x_3 =$	0	1	−2
$0 =$	0	−2	2
$0 =$	−1	−1	2

.

The third step is over the fourth row and second column, which yields

	x_1	1
$x_4 =$	−1	0
$x_3 =$	−1	0
$0 =$	2	−2
$x_2 =$	−1	2

.

After the fourth step, we find that

	1
$x_4 =$	−1
$x_3 =$	−1
$x_1 =$	1
$x_2 =$	1

.

3) *Gaussian elimination.* Gaussian elimination differs from Jordan elimination only in the fact that after each step in a Jordan elimination we eliminate not only the resolvent column, but the resolvent row as well while we write a separate expression for the corresponding x_i. In the last step we obtain the value of one of the unknowns, and the values of the remaining unknowns are successively computed by substitution of evaluated unknowns into expressions for the x_i (in the order opposite to the order in which they are eliminated).

Example. We shall use Gaussian elimination to solve the system

	x_1	x_2	x_3	x_4	1
0 =	2	2	—1	1	— 4
0 =	4	3	—1	2	— 6
0 =	8	5	—3	4	—12
0 =	3	3	—2	2	— 6

,

which was solved above in Paragraph 2.

Jordan elimination over the first row and fourth column, with subsequent elimination of this row and column, yields the table

	x_1	x_2	x_3	1
0 =	0	—1	[1]	2
0 =	0	—3	1	4
0 =	—1	—1	0	2

and the following expression for x_4:

$$x_4 = -2x_1 - 2x_2 + x_3 + 4.$$

We then execute a Jordan elimination over the first row and third column, which, after this row and column are eliminated, yields

	x_1	x_2	1
0 =	0	—2	2
0 =	—1	[—1]	2

and the following expression for x_3:

$$x_3 = x_2 - 2.$$

We now apply Jordan elimination to the second row and second column, which yields the table

	x_1	1
0 =	2	—2

and the following expression for x_2:

$$x_2 = -x_1 + 2.$$

The last table yields

$$x_1 = 1.$$

Substituting the value we have obtained for x_1 into the expression for x_2, we find that $x_2 = 1$, $x_3 = -1$, and $x_4 = -1$.

5. General Systems of Linear Equations

We now consider the general linear system

$$y_i \equiv a_{i1}x_1 + a_{i2}x_2 + \ldots + a_{in}x_n - a_i = 0 \quad (i = 1, \ldots, m), \quad (1.5)$$

where we assume that the rank of the coefficient matrix $\|a_{ij}\|$ is r. We write system (1.5) in the form

$$
\begin{array}{c|ccc|c}
 & x_1 & x_2 \ \ldots \ x_n & & 1 \\
\hline
y_1 = & a_{11} & a_{12} \ \ldots \ a_{1n} & & -a_1 \\
\cdots & & \cdots\cdots\cdots\cdots & & \cdots \\
y_m = & a_{m1} & a_{m2} \ \ldots \ a_{mn} & & -a_m
\end{array}
\qquad (1.6)
$$

As we noted in Paragraph 3, only r Jordan eliminations can be executed over Table (1.6). We obtain, for example, a table of the form

$$
\begin{array}{c|ccc|c}
 & y_1 \quad \ldots \ y_r & x_{r+1} \ \ldots \ x_n & 1 \\
\hline
x_1 = & c_{11} \quad \ldots \ c_{1r} & c_{1,\,r+1} \ \ldots \ c_{1n} & c_1 \\
\cdots & \cdots\cdots\cdots\cdots & \cdots\cdots\cdots\cdots & \cdots \\
x_r = & c_{r1} \quad \ldots \ c_{rr} & c_{r,\,r+1} \ \ldots \ c_{rn} & c_r \\
y_{r+1} = & c_{r+1,\,1} \ldots \ c_{r+1,\,r} & 0 \qquad \ldots \ 0 & c_{r+1} \\
\cdots & \cdots\cdots\cdots\cdots & \cdots\cdots\cdots\cdots & \cdots \\
y_m = & c_{m1} \quad \ldots \ c_{mr} & 0 \qquad \ldots \ 0 & c_m
\end{array}
\qquad (1.7)
$$

System (1.5) is clearly consistent if and only if for some system of $x_1, \ldots, x_n$ all of the $y_1, \ldots, y_m$ are equal to zero, which occurs if and only if $c_{r+1} = c_{r+2} = \ldots = c_m = 0$. Here, by eliminating the first r columns (since $y_1 = \ldots = y_r = 0$) and treating $x_{r+1}, \ldots, x_n$ as parameters taking arbitrary values, we can for any system of parameter values $x_{r+1} = b_{r+1}, \ldots, x_n = b_n$, use (1.7) to obtain the corresponding values for the remaining unknowns $x_1, \ldots, x_r$:

$$x_1 = c_{1,\,r+1}b_{r+1} + \ldots + c_{1n}b_n + c_1,$$
$$\cdots\cdots\cdots\cdots\cdots\cdots\cdots\cdots\cdots$$
$$x_r = c_{r,\,r+1}b_{r+1} + \ldots + c_{rn}b_n + c_r.$$

The entries $c_{i1}, c_{i2}, \ldots, c_{ir}$ $(i = r+1, r+2, \ldots, m)$ in Table (1.7) are the coefficients of the linear combination of the first r equations that is equal to the ith equation.

Remark. When we are not interested in the coefficients of the linear relationship among the equations of the system, it is desirable, as in 2) of Paragraph 4, to eliminate the resolvent column after each Jordan elimination, which considerably shortens the computation.

The following examples illustrate the foregoing discussion.

Example 1. Consider the system

$$
\begin{aligned}
y_1 &= 2x_1 + x_2 + 4x_3 - 4 = 0, \\
y_2 &= x_1 - 3x_2 - x_3 + 5 = 0, \\
y_3 &= 3x_1 - 2x_2 + 2x_3 + 1 = 0, \\
y_4 &= 5x_1 - x_2 + 6x_3 - 3 = 0.
\end{aligned}
$$

We now write this system in the form of a table, subject it to three Jordan eliminations and place the resolvent element of each elimination in a box:

	x_1	x_2	x_3	1
$y_1 =$	2	1	4	−4
$y_2 =$	$\boxed{1}$	−3	−1	5
$y_3 =$	3	−2	2	1
$y_4 =$	5	−1	6	−3

→

	y_2	x_2	x_3	1
$y_1 =$	2	$\boxed{7}$	6	−14
→ $x_1 =$	1	3	1	−5
$y_3 =$	3	7	5	−14
$y_4 =$	5	14	11	−28

→

	y_2	y_1	x_3	1
$x_2 =$	$-\frac{2}{7}$	$\frac{1}{7}$	$-\frac{6}{7}$	2
→ $x_1 =$	$\frac{1}{7}$	$\frac{3}{7}$	$-\frac{11}{7}$	1
$y_3 =$	1	1	$\boxed{-1}$	0
$y_4 =$	1	2	−1	0

→

	0	0	0	
	y_2	y_1	y_3	1
$x_2 =$	$-\frac{8}{7}$	$-\frac{5}{7}$	$\frac{6}{7}$	2
→ $x_1 =$	$-\frac{10}{7}$	$-\frac{8}{7}$	$\frac{11}{7}$	1
$x_3 =$	1	1	−1	0
$y_4 =$	0	1	1	0

The system has the unique solution

$$x_1 = 1, \quad x_2 = 2, \quad x_3 = 0.$$

It follows from the last row that

$$y_4 = y_1 + y_3,$$

so that the fourth equation is a linear combination of the first and third; the coefficients of this combination are 1 and 1.

Example 2. Consider the system

$$
\begin{aligned}
y_1 &= 2x_1 - x_2 + 4x_3 - 2 = 0, \\
y_2 &= x_1 + 2x_2 - 3x_3 + 4 = 0, \\
y_3 &= 4x_1 + 3x_2 - 2x_3 + 6 = 0.
\end{aligned}
$$

We have

	x_1	x_2	x_3	1
$y_1 =$	2	−1	4	−2
$y_2 =$	[1]	2	−3	4
$y_3 =$	4	3	−2	6

→

	y_2	x_2	x_3	1
$y_1 =$	2	[−5]	10	−10
$x_1 =$	1	−2	3	−4
$y_3 =$	4	−5	10	−10

→

	y_2	y_1	x_3	1
$x_2 =$	$\frac{2}{5}$	$-\frac{1}{5}$	2	−2
$x_1 =$	$\frac{1}{5}$	$\frac{2}{5}$	−1	0
$y_3 =$	2	1	0	0

Treating x_3 as a parameter taking arbitrary values, we obtain an infinite set of solutions for the system:

$$x_1 = -x_3,$$
$$x_2 = 2x_3 - 2,$$

and $y_3 = y_1 + 2y_2$.

Example 3. Consider the system

$$y_1 = x_1 + 2x_2 + 3x_3 + x_4 - 1 = 0,$$
$$y_2 = x_1 - x_2 + 2x_3 - x_4 + 3 = 0,$$
$$y_3 = 3x_1 + 3x_2 + 8x_3 + x_4 + 3 = 0$$

which has the table

	x_1	x_2	x_3	x_4	1
$y_1 =$	1	2	3	1	−1
$y_2 =$	1	−1	2	−1	3
$y_3 =$	3	3	8	1	3

Two Jordan eliminations with the resolvent columns being eliminated yields

	x_2	x_3	x_4	1
$x_1 =$	−2	−3	−1	1
$y_2 =$	−3	[−1]	−2	4
$y_3 =$	−3	−1	−2	6

→

	x_2	x_4	1
$x_1 =$	7	5	−11
$x_3 =$	−3	−2	4
$y_3 =$	0	0	2

The system is inconsistent, since $y_3 = 2 \neq 0$.

3. MODIFIED JORDAN ELIMINATION

1. Definition

In certain applications of the computational apparatus provided by Jordan elimination [for example, in the simplex method (see Chapter II)], it is important to ensure that the entries in the resolvent row maintain their signs and that the entries of the resolvent column change their signs. Under these circumstances, ordinary Jordan elimination is replaced by so-called *modified* Jordan elimination, which requires us to write system (1.1) in the form

$$y_i = -a_{i1}(-x_1) - a_{i2}(-x_2) - \dots - a_{in}(-x_n) \quad (i = 1, \dots, m) \tag{1.1'}$$

and to use the table

	$-x_1$	$-x_2$	...	$-x_s$	...	$-x_n$
$y_1 =$	α_{11}	α_{12}	...	α_{1s}	...	α_{1n}
...	...	...	...	...	...	...
$y_r =$	α_{r1}	α_{r2}	...	α_{rs}	...	α_{rn}
...	...	...	...	...	...	...
$y_m =$	α_{m1}	α_{m2}	...	α_{ms}	...	α_{mn}

, (1.2′)

where for convenience, we have $\alpha_{ik} = -a_{ik}$ $(i = 1, \dots, m; k = 1, \dots, n)$.

A single modified Jordan elimination over α_{rs} is the process required for passage to the new table

	$-x_1$	$-x_2$	...	$-y_r$	...	$-x_n$
$y_1 =$	b_{11}	b_{12}	...	$-\alpha_{1s}$	...	b_{1n}
...	...	...	...	...	...	...
$x_s =$	α_{r1}	α_{r2}	...	1	...	α_{rn}
...	...	...	...	...	...	...
$y_m =$	b_{m1}	b_{m2}	...	$-\alpha_{ms}$	...	b_{mn}

$:\alpha_{rs}$,

which is obtained from the preceding table by rules 1)-5) of ordinary Jordan elimination, with rules 2) and 3) changed to read as follows:

2) the remaining entries (except for the resolvent) in the resolvent row are retained without change;

3) the remaining entries in the resolvent column change only in their signs.

2. *Example.* We write the system

$$\begin{aligned} y_1 &= 2x_1 - x_2 + 3x_3, \\ y_2 &= -x_1 + 4x_2 - 2x_3, \\ y_3 &= 5x_1 + 2x_2 - 4x_3 \end{aligned}$$

in the form of the table

$$\begin{array}{r|ccc|}
 & -x_1 & -x_2 & -x_3 \\
\hline
y_1 = & -2 & 1 & -3 \\
y_2 = & 1 & -4 & \boxed{2} \\
y_3 = & -5 & -2 & 4 \\
\hline
\end{array}$$

and execute modified Jordan elimination over the second row and third column. This yields

$$\begin{array}{r|ccc|}
 & -x_1 & -x_2 & -y_2 \\
\hline
y_1 = & -\frac{1}{2} & -5 & \frac{3}{2} \\
x_3 = & \frac{1}{2} & -2 & \frac{1}{2} \\
y_3 = & -7 & 6 & -2 \\
\hline
\end{array}.$$

2

The Basic Linear Programming Problem and Its Solution by the Simplex Method

1. THE BASIC LINEAR PROGRAMMING PROBLEM

1. Statement of the Problem

The basic linear programming problem can be stated as follows: *Given a linear form (target function)*

$$z = p_1x_1 + p_2x_2 + \dots + p_nx_n \tag{2.1}$$

and a system of $m > n$ linear inequalities (constraints)

$$a_{i1}x_1 + a_{i2}x_2 + \dots + a_{in}x_n \leqslant a_i \quad (i = 1, \dots, m),$$

which we rewrite in the form

$$y_i \equiv -a_{i1}x_1 - a_{i2}x_2 - \dots - a_{in}x_n + a_i \geqslant 0 \quad (i = 1, \dots, m), \tag{2.2}$$

maximize (minimize) (2.1) under conditions (2.2).

In other words, among the solutions of system (2.2) (which constitute a polyhedron Ω), find one for which form (2.1) takes a maximal (minimal) value.

As we shall show in the next chapter, this problem is a mathematical model of many important practical problems.

2. Geometric Interpretation

The basic linear programming problem can easily be interpreted geometrically. Each inequality

$$y_i \equiv -a_{i1}x_1 - \dots - a_{in}x_n + a_i \geqslant 0$$

of system (2.2) defines, in Euclidean n-space, a half-space consisting of the points $x(x_1, \ldots, x_n)$ located "on one side" of the plane

$$y_i \equiv -a_{i1}x_1 - \ldots - a_{in}x_n + a_i = 0$$

and the set of points on the other side. Those points that belong to all the half-spaces (2.2) [i.e., the set of all solutions of system (2.2)] form, as the intersection of convex sets, some convex polyhedron Ω.

The value of the function

$$z(x) = p_1x_1 + \ldots + p_nx_n$$

at the point $x'(x'_1, \ldots, x'_n)$ can be treated as the deviation of the point $x'(x'_1, \ldots, x'_n)$ from the plane

$$p_1x_1 + \ldots + p_nx_n = 0, \qquad (*)$$

where, by the deviation (as in Paragraph 2 of Section 1, Chapter 1), we mean the number that appears in the left side of Eq. (*) when the coordinates $x'_1, \ldots, x'_n$ are substituted for $x_1, \ldots, x_n$. Thus, for example, the deviation of the point $x(1, -2, 5)$ from the plane

$$2x_1 - x_2 + 3x_3 = 0$$

is $2 \cdot 1 - 1 \cdot (-2) + 3 \cdot 5 = 19$.

The deviation of the point x from the plane (*) is proportional to the distance of the point x from this plane.

Thus, the geometric meaning of the basic linear programming problem consists in finding points in the polyhedron Ω that have maximal (minimal) deviation from the plane (*).

In the case of a two-dimensional space, we have the pattern shown in Figs. 1-4.

Here the polyhedron Ω is a polygon, while the planes $y_i \equiv -a_{i1}x_1 - a_{i2}x_2 + a_i = 0$ are lines and the half-spaces $y_i \geqslant 0$ are half-planes (they are partly shaded in the figures).

It is clear that a solution of a linear programming problem lies at some *vertex* of the polyhedron Ω. In Fig. 1 a solution of a problem of maximizing form (2.1) is given by the vertex P_1, while the problem of minimizing this form has its solution at the vertex P_2. Both of these solutions are unique.

Figures 2-4 illustrate the following cases: a case in which there is an infinite set of solutions (Fig. 2), a case in which the function z is unbounded on Ω (Fig. 3), and, finally, a case in which there is no solution (Fig. 4).

Another geometric interpretation can be obtained by considering the basic linear programming problem in the $(n+1)$-dimensional space of variables $x_1, \ldots, x_n, z$, in which the linear form

$$z = p_1x_1 + \ldots + p_nx_n \qquad (2.1)$$

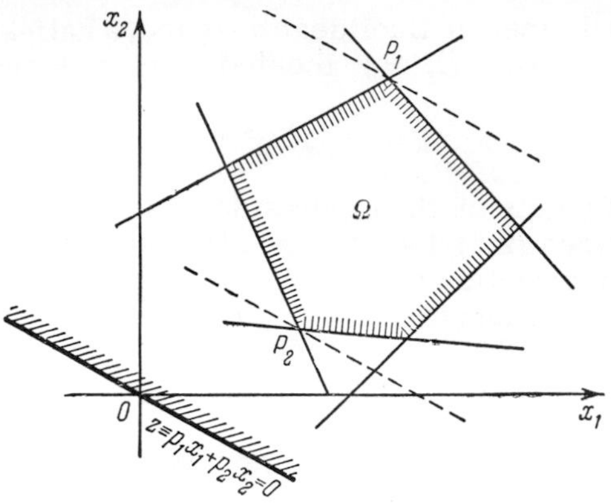

Fig. 1.

is the equation of a plane (passing through the coordinate origin). The system of inequalities

$$-a_{i1}x_1 - \dots - a_{in}x_n + a_i \geqslant 0 \quad (i = 1, \dots, m) \tag{2.2}$$

defines, in this space, some convex prism whose (n-dimensional) faces are the planes

$$-a_{i1}x_1 - \dots - a_{in}x_n + a_i = 0 \quad (i = 1, \dots, m)$$

parallel to the Oz axis. In the "horizontal" plane $z = 0$, i.e., in the n-dimensional space of variables $x_1, \dots, x_n$, these planes define a

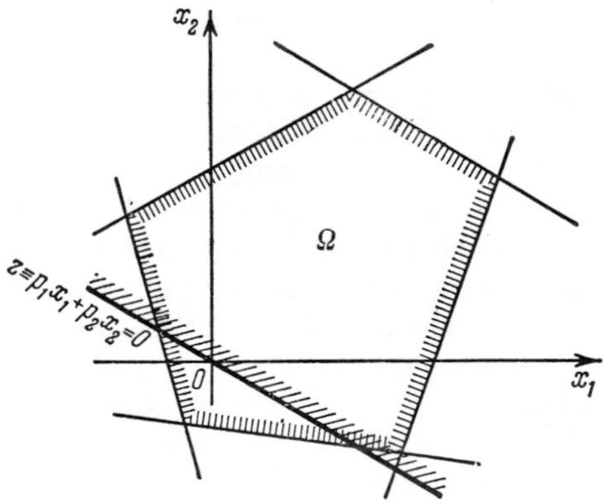

Fig. 2.

polyhedron Ω on which part of plane (2.1) a "cut" through prism (2)--is projected, so that Ω can be treated as the domain of existence of linear function (2.1). We must find the vertex of Ω onto which the "cut" vertex with the largest (smallest) coordinate (in three-space, the z-coordinate) z is projected.

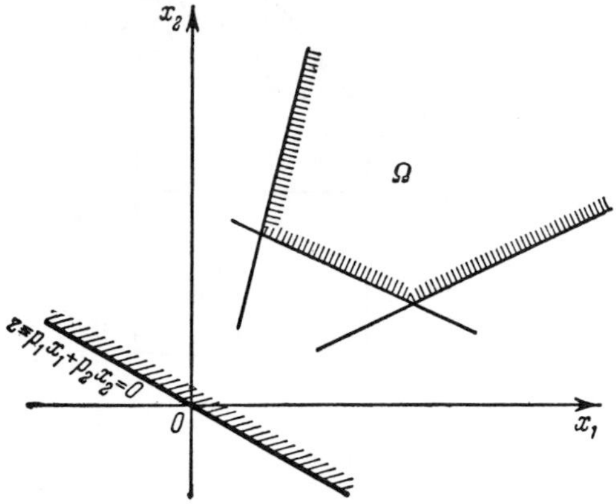

Fig. 3.

Figure 5 illustrates the situation (the "cut" is shaded) for the case $n=2$. The linear function (2.1) achieves its largest value on Ω on the vertex A', onto which the vertex A of the "cut" with the largest z-coordinate is projected.

3. A Method for Solving Linear Programming Problems

It is not difficult to see that the usual methods of classical mathematical analysis for solution of problems on local extrema do not apply to the problem under discussion: Difficulties appear because linear form (2.1), which is defined in the region Ω given by inequalities (2.2) (see Fig. 5), achieves its maximum and minimum values on the boundary (at the vertices) of this region (i.e., at points

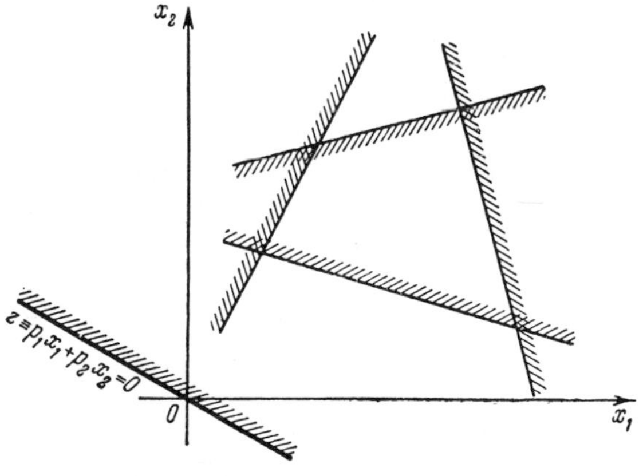

Fig. 4.

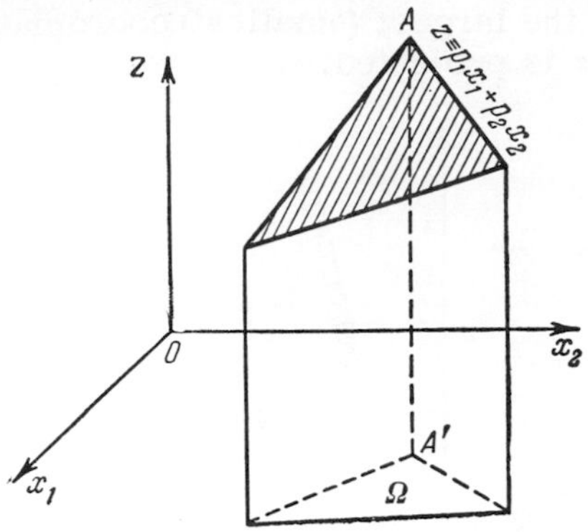

Fig. 5

at which the partial derivatives are generally nonzero); the methods of differential calculus for finding extrema are valid only for points inside the domain of existence of the function under investigation, and hold only when the number of variables is small and constraints are given in the form of equations, and not inequalities. Inspection of the values of function (2.1) at all the vertices of the polyhedron Ω (2.2) is, in practice, out of the question because the number of such vertices is generally large.

The fundamental method of solving the general linear programming problem without stumbling on these difficulties is Dantzig's so-called simplex method [17], which is described in detail in Sections 2 and 3.

The simplex method is an algorithm for finding a basic solution among the solutions of system (2.2), (or proving that the system is inconsistent), i.e., a solution at a vertex of the polyhedron Ω, and then successively transforming the basic solution to a new basic solution for which form (2.1) has a larger (smaller) value [until a maximizing (minimizing) solution is obtained, i.e., until an optimal solution is obtained].

The basis of the computational aspects of the simplex method is modified Jordan elimination.

2. THE SIMPLEX METHOD FOR FINDING A BASIC SOLUTION FOR A SYSTEM OF LINEAR INEQUALITIES

In the interest of clarity, we shall describe this method step by step.

1. Construction of a Table

We write form (2.1) and conditions (2.2) in tabular form:

	$-x_1$	$-x_2$	$\dots$	$-x_n$	1
$y_1 =$	a_{11}	a_{12}	$\dots$	a_{1n}	a_1
$\dots$	$\dots$	$\dots$	$\dots$	$\dots$	$\dots$
$y_m =$	a_{m1}	a_{m2}	$\dots$	a_{mn}	a_m
$z =$	$-p_1$	$-p_2$	$\dots$	$-p_n$	0

(2.3)

2. Elimination of $x_1, \dots, x_n$ (Variables)

Assume that the rank of the coefficient matrix $\|a_{ij}\|$ of system (2.2) is n. Then (see Paragraph 1, Section 2, Chapter 1), n successive modified Jordan eliminations are required to carry all the x_j from the top of table (2.3) to the column on the left and replace them with the corresponding y_i. Here no constraints are placed on the resolvent elements, except that they be nonzero.

For convenience in notation, we can assume that $y_1, \dots, y_n$ have been carried to the top of the table, so that, for example, we obtain a table of the form

	$-y_1$	$-y_2$	$\dots$	$-y_n$	1
$x_1 =$	b_{11}	b_{12}	$\dots$	b_{1n}	b_1
$\dots$	$\dots$	$\dots$	$\dots$	$\dots$	$\dots$
$x_n =$	b_{n1}	b_{n2}	$\dots$	b_{nn}	b_n
$y_{n+1} =$	$b_{n+1,1}$	$b_{n+1,2}$	$\dots$	$b_{n+1,n}$	b_{n+1}
$\dots$	$\dots$	$\dots$	$\dots$	$\dots$	$\dots$
$y_r =$	b_{r1}	b_{r2}	$\dots$	b_{rn}	b_r
$\dots$	$\dots$	$\dots$	$\dots$	$\dots$	$\dots$
$y_m =$	b_{m1}	b_{m2}	$\dots$	b_{mn}	b_m
$z =$	q_1	q_2	$\dots$	q_n	Q

(2.4)

It is only after we obtain a solution that we shall require expressions for the variables $x_1, \dots, x_n$ so that the solution can be expressed in terms of the old coordinates. We therefore write these expressions separately,

$$x_1 = -b_{11}y_1 - b_{12}y_2 - \dots - b_{1n}y_n + b_1,$$
$$\dots\dots\dots\dots\dots\dots$$
$$x_n = -b_{n1}y_1 - b_{n2}y_2 - \dots - b_{nn}y_n + b_n,$$

and proceed with the remaining part of the table

	$-y_1$	$\dots$	$-y_s$	$\dots$	$-y_n$	1
$y_{n+1} =$	$b_{n+1,1}$	$\dots$	$b_{n+1,s}$	$\dots$	$b_{n+1,n}$	b_{n+1}
$\dots$	$\dots$	$\dots$	$\dots$	$\dots$	$\dots$	$\dots$
$y_r =$	b_{r1}	$\dots$	b_{rs}	$\dots$	b_{rn}	b_r
$\dots$	$\dots$	$\dots$	$\dots$	$\dots$	$\dots$	$\dots$
$y_m =$	b_{m1}	$\dots$	b_{ms}	$\dots$	b_{mn}	b_m
$z =$	q_1	$\dots$	q_s	$\dots$	q_n	Q

(2.4′)

Since, by conditions (2.2), $y_1 \geqslant 0, \ldots, y_n \geqslant 0$, we have the following statement of the basic linear programming problem:

Given the linear function

$$z = -q_1y_1 - q_2y_2 - \ldots - q_ny_n + Q \tag{2.1'}$$

and the system of inequalities (constraints)

$$\left.\begin{array}{r} y_i = -b_{i1}y_1 - b_{i2}y_2 - \ldots - b_{in}y_n + b_i \geqslant 0 \\ (i = n+1,\ n+2,\ \ldots,\ m), \\ y_1 \geqslant 0,\ y_2 \geqslant 0,\ \ldots,\ y_n \geqslant 0, \end{array}\right\} \tag{2.2'}$$

find a solution of system (2.2') that maximizes linear function (2.1').

Remark. System (2.2) frequently contains inequalities of the form $x_1 \geqslant 0, \ldots, x_n \geqslant 0$. It is clear that here we need not eliminate the coordinates $x_1, \ldots, x_n$ and we can, after step 1, proceed immediately to steps 3 and 4. If (2.2) contains, for example, the inequalities $x_1 \geqslant 0, \ldots, x_k \geqslant 0$, where $k < n$, we need eliminate only the coordinates $x_{k+1}, \ldots, x_n$.

To find a basic solution after Table (2.4') is obtained, we must distinguish the cases in which this table contains or does not contain negative slack terms.

3. All Slack Terms Are Nonnegative

Assume that $b_{n+1} \geqslant 0, \ldots, b_m \geqslant 0$. In this case Table (2.4') permits us to obtain immediately a basic solution for system (2.2'), and consequently a basic solution for (2.2). This solution (vertex of the polyhedron Ω) is given by the equations

$$y_1 = 0, \quad y_2 = 0, \ \ldots, \ y_n = 0,$$

since here

$$y_{n+1} = b_{n+1} \geqslant 0, \ \ldots, \ y_m = b_m \geqslant 0,$$

and, consequently, all of the y_i are nonnegative and satisfy system (2.2).

4. A Rule for Choosing the Resolvent Element for Finding a Basic Solution (Some Slack Terms Are Negative)

Assume that table (2.4') has at least one negative slack term, say, $b_r < 0$, where $r \geqslant n+1$. Now

$$y_1 = y_2 = \ldots = y_n = 0$$

does not provide a solution of system (2.2′) [or, consequently, of (2.2)], since we have $y_r = b_r < 0$ for these values.*

The simplex method for finding a basic solution provides a special rule for passing from the given vertex $y_1 = y_2 = \ldots = y_n = 0$ to some adjacent vertex that separates a smaller number of planes from the polyhedron Ω, i.e., for which the corresponding table contains a smaller number of negative slack terms.

To pass from the vertex $y_1 = \ldots = y_n = 0$ to the indicated adjacent vertex, we execute a modified Jordan elimination over a resolvent element chosen in accordance with the following rule.

*Rule for choosing resolvent elements.***

1) We choose a row with a *negative* slack term (say, for example, $b_r < 0$). If none of the coefficients in this row is negative, then system (2.2) is *inconsistent*.

2) If, however, the row under discussion contains negative coefficients, we choose one of them (say, $b_{rs} < 0$) and we take the column containing this coefficient as the resolvent column.

3) The resolvent row is chosen as follows: We compute all of the nonnegative ratios $b_i / b_{is} \geqslant 0$ of slack terms to the corresponding nonzero coefficients in the resolvent column, find the smallest of them and the element $b_{i_0 s}$ on which this minimum is achieved, and use this element as the resolvent element.

In the case of *degeneration*, when $\min\limits_i \frac{b_i}{b_{is}} = \frac{b_{i_0}}{b_{i_0 s}} = 0$, we choose $b_{i_0 s}$ as the resolvent element only when $b_{i_0 s} > 0$.***

If, by applying the above rule, we choose the coefficient b_{rs} as the resolvent element, the slack term b_r' in the rth row under discussion will, after modified Jordan elimination, be positive:

$$b_r' = \frac{b_r}{b_{rs}} > 0.$$

If b_{ls} is the resolvent coefficient, where $l \neq r$, the new slack term b_r' in our rth row will still be negative, and we shall not yet have made it positive. In this case we continue to operate on this (rth) row, apply the above rule to it and use modified Jordan elimination until either system (2.2) is proved inconsistent (all of the coefficients in this row are nonnegative) or we demonstrate that we cannot make this slack term positive (the resolvent element belongs to this row).****

---

* They determine only the point at which the n planes $y_1 = 0, \ldots, y_n = 0$ intersect, i.e., a vertex that lies outside the polyhedron Ω.

** This rule is proved below in Paragraph 6.

***If, in the case under discussion ($b_r < 0$, $b_{i_0} = 0$), we have, not only $b_{rs} < 0$ but also $b_{rj} < 0$, where $b_{i_0 j} \leqslant 0$, it is better to use the jth column instead of the sth column as the resolvent. Then the i_0th row is not the resolvent row; here the resolvent row is a row with nonzero slack term (if b_{i_0} is the only zero).

**** On the possibility of *cycling* here, see below, Section 6.

A finite number of applications of the above sequence of steps will ultimately either prove the inconsistency of system (2.2) or lead to a table with no negative slack terms, i.e., we shall obtain a basic solution for our system by equating all of the y at the top of the table to zero.

Remark. If some row containing, say, y_k, has slack term b_k equal to zero and all coefficients nonnegative, then, in finding a basic solution, we can eliminate all of the columns containing these coefficients with plus signs, as well as the row itself. Indeed, in the case under discussion the kth equation is satisfied only when the unknowns over the positive coefficients are equal to zero, and so, consequently, are the y_k.

5. Examples

Example 1. Find a basic solution for the system

$$\begin{aligned} y_1 &= -x_1 + 2x_2 - 3x_3 - 1 \geqslant 0, \\ y_2 &= -3x_1 - 4x_3 + 2 \geqslant 0, \\ y_3 &= -5x_1 + 4x_2 - x_3 - 10 \geqslant 0, \\ y_4 &= -3x_1 - x_2 + 4 \geqslant 0, \\ x_1 &\geqslant 0, \quad x_2 \geqslant 0, \quad x_3 \geqslant 0. \end{aligned}$$

In this case (see the remark at the end of Paragraph 2), we need not eliminate coordinates. Consider the table

	$-x_1$	$-x_2$	$-x_3$	1
$y_1 =$	1	[−2]	3	−1
$y_2 =$	3	0	4	2
$y_3 =$	5	−4	1	−10
$y_4 =$	3	1	0	4

The first and third rows of this table contain negative slack terms, while the first row contains one more negative coefficient, -2. We now compare all of the nonnegative ratios of the slack terms to the corresponding coefficients in the second column:

$$\frac{-1}{-2}, \quad \frac{-10}{-4}, \quad \frac{4}{1}.$$

The first of them is the smallest, so we choose the coeffecient -2 as the resolvent element. Modified Jordan elimination yields the table

	$-x_1$	$-y_1$	$-x_3$	1
$x_2 =$	$-\frac{1}{2}$	$-\frac{1}{2}$	$-\frac{3}{2}$	$\frac{1}{2}$
$y_2 =$	3	0	4	2
$y_3 =$	3	$\boxed{-2}$	-5	-8
$y_4 =$	$\frac{7}{2}$	$\frac{1}{2}$	$\frac{3}{2}$	$\frac{7}{2}$

,

which contains one negative slack term, -8. We convert it to a positive term by executing a modified Jordan elimination over the -2 shown in a box, since the first of the two ratios

$$\frac{-8}{-2} \text{ and } \frac{7}{2} : \frac{1}{2}$$

is the smaller. We use the table thus obtained

	$-x_1$	$-y_3$	$-x_3$	1
$x_2 =$	$-\frac{5}{4}$	$-\frac{1}{4}$	$-\frac{1}{4}$	$\frac{5}{2}$
$y_2 =$	3	0	4	2
$y_1 =$	$-\frac{3}{2}$	$-\frac{1}{2}$	$\frac{5}{2}$	4
$y_4 =$	$\frac{17}{4}$	$\frac{1}{4}$	$\frac{1}{4}$	$\frac{3}{2}$

,

which has no negative slack terms, to find a basic solution for our system. We set

$$x_1 = y_3 = x_3 = 0.$$

Then

$$x_2 = \frac{5}{2}.$$

We have thus obtained the basic solution

$$x_1 = 0, \quad x_2 = \frac{5}{2}, \quad x_3 = 0.$$

Example 2. Find a basic solution for the system

$$\begin{aligned} y_1 &= -\ x_1 - 2x_2 - 3x_3 + \ 6 \geqslant 0, \\ y_2 &= \ 2x_1 + \ x_2 - 3x_3 + 12 \geqslant 0, \\ y_3 &= \ x_1 + 3x_2 + 4x_3 + 12 \geqslant 0, \\ y_4 &= \ x_1 + \ x_2 + \ x_3 - \ 7 \geqslant 0, \\ & x_1 \geqslant 0, \quad x_2 \geqslant 0, \quad x_3 \geqslant 0. \end{aligned}$$

We construct the table

	$-x_1$	$-x_2$	$-x_3$	1
$y_1 =$	[1]	2	3	6
$y_2 =$	−2	−1	3	12
$y_3 =$	−1	−3	−4	12
$y_4 =$	−1	−1	−1	−7

and we shall attempt to find a basic solution without eliminating coordinates.

The fourth row contains a negative slack term, -7. We examine, for example, the first column of coefficients over the negative coefficient -1 of this row and compose the nonnegative ratios of the slack terms to the coefficients of this column:

$$\frac{6}{1}, \quad \frac{-7}{-1}.$$

The first ratio is smaller, so we will use the entry 1 in the first row as the resolvent element.

Modified Jordan elimination over this resolvent element yields the table

	$-y_1$	$-x_2$	$-x_3$	1
$x_1 =$	1	2	3	6
$y_2 =$	2	3	9	24
$y_3 =$	1	−1	−1	18
$y_4 =$	1	1	2	−1

,

which still contains a negative slack term, -1, but the row in which it is located contains no negative coefficients, so the system is inconsistent.

6. Justification of the Rule for Choosing Resolvent Elements

The presence of a negative slack term, say, $b_r < 0$, indicates, geometrically, that the point (vertex)

$$y_1 = y_2 = \dots = y_n = 0$$

lies outside the polyhedron Ω and is separated from it by the plane $y_r = 0$ (if it is nonempty), or that system (2.2′) is inconsistent and, consequently, Ω is the empty set.

If all the slack terms in (2.4′) are nonzero, then exactly n planes $y_1 = 0$, ..., $y_n = 0$ pass through the vertex $y_1 = \dots y_n = 0$ and, consequently, there are exactly n edges, each formed at the intersection of $n-1$ of these planes. If some of the slack terms are equal to zero, then, in addition to the planes $y_1=0, \dots, y_n=0$, the planes $y_i=0$ $(i>n)$ for which the slack terms are equal to zero pass through the vertex under discussion. In this case, which is called *degenerate* (for more details about this, see below, Section 6), more than n edges meet at the vertex under discussion.

The parametric equation of any "upper" edge, i.e., an edge obtained at the intersection of $n-1$ planes $y_1=0, \dots, y_n=0$ at the top of the table, can be obtained by setting one of these y equal to the parameter $t \geqslant 0$, and setting the remaining y equal to zero. For example,

$$y_1 = t, \quad y_2 = \dots = y_n = 0$$

is the equation of the edge formed by the planes $y_2=0, \dots, y_n=0$.

Each step in the simplex method provides for *movement* from the vertex $y_1 = \dots = y_n = 0$, obtained in the previous step, along one of the edges leaving the vertex in the direction of a *separating* plane $y_r=0$ until some plane $y_i=0$ $(i>n)$ encountered, i.e., until we encounter an adjacent vertex. This direction of motion is chosen because we are attempting to find a basic solution, i.e., some vertex of the polyhedron Ω, and it is natural to decrease, step by step, the number of planes $y_i=0$ separating the vertex previously obtained from the polyhedron Ω.

Upon motion along the edge

$$y_1 = \dots = y_{s-1} = 0, \; y_s = t > 0, \; y_{s+1} = \dots = y_n = 0 \tag{2.5}$$

we obtain

$$y_r = -b_{rs}t + b_r,$$

and, for the motion to proceed in the necessary direction relative to the separating plane $y_r=0$, it is necessary and sufficient that the value of $|y_r|$ decrease when the vertex $y_1 = \dots = y_n = 0$ at which $|y_r| = |b_r|$ is left, i.e., it is necessary and sufficient that the inequality

$$|-b_{rs}t + b_r| < |b_r|$$

be satisfied for sufficiently small $t>0$.

Since $b_r<0$, this last inequality indicates that $-(-b_{rs}t+b_r) < -b_r$ or $-b_{rs}t + b_r > b_r$ and, because t is positive, that $b_{rs}<0$. Thus, the motion is along edge (2.5) if and only if the sth column (under the nonzero coordinate $y_s=t$) contains a negative coefficient in the rth row.

If the rth row has no negative coefficients, then motion toward the separating plane $y_r=0$ is impossible, and this is a test for inconsistency (unsolvability) of system (2.2), i.e., it indicates that the polyhedron Ω is empty. In this case we have

$$y_r = -b_{r1}y_1 - b_{r2}y_2 - \dots - b_{rn}y_n + b_r \leqslant b_r < 0$$

and nonnegativity of $y_1, \ldots, y_n$ is inconsistent with the requirement of nonnegativity for y_r.

Now assume that $b_{rs} < 0$. Then motion along edge (2.5) is admissible until the first encounter with a plane $y_i = 0$ $(i > n)$ that does not separate our vertex from Ω (i.e., $b_i > 0$).

If an encounter with such a plane (Fig. 6) is impossible, motion can proceed along an edge until an encounter with a plane $y_i = 0$ separating vertex A from Ω (at least one such plane exists, since, for example, $y_r = 0$ is such a plane).

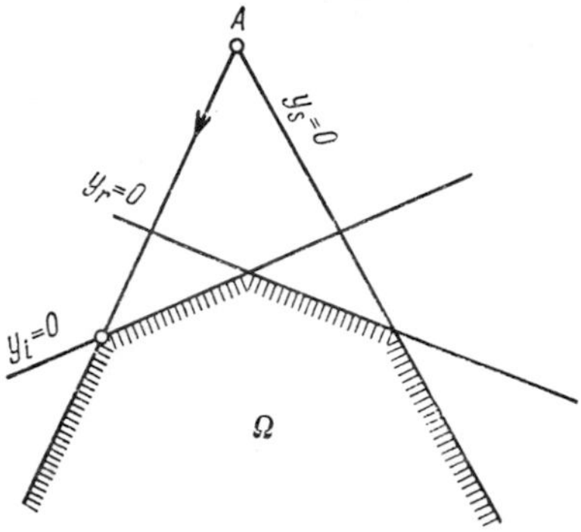

Fig. 6.

The simplex method takes its simplest form when motion from a given vertex proceeds along edge (2.5) until the first encounter with a new plane (which need not be a separating plane).

We shall now describe a computational procedure for obtaining this motion. Since

$$0 = -b_{is}t_0 + b_i$$

upon encounter with a plane $y_{i_0} = 0$, we have $b_{is} \neq 0$ and

$$\frac{b_i}{b_{is}} = t_0 > 0,$$

so that b_i and b_{is} must have the same signs; the first encounter with the plane $y_{i_0} = 0$ clearly occurs when the ratio $\frac{b_{i_0}}{b_{i_0 s}} = t_0$ takes its smallest value. Such a ratio must exist, since $\frac{b_r}{b_{rs}} > 0$. To obtain a new vertex, therefore, we execute a modified Jordan elimination over $b_{i_0 s}$. Then the new plane $y_{i_0} = 0$ that appears at the first intersection with edge (2.5) appears, instead of the plane $y_s = 0$, at the top of the table.

All the coordinates of the new vertex are equal to zero in the new coordinate system $y_1, \ldots, y_{s-1}, y_{i_0}, y_{s+1}, \ldots, y_n$ (in the old system $y_1, \ldots, y_{s-1}, y_s, y_{s+1}, \ldots, y_n$ all the coordinates except $y_s = t_0 = b_{i_0}/b_{i_0 s}$ were equal to zero).

If the smallest positive ratio $\frac{b_{i_0}}{b_{i_0 s}}$ is obtained when $b_{i_0 s} < 0$, $b_{i_0} < 0$ (which is desirable), then modified Jordan elimination leads us to a vertex that is separated from Ω by a smaller number of planes than the preceding vertex. In other words, the number of negative slack terms in the table decreases, and so does $|b_r|$.

If, however, the smallest positive ratio $\frac{b_{i_0}}{b_{i_0 s}}$ is obtained with $b_{i_0 s} > 0$ and $b_{i_0} > 0$, then, although the number of negative slack terms in the table has not changed, we shall have decreased $|b_r|$, i.e., gotten closer to the separating plane $y_r = 0$.

Now assume that degeneration occurs, i.e., assume that among the slack terms there is at least one that is equal to zero, say, $b_l = 0$ $(l > n)$, so that the plane $y_l = 0$ passes through the vertex $y_1 = \dots = y_n = 0$. In this case, care must be taken in moving along edge (2.5) to prevent exit from the half-space $y_l < 0$, i.e., when $t > 0$

$$y_l = -b_{ls}t + b_l = -b_{ls}t < 0.$$

This is possible only when $b_{ls} > 0$, at which time motion along edge (2.5) is not admissible.

If, however, $b_{ls} < 0$ when $b_l = 0$, then, for $t > 0$, we have

$$y_l = -b_{ls}t + b_l = -b_{ls}t > 0,$$

and motion along edge (2.5) is admissible, but choosing b_{ls} as the resolvent element is meaningless, since it leads to $b_l = 0$, so that $t = 0$ and no motion occurs, i.e., no progress is made away from the vertex. If we choose another resolvent element b_{is} such that $t = \frac{b_i}{b_{is}} > 0$, movement will occur along the edge until an adjacent vertex is met.

Let $b_{ls} > 0$. Then, if there are no negative coefficients among the remaining coefficients (except b_{rs}) in the rth row, or there are negative coefficients but the corresponding coefficients in the lth row (in the same columns) are positive, then motion along upper edges is impossible. In this case we must test the remaining edges (not the upper edges) obtained by using modified Jordan elimination to substitute the plane $y_l = 0$ for $y_s = 0$, even though this Jordan elimination will not lead to any motion ($t = 0$!), i.e., we shall remain at the vertex.

Thus, only a finite number of steps is required to obtain an edge along which motion is possible or to demonstrate that the system of constraints is inconsistent.

7. Another Rule for Choosing Resolvent Elements

The process of moving toward the polyhedron Ω from a vertex separated from the polyhedron by several planes can be accelerated by using the following, somewhat different rule for choosing resolvent elements.

1) We choose a row with a *negative* slack term (say, for example, $b_r < 0$). If there are no negative coefficients in this row, system (2.2) is inconsistent.

2) If the row under consideration contains negative coefficients, we choose one of them (say, $b_{rs} < 0$), and we take the column containing this coefficient for the resolvent column.

3) We compute all the nonnegative ratios b_i/b_{is} of slack terms to the corresponding *positive* coefficients in the resolvent column ($b_{i_0s} > 0$), find the smallest of them, the element b_{i_0s} at which this minimum is achieved, and use this element as the resolvent element.

4) If there are no such ratios, we find the largest of the positive ratios b_i/b_{is} of negative slack terms to the corresponding *negative* coefficients in the resolvent column, find the coefficient $b_{i_0s} < 0$ at which this maximum is achieved, and use this element as the resolvent element.

This rule can be proved valid in the same way as was the other, so we shall limit the discussion to a geometric illustration (Fig. 7). Motion from the vertex A along the edge AB in the direction of the polyhedron Ω is not terminated at the vertex P_1 where the edge meets the *first separating* plane $y_1 = 0$ ($b_1 < 0$) (as recommended by the first rule); instead, the motion is continued to B, where it encounters the first plane $y_5 = 0$ ($b_5 > 0$) that is not a separating plane (as recommended in Paragraph 3 of the new rule).

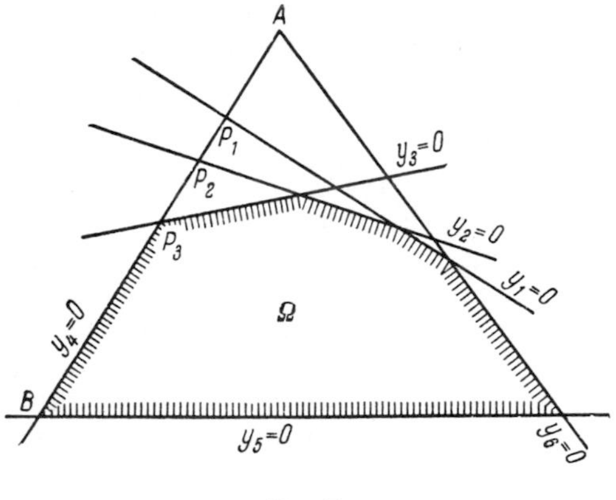

Fig. 7.

If no planes that are not separating planes are encountered, there are no positive ratios b_i/b_{is} for which $b_i > 0$ and $b_{is} >$i 0. Then, by Paragraph 4, motion can proceed to the next separating plane ($y_4 = 0$ in Fig. 8), for which the ratio $\frac{b_i}{b_{is}}$ ($b_i < 0$, $b_{is} < 0$) is maximal.

Remark. It is clear from Fig. 7 that the motion from the vertex A toward the polyhedron Ω can be terminated at the point P_3 instead of B if Paragraphs 3 and 4 of the second rule for choosing resolvent elements are somewhat complicated.

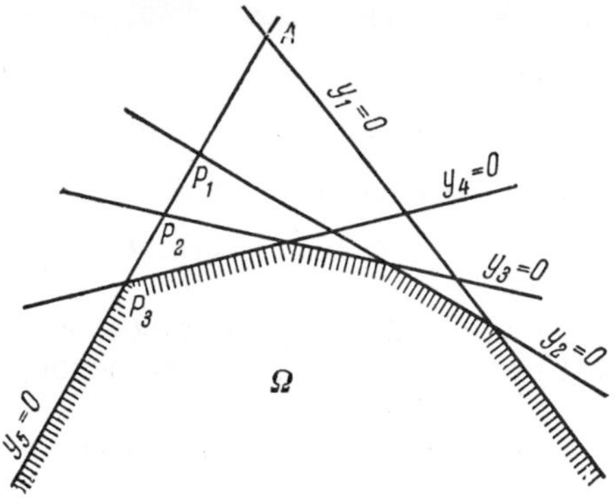

Fig. 8.

3. THE SIMPLEX METHOD FOR FINDING OPTIMAL SOLUTIONS TO THE BASIC LINEAR PROGRAMMING PROBLEM

Assume that we are faced with the problem of maximizing form (2.1)

$$z = p_1x_1 + p_2x_2 + \dots + p_nx_n$$

under constraints (2.2)

$$y_i = -a_{i1}x_1 - a_{i2}x_2 - \dots - a_{in}x_n + a_i \geqslant 0$$
$$(i = 1, 2, \dots, m),$$

and assume that after coordinates have been eliminated and basic solution has been obtained we have the table

	$-y_1$	$-y_2$	$\dots -y_s$	$\dots -y_n$	1
$y_{n+1} =$	$b_{n+1,1}$	$b_{n+1,2}$	$\dots b_{n+1,s}$	$\dots b_{n+1,n}$	b_{n+1}
$\dots$	$\dots$	$\dots$	$\dots$	$\dots$	$\dots$
$y_r =$	b_{r1}	b_{r2}	$\dots b_{rs}$	$\dots b_{rn}$	b_r
$\dots$	$\dots$	$\dots$	$\dots$	$\dots$	$\dots$
$y_m =$	b_{m1}	b_{m2}	$\dots b_{ms}$	$\dots b_{mn}$	b_m
$z =$	q_1	q_2	$\dots q_s$	$\dots q_n$	Q

, (2.4′)

so that $b_{n+1} \geqslant 0, b_{n+2} \geqslant 0, \dots, b_m \geqslant 0$.

Corresponding to the sign of the coefficients of the z-row, the following two cases must be distinguished.

1. All Coefficients in the z-Row Are Nonnegative

If $q_1 \geqslant 0, q_2 \geqslant 0, \dots, q_n \geqslant 0$, then the linear programming problem is solved, and

$$\max z = Q$$

is achieved at the point

$$y_1 = y_2 = \dots = y_n = 0.$$

Indeed, at this point we have

$$y_{n+1} = b_{n+1} \geqslant 0, \dots, y_m = b_m \geqslant 0,$$

i.e., constraints (2.2) are satisfied, and since, at any other point of the polyhedron Ω all of the y_1, y_2, ..., y_n are nonnegative,

$$z = -q_1 y_1 - \dots - q_n y_n + Q \leqslant Q,$$

i.e., Q is the maximum of z.

2. Rule for Choosing Resolvent Elements for Finding Optimal Solutions (Some Coefficients in the z-Row Are Negative)

Assume that there are negative coefficients in the z-row, say, $q_s < 0$. It is clear that in this case we cannot assert that the value Q of the function z at the point $y_1 = \dots = y_n = 0$ is maximal. Indeed, if, for example, the point $y_1 = \dots = y_{s-1} = 0$, $y_s > 0$, $y_{s+1} = \dots = y_n = 0$ satisfies constraints (2.2) (i.e., $y_i = -b_{is} y_s + b_i \geqslant 0$, $i = n+1, \dots, m$), then $z = -q_s y_s + Q > Q$ at this point.

The simplex method for finding an optimal solution provides a special rule for passing from a point $y_1 = \dots = y_n = 0$ (vertex of the polyhedron Ω) to an adjacent vertex at which z is larger (not less than) Q; this process continues until a vertex at which z is maximal is found, i.e., until all the coefficients in the z-row are nonnegative (or until it has been proved that the function z is not bounded above).

To pass from the vertex $y_1 = \dots = y_n = 0$ to the above-noted adjacent vertex, we execute a modified Jordan elimination over the resolvent element given by the following rule.

*Rule for choosing resolvent elements.**

1) For the resolvent column, we take one containing a negative entry in the z-row (in the case under discussion, the sth column);

2) We find all positive coefficients in this column (if there are any), divide the corresponding slack terms by them, compare the ratios thus obtained, and, for the resolvent element, choose the coefficient for which the ratio takes a minimal value (if there is more than one, we choose one arbitrarily).**

---

* This rule is justified below in Paragraph 4.

** For a detailed analysis, see Section 6. In the case of degeneration, when $\min \frac{b_i}{b_{is}} = \frac{b_{i_0}}{b_{i_0 s}} = 0$, if, in addition to $q_s < 0$, $q_j < 0$, but $b_{i_0 j} \leqslant 0$, then it is better to use the jth column than the sth (the i_0th row will not be the resolvent row) as the resolvent column.

After modified Jordan elimination over the resolvent element given by the rule formulated above, the sign of q_s reverses, so that the new coefficient q'_s is positive. If all of the remaining coefficients in the z-row are nonnegative, we obtain the case of Paragraph 1 (in which nonnegativity of the new slack terms is guaranteed by the rule for choosing resolvent elements), and the problem is solved.

If there are still negative coefficients in the new z-row, we proceed with each of them as we did with q_s, and after a finite number of steps, either the z-row will have no negative coefficients, i.e., we shall have been led to the case of Paragraph 1 (the problem is solved), or there will be no positive coefficients in some column containing a negative coefficient in the z-row, which, as we can see with little difficulty, means that the function z is unbounded above.*

Indeed, assume that q_s, for example, is less than zero, and that there are no positive coefficients in the sth column. In this case we can, for example, set $y_1 = \ldots = y_{s-1} = 0, y_s = t > 0, y_{s+1} = \ \ldots \ = y_n =$. Then, for $i \geqslant n+1$, we have

$$y_i = -b_{is}t + b_i \geqslant 0,$$

i.e., system (2.2) is satisfied for all $t \geqslant 0$. Accordingly, the value of the function

$$z = -q_s t + Q$$

can be made arbitrarily large by choosing sufficiently large t.

3. Examples. Preliminary Remark

In solving the following problems, it is suggested that the first step in filling the table be entering the column of slack terms and the coefficients of the z-row. If there are no negative coefficients in the z-row, it is meaningless to compute the remainder of the table.

Example 1 [35]. Maximize the linear form

$$z = -3x_1 + 6x_2$$

under the constraints

$$\begin{aligned} y_1 &= x_1 + 2x_2 + 1 \geqslant 0, \\ y_2 &= 2x_1 + x_2 - 4 \geqslant 0, \\ y_3 &= x_1 - x_2 + 1 \geqslant 0, \\ y_4 &= x_1 - 4x_2 + 13 \geqslant 0, \\ y_5 &= -4x_1 + x_2 + 23 \geqslant 0. \end{aligned}$$

The table for the problem is

*Concerning the possibility of cycling, see below, Section 6.

	$-x_1$	$-x_2$	1
$y_1 =$	-1	-2	1
$y_2 =$	-2	-1	-4
$y_3 =$	-1	1	1
$y_4 =$	-1	4	13
$y_5 =$	4	-1	23
$z =$	3	-6	0

.

Elimination of the coordinate x_1 yields

	$-y_1$	$-x_2$	1
$x_1 =$	-1	2	-1
$y_2 =$	-2	3	-6
$y_3 =$	-1	3	0
$y_4 =$	-1	6	12
$y_5 =$	4	-9	27
$z =$	3	-12	3

.

We write an expression for x_1,

$$x_1 = y_1 - 2x_2 - 1,$$

and then the remaining part of the table:

	$-y_1$	$-x_2$	1
$y_2 =$	-2	3	-6
$y_3 =$	-1	3	0
$y_4 =$	-1	6	12
$y_5 =$	4	-9	27
$z =$	3	-12	3

.

We now eliminate the coordinate x_2:

	$-y_1$	$-y_2$	1
$x_2 =$	$-\frac{2}{3}$	$\frac{1}{3}$	-2
$y_3 =$	1	-1	6
$y_4 =$	3	-2	24
$y_5 =$	-2	3	9
$z =$	-5	4	-21

.

The expression for x_2 is

$$x_2 = \frac{2}{3} y_1 - \frac{1}{3} y_2 - 2,$$

and the remaining part of the table is

	$-y_1$	$-y_2$	1
$y_3 =$	[1]	−1	6
$y_4 =$	3	−2	24
$y_5 =$	−2	3	9
$z =$	−5	4	−21

In the last table all the slack terms are nonnegative, so (see Section 2, Paragraph 3) $y_1 = y_2 = 0$ yields a basic solution for our system of constraints.

We shall now find an optimal solution. The z-row contains the negative coefficient -5, so that we have the case of Paragraph 2. There are two positive coefficients 1 and 3 in the column of coefficients over -5. We divide these coefficients by the corresponding constant terms: $\frac{6}{1}$ and $\frac{24}{3}$. Of these ratios, the smaller is $\frac{6}{1}$, so we use 1 as the resolvent element. Modified Jordan elimination yields the table

	$-y_3$	$-y_2$	1
$y_1 =$	1	−1	6
$y_4 =$	−3	[1]	6
$y_5 =$	2	1	21
$z =$	5	−1	9

in which the z-row contains the negative coefficient -1. Of the two positive entries above -1, we choose the 1 in the box, since $\frac{6}{1} < \frac{21}{1}$. We thus obtain the table

	$-y_3$	$-y_4$	1
$y_1 =$			12
$y_2 =$			6
$y_5 =$			15
$z =$	2	1	15

in which the z-row has no negative coefficients. This completes the solution. The last table shows us that max $z = 15$, which is achieved at $y_3 = y_4 = 0$, and in this case $y_1 = 12$, $y_2 = 6$, $y_5 = 15$. Substituting into the expressions for x_1 and x_2, we find that

$$x_2 = 4, \quad x_1 = 3.$$

Example 2. Maximize the form

$$z = x_1 + x_2 + x_3$$

under the constraints

$$\begin{aligned} y_1 &= 2x_1 + 2x_2 + x_3 - 2 \geqslant 0, \\ y_2 &= -3x_1 + 3x_2 - 2x_3 + 6 \geqslant 0, \\ y_3 &= -3x_1 + 3x_2 + 2x_3 + 6 \geqslant 0, \\ y_4 &= -2x_2 + 2x_3 + 2 \geqslant 0, \\ x_1 \geqslant 0,& \quad x_2 \geqslant 0, \quad x_3 \geqslant 0. \end{aligned}$$

The initial table for this problem is

	$-x_1$	$-x_2$	$-x_3$	1
$y_1 =$	-2	-2	[-1]	-2
$y_2 =$	3	-3	2	6
$y_3 =$	3	-3	-2	6
$y_4 =$	0	2	-2	2
$z =$	-1	-1	-1	0

.

The variables x_1, x_2, and x_3 are nonnegative, so we shall not eliminate them (see the remark at the end of Paragraph 2, Section 2) and we proceed immediately to Paragraph 4 of Section 2.

The first row contains a negative slack term. Of the negative coefficients in this row, we choose -1 and compare the nonnegative ratios of the slack terms to the coefficients of the third column:

$$\frac{-2}{-1} \text{ and } \frac{6}{2};$$

the first of these ratios is the larger, so we choose the -1 in a box as the resolvent element. Modified Jordan elimination yields the table

	$-x_1$	$-x_2$	$-y_1$	1
$x_3 =$	2	2	-1	2
$y_2 =$	-1	-7	[2]	2
$y_3 =$	7	1	-2	10
$y_4 =$	4	6	-2	6
$z =$	1	1	-1	2

,

which contains no negative slack terms, so we can proceed to find an optimal solution. There is only one positive coefficient, 2, over the negative coefficient -1 in the z-row, and we choose it as the resolvent element. Modified Jordan elimination yields

	$-x_1$	$-x_2$	$-y_2$	1
$x_3 =$	$\frac{3}{2}$	$-\frac{3}{2}$	$\frac{1}{2}$	3
$y_1 =$	$\frac{-1}{2}$	$\frac{-7}{2}$	$\frac{1}{2}$	1
$y_3 =$	6	-6	1	7
$y_4 =$	3	-1	1	8
$z =$	$\frac{1}{2}$	$-\frac{5}{2}$	$\frac{1}{2}$	3

.

There are no positive entries over the negative coefficient $-\frac{5}{2}$ in the z-row, so (see the end of Paragraph 2), the linear form is not bounded above.

4. Justification of Rules for Choosing Resolvent Elements

Assume that there is a negative coefficient in the z-row, and, consequently, that it is not true that the vertex $y_1 = \dots = y_n = 0$ maximizes the function z. The transition to an adjacent vertex means motion from the vertex $y_1 = \dots = y_n = 0$ along some edge $y_1 = \dots = y_{s-1} = 0$, $y_s = t > 0$, $y_{s+1} = \dots = y_n = 0$, chosen so that z increases, i.e., so that

$$z = -q_s t + Q > Q.$$

It follows that $-q_s t > 0$ and $q_s < 0$.

Thus, if z is to increase, it is necessary to move along an edge such that the nonzero parameter t in the parametric equation is located over the negative coefficient in the z-row.

Assume that $q_s < 0$. It is clear that motion along the indicated edge can proceed only until an encounter with an adjacent vertex of the polyhedron Ω (so that Ω is not left!), i.e., until encounter with some plane $y_i = 0$, where $i > n$, $b_i \geqslant 0$. At the point of encounter with this plane, if $b_i > 0$, we have $0 = -b_{is}t + b_i$, so $b_{is} \neq 0$, and since $\frac{b_i}{b_{is}} = t > 0$, we have $b_{is} > 0$. It is clear that the first plane $y_{i_0} = 0$ $(i_0 > n, b_{i_0} > 0)$ that is encountered is one for which $b_{i_0}/b_{i_0 s}$ is minimal (positive).

In the case of degeneration, i.e., when there are zero slack terms, it can be assumed that the desired "adjacent" vertex coincides with the initial vertex $y_1 = \dots = y_n = 0$ and there will actually be no movement ($t = 0$). This occurs if $b_{i_0} = 0$ and $b_{i_0 s} > 0$, since then $y_{i_0} = -b_{i_0 s}t + b_{i_0} = -b_{i_0 s}t$ is nonnegative only when $t = 0$, while for $t > 0$ we have $y_{i_0} < 0$ and we leave the polyhedron Ω.

If, however, $b_{i_0} = 0$ and $b_{i_0 s} < 0$, then $y_{i_0} = -b_{i_0 s}t + b_{i_0} = -b_{i_0 s}t$ remains positive when $t > 0$, so that it is not necessary to set $t = 0$ (to remain at the initial vertex) if $\min\limits_i \frac{b_i}{b_{is}} (i > n, b_{is} > 0)$ is positive.

Thus, in the case of degeneration we first examine all upper branches corresponding to columns over negative coefficients in the z-row, i.e., in each column we consider the coefficients opposite the zero slack terms. If some such column opposite a zero slack term has no positive coefficients, this column must be used as the resolvent column, since motion along the corresponding edge is permissible. Otherwise, it is impossible to move along any of the upper edges and it is necessary to examine a lateral edge. It must be converted to an upper edge by modified Jordan elimination over a resolvent element given by the rule in Paragraph 2 (no motion occurs in this case).

After a finite number of steps either we shall have left the vertex under consideration, or we shall have shown that a maximum occurs at this vertex, or we shall have shown that the function z is unbounded.

5. Monotonicity and Finiteness of the Simplex Algorithm

The simplex method, as its geometric interpretation shows, belongs to the class of so-called *monotonic algorithms*, i.e., the class of algorithms such that from step to step there is a monotonic approach toward a desired value. To prove this analytically, it is sufficient to show that in using the simplex method to pass from one trial solution to another, i.e., in using the rule of Paragraph 2 to choose a resolvent element, the value of the function z does not decrease.

Indeed, after elimination of coordinates (see Section 2, Paragraph 2) and construction of table (2.4′), in which all constant terms are nonnegative, a basic solution is provided by $y_1 = \ldots = y_n = 0$. If the z-row contains a negative coefficient, say, $q_s < 0$, then transition to the next trial solution requires a modified Jordan elimination with resolvent elements chosen with the rule of Paragraph 2 in the sth column (say, $b_{rs} > 0$). Such a coefficient exists if the problem has a bounded solution (see the end of Paragraph 2). For the new value of Q, which we denote by Q' we have (assuming that $q_s < 0, b_{rs} > 0$, $b_r \geqslant 0$)

$$Q' = \frac{Qb_{rs} - q_s b_r}{b_{rs}} = Q - \frac{q_s b_r}{b_{rs}} \geqslant Q.$$

Thus, if $b_r > 0$, then $Q' > Q$, i.e., the algorithm step under discussion is *strictly monotonic*. If $b_r = 0$, we have $Q' = Q$, i.e., strict monotonicity does not occur and a degeneracy occurs.

The phenomenon of degeneracy is discussed in detail in Section 6.

In the nondegenerate case it is easy to show that the algorithm is finite, because the polyhedron Ω has only a finite number of vertices and, because the algorithm is strictly monotonic, it is impossible to return to a vertex that has already been investigated.

In the degenerate case, however, the algorithm may prove to be infinite, since, because the process is not strictly monotonic (if no means have been provided for remembering which edges leaving a given vertex have already been investigated), it is possible to return to a previously encountered table. This procedure is called *cycling*. In Section 6 we shall show how the rule of Paragraph 2 can be changed to eliminate cycling and ensure that the algorithm is finite. There we shall also consider the analogous problem of the possibility of cycling (in the case of degeneracy) when the simplex method is used to find a basic solution.

4. METHODS FOR STATING CONSTRAINTS

1. Constraints in the Form of a System of Linear Equations

The linear programming problem is frequently encountered in the following form:

Among the solutions of the system

$$\left.\begin{array}{c} a_{11}x_1 + \ldots + a_{1n}x_n = a_1, \\ \ldots\ldots\ldots\ldots\ldots \\ a_{m1}x_1 + \ldots + a_{mn}x_n = a_m, \\ x_1 \geqslant 0, \ \ldots, \ x_n \geqslant 0 \end{array}\right\} \tag{2.6}$$

find one that maximizes (minimizes) the linear form

$$z = p_1x_1 + \ldots + p_nx_n. \tag{2.1}$$

The geometric meaning of this problem is generally the same as that of the basic problem of Section 1, except that here the space in which the problem is considered may have dimension less than n.

Indeed, assume that the matrix $\|a_{ij}\|$ has rank r. Then system (2.6) can be solved for r unknowns, say, for example, for $x_1, \ldots, x_r$:

$$\begin{array}{c} x_1 = b_{1,r+1}x_{r+1} + \ldots + b_{1n}x_n + b_1, \\ \ldots\ldots\ldots\ldots\ldots\ldots \\ x_r = b_{r,r+1}x_{r+1} + \ldots + b_{rn}x_n + b_r. \end{array}$$

When the inequalities of system (2.6) are taken into account, we find that

$$\left.\begin{array}{c} x_1 = b_{1,r+1}x_{r+1} + \ldots + b_{1n}x_n + b_1 \geqslant 0, \\ \ldots\ldots\ldots\ldots\ldots\ldots \\ x_r = b_{r,r+1}x_{r+1} + \ldots + b_{rn}x_n + b_r \geqslant 0, \\ x_{r+1} \geqslant 0, \ \ldots, \ x_n \geqslant 0. \end{array}\right\} \tag{2.7}$$

Thus, the problem has reduced to the problem (discussed in Sections 2 and 3) of maximizing a linear function

$$z = c_{r+1}x_{r+1} + \ldots + c_nx_n + c \tag{2.1'}$$

(obtained from form (2.1) by substitution for $x_1, \ldots, x_r$) under constraints (2.7).

In fact, application of the simplex method does not require preliminary transition from problem (2.1)-(2.6) to problem (2.1')-(2.7), since the simplex method can be applied directly to problem (2.1)-(2.6). We shall consider this step by step.

1) Construction of a table. Without loss of generality, we may assume that $\alpha_i \geqslant 0$ $(i=1, \ldots, m)$. Then, if some of the variables, say, $x_1, \ldots, x_k$, have positive coefficients in only one of the equations of system (2.6), we solve the corresponding equations for these variables (the right sides remain nonnegative), substitute into (2.1), and construct the table

	$-x_{k+1}$	$-x_{k+2}$	$\ldots$	$-x_n$	1
$x_1 =$	$\alpha_{1,k+1}$	$\alpha_{1,k+2}$	$\ldots$	α_{1n}	α_1
$\ldots$	$\ldots$	$\ldots$	$\ldots$	$\ldots$	$\ldots$
$x_k =$	$\alpha_{k,k+1}$	$\alpha_{k,k+2}$	$\ldots$	α_{kn}	α_k
$0 =$	$\alpha_{k+1,k+1}$	$\alpha_{k+1,k+2}$	$\ldots$	$\alpha_{k+1,n}$	α_{k+1}
$\ldots$	$\ldots$	$\ldots$	$\ldots$	$\ldots$	$\ldots$
$0 =$	$\alpha_{m,k+1}$	$\alpha_{m,k+2}$	$\ldots$	α_{mn}	α_m
$z =$	γ_{k+1}	γ_{k+2}	$\ldots$	γ_n	M

in which all of the constant terms α_j are nonnegative.

Usually, this table consists only of 0-rows and the z-row, i.e., system (2.6) cannot be solved immediately for some of the unknowns.

2) Finding a basic solution. To obtain a basic solution, it is necessary to eliminate all the 0-rows step by step. The following rule can be used to eliminate the ith 0-row: Consider the column that contains the positive coefficient α_{ij} in the ith 0-row; note all positive coefficients in this column (including α_{ij}); divide the corresponding slack terms by the coefficients that have been noted, and use the coefficient for which this ratio takes its smallest value as the resolvent element. If this coefficient proves to be α_{ij} (a favorable case), then, after a modified Jordan elimination, the zero on the left of the ith 0-row will be carried to the top of the table and will replace x_j. Thereby we shall have eliminated a 0-row.

If, however, the resolvent element is α_{lj} $(l \neq i)$, we carry out a modified Jordan elimination by working with the ith 0-row (i.e., by choosing the resolvent element from the coefficients in the column containing the positive entry α_{ij} in the ith 0-row). We then proceed until either we have eliminated the ith 0-row (the resolvent element is a member of the ith 0-row and the zero is carried to the top of the table), or we prove that system (2.6) is inconsistent (all the coefficients of the ith 0-row become nonpositive and the constant term remains positive).

After the zeros are carried to the top of the table, we eliminate the columns of coefficients under them.

We show that the new table obtained after each modified Jordan elimination has all its slack terms nonnegative. Indeed, if the resolvent element is α_{ij}, the sign of the slack term α_i in the resolvent 0-row does not change, so that α is positive and any other slack term α_l' in the new table is given by the formula

$$\alpha_l' = \frac{1}{\alpha_{ij}} (\alpha_l \alpha_{ij} - \alpha_i \alpha_{lj}),$$

where $\alpha_{lj} > 0$, $\alpha_l \geqslant 0$, $\alpha_i > 0$. Then

$$\text{if } \alpha_{lj} < 0, \text{ then } \alpha_l' > 0,$$

$$\text{if } \alpha_{lj} = 0, \text{ then } \alpha_l' \geqslant 0,$$

$$\text{if } \alpha_{lj} > 0, \text{ then } \alpha_l' = \alpha_{lj}\left(\frac{\alpha_l}{\alpha_{lj}} - \frac{\alpha_i}{\alpha_{ij}}\right) \geqslant 0,$$

since $\alpha_{lj} > 0$ and $\frac{\alpha_l}{\alpha_{lj}} \geqslant \frac{\alpha_i}{\alpha_{ij}}$ (because of the rule used to choose α_{lj} as the resolvent element). Our assertion can be proved in exactly the same way when the resolvent element is an entry α_{rj} that does not belong to a 0-row.

This method for eliminating 0-rows is applied until all 0-rows are eliminated or it is proved that system (2.6) is inconsistent.

Remark. If the constant term in some rth 0-row is equal to zero when a trial solution is found and all the nonzero coefficients in this row have the same signs, then the columns containing these coefficients, as well as the row itself, may be eliminated and the x_j eliminated here can be assumed to be equal to zero. This reduces the size of the table, which reduces the quantity of computation.

The rule formulated in the above remark is based on the fact that when the indicated x_j are not equal to zero, our 0-equation, and hence system (2.6), are clearly inconsistent.

3) Optimal solutions are found in exactly the same way as in Section 3.

2. Mixed Systems of Constraints

Sometimes the constraints are mixed, consisting of inequalities (in addition to the inequalities $x_1 \geqslant 0, \ldots, x_n \geqslant 0$) and equations. In this case the linear programming problem is stated as follows: Among the solutions of the system

$$\left.\begin{array}{ll} a_{i1}x_1 + \ldots + a_{in}x_n \leqslant a_i & (i = 1, \ldots, r), \\ a_{k1}x_1 + \ldots + a_{kn}x_n = a_k & (k = r+1, \ldots, m), \\ x_1 \geqslant 0, \ldots, x_n \geqslant 0, & \end{array}\right\} \tag{2.6'}$$

where $a_k \geqslant 0$ $(k = r+1, \ldots, m)$, find one that maximizes (minimizes) the linear form

$$z = p_1 x_1 + \ldots + p_n x_n. \tag{2.1}$$

We introduce the inequalities of (2.6′) into the table in the form

$$y_i = -(a_{i1}x_1 + \ldots + a_{in}x_n) + a_i \quad (i = 1, \ldots, r),$$

while we introduce the equations in the form of 0-equations

$$0 = -(a_{k1}x_1 + \ldots + a_{kn}x_n) + a_k \quad (k = r+1, \ldots, m).$$

Thus, we obtain the table

	$-x_1$	$\dots$	$-x_n$	1
$y_1 =$	a_{11}	$\dots$	a_{1n}	a_1
$\dots$	$\dots$	$\dots$	$\dots$	$\dots$
$y_r =$	a_{r1}	$\dots$	a_{rn}	a_r
$0 =$	$a_{r+1,1}$	$\dots$	$a_{r+1,n}$	a_{r+1}
$\dots$	$\dots$	$\dots$	$\dots$	$\dots$
$0 =$	a_{m1}	$\dots$	a_{mn}	a_m
$z =$	$-p_1$	$\dots$	$-p_n$	0

We eliminate the 0-equations as in Paragraph 2, find a basic solution as in Section 2, and find an optimal solution as in Section 3.

3. Examples

Example 1. Find the maximal value of the form

$$z = -5x_1 + 10x_2 - 7x_3 + 3x_4$$

on the set of *nonnegative* solutions of the system

$$\begin{aligned} x_1 + x_2 + 7x_3 + 2x_4 &= \frac{7}{2}, \\ -2x_1 - x_2 + 3x_3 + 3x_4 &= \frac{3}{2}, \\ 2x_1 + 2x_2 + 8x_3 + x_4 &= 4. \end{aligned}$$

The initial table for the problem is

	$-x_1$	$-x_2$	$-x_3$	$-x_4$	1
$0 =$	1	1	7	2	$\frac{7}{2}$
$0 =$	−2	−1	3	3	$\frac{3}{2}$
$0 =$	$\boxed{2}$	2	8	1	4
$z =$	5	−10	7	−3	0

To find a basic solution, we must eliminate the 0-rows. We first consider the positive coefficient 1 in the first 0-row, compare the ratios of the constant terms to the positive coefficients in the first column, and find that the resolvent element must be the 2 shown in a square.

Modified Jordan elimination and elimination of the column under the zero carried to the top of the table yields

	$-x_2$	$-x_3$	$-x_4$	1
$0=$	0	$\boxed{3}$	$\frac{3}{2}$	$\frac{3}{2}$
$0=$	1	11	4	$\frac{11}{2}$
$x_1=$	1	4	$\frac{1}{2}$	2
$z=$	-15	-13	$-\frac{11}{2}$	-10

.

We have thus eliminated one 0-row. Similarly, we obtain the following tables

	$-x_2$	$-x_4$	1
$x_3=$	0	$\frac{1}{2}$	$\frac{1}{2}$
$0=$	$\boxed{1}$	$-\frac{3}{2}$	0
$x_1=$	1	$-\frac{3}{2}$	0
$z=$	-15	1	$\frac{-7}{2}$

$\rightarrow$

	$-x_4$	1
$x_3=$	$\frac{1}{2}$	$\frac{1}{2}$
$x_2=$	$-\frac{3}{2}$	0
$x_1=$	0	0
$z=$	$\frac{-43}{2}$	$\frac{-7}{2}$

$=$

	$-x_4$	1
$x_3=$	$\boxed{\frac{1}{2}}$	$\frac{1}{2}$
$x_2=$	$-\frac{3}{2}$	0
$z=$	$-\frac{43}{2}$	$-\frac{7}{2}$

.

The last table contains no 0-rows, so we have the basic solution

$$x_4 = 0, \quad x_3 = \frac{1}{2}, \quad x_2 = 0, \quad x_1 = 0.$$

Now we shall attempt to find an optimal solution. In the column over the negative coefficient $-\frac{43}{2}$ of the z-row there is only one positive coefficient, $\frac{1}{2}$, so it must be the resolvent element.

Modified Jordan elimination yields the table

	$-x_3$	1
$x_4=$		1
$x_2=$		$\frac{3}{2}$
$z=$	43	18

,

which yields, when we set $x_3 = 0$,

$$\max z = 18,$$

which is achieved when

$$x_1 = 0, \quad x_2 = \frac{3}{2}, \quad x_3 = 0, \quad x_4 = 1.$$

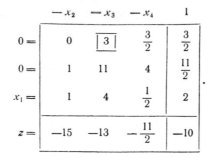

Example 2. Find the maximum of the linear form

$$z = 10x_1 - x_2 - 9x_3 - 8x_4$$

on the set of *nonnegative* solutions of the mixed system of constraints

$$\begin{aligned}
2x_1 - x_2 - 3x_3 - x_4 + 2 &= 0,\\
5x_1 - 2x_2 \qquad\quad - 3x_4 + 5 &= 0,\\
-7x_1 + 4x_2 - x_3 - 4x_4 + 1 &\geqslant 0,\\
-3x_1 - 2x_2 - 5x_3 - 6x_4 + 10 &\geqslant 0.
\end{aligned}$$

The table for the problem is

	$-x_1$	$-x_2$	$-x_3$	$-x_4$	1
$0 =$	−2	$\boxed{1}$	3	1	2
$0 =$	−5	2	0	3	5
$y_1 =$	7	−4	1	4	1
$y_2 =$	3	2	5	6	10
$z =$	−10	1	9	8	0

Modified Jordan elimination over the entry 1 in the square in the first row and elimination of the column of coefficients over the zero carried to the top of the table yield

	$-x_1$	$-x_3$	$-x_4$	1
$x_2 =$	−2	3	1	2
$0 =$	−1	−6	$\boxed{1}$	1
$y_1 =$	−1	13	8	9
$y_2 =$	7	−1	4	6
$z =$	−8	6	7	−2

Similarly, we eliminate the second 0-row:

	$-x_1$	$-x_3$	1
$x_2 =$	−1	9	1
$x_4 =$	−1	−6	1
$y_1 =$	$\boxed{7}$	61	1
$y_2 =$	11	23	2
$z =$	−1	48	−9

Now we attempt to find an optimal solution. Over the negative entry in the z-row the resolvent element must be 7, and modified Jordan elimination yields the table

	$-y_1$	$-x_3$	1
$x_2 =$			$\frac{8}{7}$
$x_4 =$			$\frac{8}{7}$
$x_1 =$			$\frac{1}{7}$
$y_2 =$			$\frac{3}{7}$
$z =$	$\frac{1}{7}$	$\frac{397}{7}$	$-\frac{62}{7}$

which contains no negative entries in the z-row. As a result, the maximum is

$$\max z = -\frac{62}{7},$$

and is achieved when $x_3 = 0$, $y_1 = 0$. Finally,

$$x_1 = \frac{1}{7}, \quad x_2 = \frac{8}{7}, \quad x_3 = 0, \quad x_4 = \frac{8}{7}.$$

5. MINIMIZATION OF LINEAR FORMS

1. Reduction to a Maximization Problem

Thus far, we have used the simplex method only to solve the problem of *maximizing* the linear form

$$z = p_1x_1 + \ldots + p_nx_n \tag{2.1}$$

under the constraints

$$-a_{i1}x_1 - \ldots - a_{in}x_n + a_i \geqslant 0 \quad (i = 1, \ldots, m). \tag{2.2}$$

In many problems it is required to *minimize* form (2.1) under constraints (2.2). To do so, it is sufficient to set

$$Z = -z = -p_1x_1 - \ldots - p_nx_n$$

and to *maximize* the form thus obtained under constraints (2.2). It is clear that

$$\min z = -\max Z.$$

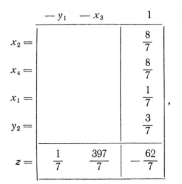

Remark. The problem of minimizing linear form (2.1) under constraints (2.2) can also be solved directly by the simplex method without, by changing signs, reducing it to a maximization problem. To do so, the optimality test and the rules for choosing resolvent elements in the simplex algorithm must be changed somewhat.

. The optimality test for a basic solution (i.e., one on which min z is achieved) is now the absence of positive coefficients in the z-row, which yields

$$\min z = Q.$$

The resolvent element must now be chosen in a column over a *positive* entry in the z-row (and not over a negative coefficient as in the case of maximization).

2. Examples

Example 1. Minimize the linear form

$$z = -3x_1 + 6x_2$$

under the constraints

$$\begin{aligned} y_1 &= x_1 + 2x_2 + 1 \geqslant 0, \\ y_2 &= 2x_1 + x_2 - 4 \geqslant 0, \\ y_3 &= x_1 - x_2 + 1 \geqslant 0, \\ y_4 &= x_1 - 4x_2 + 13 \geqslant 0, \\ y_5 &= -4x_1 + x_2 + 23 \geqslant 0. \end{aligned}$$

We reduce this problem to the problem of maximizing the form

$$Z = -z = 3x_1 - 6x_2$$

under the same constraints.

1) The table for the problem is

	$-x_1$	$-x_2$	1
$y_1 =$	$\boxed{-1}$	−2	1
$y_2 =$	−2	−1	−4
$y_3 =$	−1	1	1
$y_4 =$	−1	4	13
$y_5 =$	4	−1	23
$Z =$	−3	6	0

2) Elimination of the coordinate x_1 leads to the table

	$-y_1$	$-x_2$	1
$y_2 =$	−2	3	−6
$y_3 =$	−1	3	0
$y_4 =$	−1	6	12
$y_5 =$	4	−9	27
$Z =$	−3	12	−3

and a separate expression for x_1:

$$x_1 = y_1 - 2x_2 - 1.$$

Elimination of the coordinate x_2 yields

	$-y_1$	$-y_2$	1
$y_3 =$	1	−1	6
$y_4 =$	3	−2	24
$y_5 =$	−2	$\boxed{3}$	9
$Z =$	5	−4	21

,

and for x_2 we have the expression

$$x_2 = \frac{2}{3} y_1 - \frac{1}{3} y_2 - 2.$$

The slack terms are nonnegative, so that $y_1 = y_2 = 0$ is a trial solution for our system of constraints.

3) Now we attempt to find an optimal solution. The Z-row contains the negative entry -4, while the column of coefficients over it contains only one positive entry, 3, so it must be the resolvent element. Modified Jordan elimination yields the table

	$-y_1$	$-y_5$	1
$y_3 =$			9
$y_4 =$			30
$y_2 =$			3
$Z =$	$\frac{7}{3}$	$\frac{4}{3}$	33

,

which contains no negative coefficients in the Z-row. The problem is solved:

$$\max Z = 33,$$

so that min $z = -33$, which is achieved at $y_1 = y_5 = 0$; here

$$y_3 = 9, \quad y_4 = 30, \quad y_2 = 3 \text{ and } x_2 = -3, \quad x_1 = 5.$$

Example 2. Now we shall solve the problem of Example 1 without reducing it to a maximization problem. After elimination of x_1 and x_2, the initial table

	$-x_1$	$-x_2$	1
$y_1 =$	$\boxed{-1}$	−2	1
$y_2 =$	−2	−1	−4
$y_3 =$	−1	1	1
$y_4 =$	−1	4	13
$y_5 =$	4	−1	23
$z =$	3	−6	0

takes the form

	$-y_1$	$-y_2$	1
$y_3 =$	1	—1	6
$y_4 =$	3	—2	24
$y_5 =$	—2	[3]	9
$z =$	—5	4	—21

,

where

$$x_1 = y_1 - 2x_2 - 1,$$

$$x_2 = \frac{2}{3}y_1 - \frac{1}{3}y_2 - 2.$$

The basic solution is

$$y_1 = y_2 = 0,$$

and now we can turn to finding an optimal solution.

In contrast to the case of maximizing a linear form, in the minimization problem we choose the resolvent element from the column of coefficients located above a positive coefficient in the z-row; in our case, we must choose the resolvent element from the column over the coefficient 4. Here the column contains only one positive coefficient, 3, so we must use it as the resolvent element. Modified Jordan elimination yields the table

	$-y_1$	$-y_5$	1
$y_3 =$			9
$y_4 =$			30
$y_2 =$			3
$z =$	$-\frac{7}{3}$	$-\frac{4}{3}$	—33

,

in which all the entries in the z-row are nonpositive. The process terminates here, and min $z = -33$ is achieved when

$$y_1 = y_5 = 0, \quad y_3 = 9, \quad y_4 = 30, \quad y_2 = 3,$$

i.e., when

$$x_2 = -3, \quad x_1 = 5.$$

6. DEGENERACY

1. Cycling

Assume that in the process of solving a linear programming problem, say, the problem of maximizing the linear form (2.1) under constraints (2.2), we have obtained some basic solution that has led to a table of the form

	$-y_1$	$\ldots$	$-y_n$	1
$y_{n+1}=$	$b_{n+1,1}$	$\ldots$	$b_{n+1,n}$	b_{n+1}
$\ldots$	$\ldots$	$\ldots$	$\ldots$	$\ldots$
$y_m=$	b_{m1}	$\ldots$	b_{mn}	b_m
$z=$	q_1	$\ldots$	q_n	Q

(2.4′)

in which all the slack terms are nonnegative. If, in this case, the simplex method does not provide a unique resolvent element at some step, i.e., if there is more than one least ratio of slack terms to the corresponding positive coefficients in the resolvent column, then, after this step, all the above-mentioned slack terms, except for the slack term in the resolvent row, will clearly be equal to zero. Then more than n planes pass through the vertex $y_1 = \ldots = y_n = 0$ of the polyhedron Ω (basic solution). This case, as we mentioned above, is called the *degenerate case.*

The phenomenon of degeneracy can be treated as a case in which two or more vertices of the polyhedron Ω merge, and the edge (or edges) connecting these vertices contracts to a point.

As we noted in Paragraph 5 of Section 3, the simplex method can lose its strict monotonicity only in the case of degeneracy.

Geometrically, this is quite understandable, when we realize that the step in the simplex algorithm is equivalent to passage along an edge from one basic solution to another, i.e., passage from a given vertex of the polyhedron Ω to an adjacent vertex (located on the same edge). In the case of degeneracy—coincidence of two adjacent vertices—it can be seen that after such a step we remain at the same vertex, except this time it is expressed in terms of the different set of n planes (equations) passing through this vertex.

If we continue to apply the simplex method and do not remember the edges considered, we are faced with the possibility of so-called *cycling,* when, after some given number of steps, each of which leads to some choice of n planes passing through the given vertex, we return to some previous choice and the process repeats.

2. The ε-Method for Elimination of Cycling

A. Charnes [16] has developed a simple method (the so-called ε-method) for eliminating cycling. The basis of this method is an appropriate parallel shift of each of the planes that are not at the top of the table, "separation" of merged vertices, and solution of a new, no longer degenerate problem (such that the algorithm is strictly monotonic), after which the shifted planes are returned to their initial position and a solution is obtained for the original problem.

Application of the ε-method begins with introduction of the following new indexing of the variables in table (2.4′):

$$\begin{array}{r|ccccc|c|} & -y'_{p+1} & \cdots & -y'_{p+s} & \cdots & -y'_{p+n} & 1 \\ \hline y'_1= & b_{1,p+1} & \cdots & b_{1,p+s} & \cdots & b_{1,p+n} & b_1 \\ \cdots & \cdots & \cdots & \cdots & \cdots & \cdots & \cdots \\ y'_i= & b_{i,p+1} & \cdots & b_{i,p+s} & \cdots & b_{i,p+n} & b_i \\ \cdots & \cdots & \cdots & \cdots & \cdots & \cdots & \cdots \\ y'_p= & b_{p,p+1} & \cdots & b_{p,p+s} & \cdots & b_{p,p+n} & b_p \\ \hline z= & q_{p+1} & \cdots & q_{p+s} & \cdots & q_{p+n} & Q \\ \hline \end{array}, \qquad (2.8)$$

where

$$p+n=m,\ y'_1=y_{n+1},\ y'_2=y_{n+2},\ \ldots,\ y'_p=y_m,$$
$$y'_{p+1}=y_1,\ \ldots,\ y'_{p+n}=y_n,$$

and the coefficients are denoted by the same letter b, but have new indices. Then the plane $y'_i=0$ ($i=1, \ldots, p$) is subjected to a parallel shift by adding the polynomial

$$P_i(\varepsilon)=\varepsilon^i+b_{i,p+1}\,\varepsilon^{p+1}+b_{i,p+2}\,\varepsilon^{p+2}+\ \ldots\ +b_{i,p+n}\,\varepsilon^{p+n}$$
$$(i=1,\ \ldots,\ p)$$

to the slack term of the equation of the plane in question, where ε is a positive number that is smaller than any of the numbers encountered in later computations. We thus obtain the table

$$\begin{array}{r|ccccc|c|} & \varepsilon^{p+1} & \cdots & \varepsilon^{p+s} & \cdots & \varepsilon^{p+n} & \\ & -y'_{p+1} & \cdots & -y'_{p+s} & \cdots & -y'_{p+n} & 1 \\ \hline y'_1= & b_{1,p+1} & \cdots & b_{1,p+s} & \cdots & b_{1,p+n} & b_1+\varepsilon+b_{1,p+1}\varepsilon^{p+1}+\ldots+b_{1,p+n}\varepsilon^{p+n} \\ \cdots & \cdots & \cdots & \cdots & \cdots & \cdots & \cdots \\ y'_i= & b_{i,p+1} & \cdots & b_{i,p+s} & \cdots & b_{i,p+n} & b_i+\varepsilon^i+b_{i,p+1}\varepsilon^{p+1}+\ldots+b_{i,p+n}\varepsilon^{p+n} \\ \cdots & \cdots & \cdots & \cdots & \cdots & \cdots & \cdots \\ y'_p= & b_{p,p+1} & \cdots & b_{p,p+s} & \cdots & b_{p,p+n} & b_p+\varepsilon^p+b_{p,p+1}\varepsilon^{p+1}+\ldots+b_{p,p+n}\varepsilon^{p+n} \\ \hline z= & q_{p+1} & \cdots & q_{p+s} & \cdots & q_{p+n} & Q \\ \hline \end{array},$$

in which all of the slack terms $b_i(\varepsilon)=b_i+P_i(\varepsilon)$ ($i=1, \ldots, p$) are strictly positive.

Indeed, if $b_i>0$, then $b_i(\varepsilon)=b_i+P_i(\varepsilon)>0$ because ε is small. If, however, $b_i=0$, then $b_i(\varepsilon)=P_i(\varepsilon)>0$, since, because $\varepsilon>0$ is small, the sign of the polynomial is determined by the term $\varepsilon^i>0$.

We can now see that the resolvent element in the new table is uniquely determined. Indeed, assume that the sth column is the resolvent column. Then, if

$$\frac{b_k}{b_{k,p+s}}<\frac{b_i}{b_{i,p+s}} \qquad (i=1,\ \ldots;\ k-1,\ k+1,\ \ldots,\ p)$$

and, therefore, the resolvent element $b_{k,p+s}$ is uniquely determined in the old table, we have

$$\frac{b_k + P_k(\varepsilon)}{b_{k,\,p+s}} < \frac{b_i + P_i(\varepsilon)}{b_{i,\,p+s}} \qquad (i = 1, \ldots, k-1, k+1, \ldots, p)$$

in the new table, because ε is small.

If, however, for the old table there is more than one minimal ratio $\frac{b_i}{b_{i,\,p+s}}$ $(i = 1, \ldots, p)$, say, $\frac{b_k}{b_{k,\,p+s}} = \frac{b_l}{b_{l,\,p+s}}$, and the resolvent element in the old table is therefore not uniquely determined, the ratios

$$\frac{b_k + P_k(\varepsilon)}{b_{k,\,p+s}} \text{ and } \frac{b_l + P_l(\varepsilon)}{b_{l,\,k+s}}$$

are not equal, because $P_k(\varepsilon) \neq P_l(\varepsilon)$ and, consequently, the resolvent element is uniquely determined.

It is not difficult to show that, instead of computing with polynomials in ε in each modified Jordan elimination, we need compute only the slack terms (without the polynomials), and then add polynomials in ε that are composed as above so that no two of the new polynomials are identical. The resolvent element will again be uniquely determined.

It can be shown (see, for example, [14]), that, because ε is sufficiently small, an optimal solution of our problem with constant terms perturbed by the $P_i(\varepsilon)$ corresponds to the optimal solution of the initial problem that is obtained by setting $\varepsilon = 0$ in the modified problem.

Cycling in the search for a trial solution can be eliminated analogously.

7. DUALITY IN LINEAR PROGRAMMING

1. Dual Tables

Consider the system

$$y_i = \sum_{j=1}^{n} a_{ij}(-x_j) \qquad (i = 1, \ldots, m) \tag{2.9}$$

and the table

(2.10)

	$-x_1$	....	$-x_s$	...	$-x_n$
$y_1 =$	a_{11}	...	a_{1s}	...	a_{1n}
...	...	...	...	...	...
$y_r =$	a_{r1}	...	a_{rs}	...	a_{rn}
...	...	...	...	...	...
$y_m =$	a_{m1}	...	a_{ms}	...	a_{mn}

with matrix $A = \|a_{ij}\|$.

Modified Jordan elimination exchanging the dependent variable y_r and the independent variable x_s leads to the table

$$
\begin{array}{r|ccccc|l}
 & -x_1 & \ldots & -y_r & \ldots & -x_n & \\
\hline
y_1 = & b_{11} & \ldots & -a_{1s} & \ldots & b_{1n} & \\
\cdots & \cdots & \cdots & \cdots & \cdots & \cdots & \\
x_s = & a_{r1} & \ldots & 1 & \ldots & a_{rn} & : a_{rs} \, . \\
\cdots & \cdots & \cdots & \cdots & \cdots & \cdots & \\
y_m = & b_{m1} & \ldots & -a_{ms} & \ldots & b_{mn} & \\
\hline
\end{array}
\qquad (2.11)
$$

$$(b_{ij} = a_{ij}a_{rs} - a_{rj}a_{is}).$$

Now, consider the system of linear forms

$$v_j = \sum_{i=1}^{m} a_{ij}u_i \qquad (j = 1, \ldots, n) \qquad (2.12)$$

whose matrix A^* is the transpose of A. We construct a table for this system with independent variables u_i at the left and dependent variables v_j at the top, and thus obtain the table

$$
\begin{array}{r|ccccc|l}
 & v_1 = & \ldots & v_s = & \ldots & v_n = & \\
\hline
u_1 & a_{11} & \ldots & a_{1s} & \ldots & a_{1n} & \\
\cdots & \cdots & \cdots & \cdots & \cdots & \cdots & \\
u_r & a_{r1} & \ldots & a_{rs} & \ldots & a_{rn} & , \\
\cdots & \cdots & \cdots & \cdots & \cdots & \cdots & \\
u_m & a_{m1} & \ldots & a_{ms} & \ldots & a_{mn} & \\
\hline
\end{array}
\qquad (2.13)
$$

whose matrix coincides with the matrix A of table (2.10).

Tables (2.10) and (2.13) are said to be *dual to each other.*

Exchanging u_r and v_s by ordinary Jordan elimination over a_{rs}, we obtain the table

$$
\begin{array}{r|ccccc|l}
 & v_1 = & \ldots & u_r = & \ldots & v_n = & \\
\hline
u_1 & b_{11} & \ldots & -a_{1s} & \ldots & b_{1n} & \\
\cdots & \cdots & \cdots & \cdots & \cdots & \cdots & \\
v_s & a_{r1} & \ldots & 1 & \ldots & a_{rn} & : a_{rs}, \\
\cdots & \cdots & \cdots & \cdots & \cdots & \cdots & \\
u_m & b_{m1} & \ldots & -a_{ms} & \ldots & b_{mn} & \\
\hline
\end{array}
$$

which is the same as table (2.11).

Thus, modified Jordan elimination over the entries in table (2.10) is equivalent to ordinary Jordan elimination over the entries in the dual table (2.13).

This justifies the desirability of the following combination of dual tables (2.10) and (2.13):

$$
\begin{array}{r|ccccc|l}
 & v_1 = & \ldots & v_s = & \ldots & v_n = & \\
 & -x_1 & \ldots & -x_s & \ldots & -x_n & \\
\hline
u_1 \;\; y_1 = & a_{11} & \ldots & a_{1s} & \ldots & a_{1n} & \\
\cdots & \cdots & \cdots & \cdots & \cdots & \cdots & \\
u_r \;\; y_r = & a_{r1} & \ldots & a_{rs} & \ldots & a_{rn} & . \\
\cdots & \cdots & \cdots & \cdots & \cdots & \cdots & \\
u_m \;\; y_m = & a_{m1} & \ldots & a_{ms} & \ldots & a_{mn} & \\
\hline
\end{array}
$$

In this table each Jordan elimination appropriately transforms both tables simultaneously.

2: Dual Linear Programming Problems

Together with the basic linear programming problem, i.e., the problem of maximizing the linear form

$$z = p_1 x_1 + \dots + p_n x_n \tag{2.14}$$

under the constraints

$$\left.\begin{aligned} a_{i1}x_1 + \dots + a_{in}x_n \leqslant a_i \quad (i = 1, \dots, m),\\ x_1 \geqslant 0, \dots, x_n \geqslant 0, \end{aligned}\right\} \tag{2.15}$$

we can consider the so-called *dual* (or *conjugate*) problem, which consists in minimizing the linear form

$$w = a_1 u_1 + \dots + a_m u_m \tag{2.16}$$

under the constraints

$$\left.\begin{aligned} a_{1j}u_1 + \dots + a_{mj}u_m \geqslant p_j \quad (j = 1, \dots, n),\\ u_1 \geqslant 0, \dots, u_m \geqslant 0, \end{aligned}\right\} \tag{2.17}$$

i.e., the problem obtained from the basic linear programming problem by way of the following four rules:

1) the slack terms $a_1, \dots, a_m$ of the constraints are used as the coefficients of a new linear form, while the coefficients $p_1, \dots, p_n$ of the original target function are used as the slack terms in a new set of constraints;

2) the coefficient matrix of the new set of constraints is the matrix A^*, the transpose of A (the coefficient matrix of the old constraints);

3) in the new constraints the inequalities are reversed ($\leqslant$ is replaced by $\geqslant$; nonnegativity of variables, however, is retained);

4) maximization of the original linear form is replaced by minimization of the new one.

As we can easily show, the basic problem can be replaced by the dual of its dual. If we write the constraints of the basic problem in the form

$$\begin{aligned} y_1 &= -a_{11}x_1 - \dots - a_{1n}x_n + a_1 \geqslant 0,\\ &\dots\dots\dots\dots\dots\dots\dots\\ y_m &= -a_{m1}x_1 - \dots - a_{mn}x_n + a_m \geqslant 0,\\ &\quad x_1 \geqslant 0, \dots, x_n \geqslant 0, \end{aligned}$$

and we write the constraints of the dual problem in the form

$$
\begin{aligned}
v_1 &= a_{11}u_1 + \dots + a_{m1}u_m - p_1 \geqslant 0, \\
&\dots\dots\dots\dots\dots\dots\dots\dots \\
v_n &= a_{1n}u_1 + \dots + a_{mn}u_m - p_n \geqslant 0, \\
& u_1 \geqslant 0, \ \dots, \ u_m \geqslant 0,
\end{aligned}
$$

we immediately see that the constraints of these two dual problems can be combined in the single table

$$
\begin{array}{lll|ccccc|c}
 & & & v_1 = & \dots & v_s = & \dots & v_n = & w = \\
 & & & -x_1 & \dots & -x_s & \dots & -x_n & 1 \\
\hline
u_1 & y_1 & = & a_{11} & \dots & a_{1s} & \dots & a_{1n} & a_1 \\
\cdot & \cdot & \cdot & \cdot & \cdot & \cdot & \cdot & \cdot & \cdot \\
u_r & y_r & = & a_{r1} & \dots & a_{rs} & \dots & a_{rn} & a_r \\
\cdot & \cdot & \cdot & \cdot & \cdot & \cdot & \cdot & \cdot & \cdot \\
u_m & y_m & = & a_{m1} & \dots & a_{ms} & \dots & a_{mn} & a_m \\
\hline
1 & z & = & -p_1 & \dots & -p_s & \dots & -p_n & 0
\end{array} \qquad (2.18)
$$

Then, as we shall show in Paragraph 3 below, by solving the basic linear programming problem (2.14)-(2.15), we shall have solved simultaneously the dual problem (2.16)-(2.17), and, conversely, the solution obtained by maximizing z in the basic problem provides the minimum for the form w.

3. The Fundamental (First) Duality Theorem of Linear Programming

Consider a pair of dual problems (2.18). If one of them has an optimal solution, then so does the other, and the extremal values of the corresponding linear forms z and w are equal:

$$\max z = \min w^*.$$

If the linear form in one of these problems is unbounded, then the dual problem is inconsistent.

Proof. Assume that the basic problem has a finite solution and that we have obtained, for example, the table

$$
\begin{array}{lll|cccccc|c}
 & & & u_1 = & \dots & u_s = & v_{s+1} = & \dots & v_n = & w = \\
 & & & -y_1 & \dots & -y_s & -x_{s+1} & \dots & -x_n & 1 \\
\hline
v_1 & x_1 & = & b_{11} & \dots & b_{1s} & b_{1,s+1} & \dots & b_{1n} & b_1 \\
\cdot & \cdot & \cdot & \cdot & \cdot & \cdot & \cdot & \cdot & \cdot & \cdot \\
v_s & x_s & = & b_{s1} & \dots & b_{ss} & b_{s,s+1} & \dots & b_{sn} & b_s \\
u_{s+1} & y_{s+1} & = & b_{s+1,1} & \dots & b_{s+1,s} & b_{s+1,s+1} & \dots & b_{s+1,n} & b_{s+1} \\
\cdot & \cdot & \cdot & \cdot & \cdot & \cdot & \cdot & \cdot & \cdot & \cdot \\
u_m & y_m & = & b_{m1} & \dots & b_{ms} & b_{m,s+1} & \dots & b_{mn} & b_m \\
\hline
1 & z & = & q_1 & \dots & q_s & q_{s+1} & \dots & q_n & Q
\end{array}, \qquad (2.19)
$$

---

* As we shall show below (Paragraph 4), if the linear forms z and w are equal on a pair of basic solutions of dual problems, these solutions are optimal.

in which

$$b_1 \geqslant 0, \ldots, b_m \geqslant 0; \; q_1 \geqslant 0, \ldots, q_n \geqslant 0;$$

max $z = Q$ and the maximum is achieved on $y_1 = \ldots = y_s = x_{s+1} = \ldots = x_n = 0$.

We shall now analyze the table obtained here for the dual problem. By setting the variables on the left equal to zero,

$$v_1 = \ldots = v_s = u_{s+1} = \ldots = u_m = 0,$$

we find that

$$u_1 = q_1 \geqslant 0, \ldots, u_s = q_s \geqslant 0;$$
$$v_{s+1} = q_{s+1} \geqslant 0, \ldots, v_n = q_n \geqslant 0.$$

As a result, we obtain the basic solution

$$u_1 = q_1, \ldots, u_s = q_s, \; u_{s+1} = \ldots = u_m = 0,$$

and it is clear from the last column that the value of the linear function

$$w = b_1 v_1 + \ldots + b_s v_s + b_{s+1} u_{s+1} + \ldots + b_m u_m + Q$$

at the point $v_1 = \ldots = v_s = u_{s+1} = \ldots = u_m = 0$ will be minimal because the $b_1, \ldots, b_m$ are nonnegative. Thus, min $w = Q$ coincides with max z.

Now assume that the linear form z of the basic problem is not bounded. This means* that for some upper variable, say, y_s, the corresponding coefficient q_s is negative ($q_s < 0$) in (2.19), while all the coefficients in its column $b_{1s}, \ldots, b_{ms}$ are not positive: $b_{1s} \leqslant 0, \ldots, b_{ms} \leqslant 0$. It then follows from the dual table that

$$u_s = b_{1s} v_1 + \ldots + b_{ss} v_s + b_{s+1,\, s} u_{s+1} + \ldots + b_{ms} u_m + q_s \leqslant q_s < 0,$$

so that the system of constraints for the dual problem is inconsistent, i.e., nonnegativity of u_s is inconsistent with nonnegativity of $v_1, \ldots, v_s, u_{s+1}, \ldots, u_m$.

Remark 1. Inconsistency of one linear programming problem does not imply that the linear form of the dual problem is unbounded. It turns out that here the dual problem may also be inconsistent, which is clear from the following example:

---

* If the function z is not bounded above, then in searching for max z we shall obtain ultimately a *final* table whose z-column contains only negative coefficients (since otherwise max z is finite), say, $q_s < 0$, and nonpositive coefficients. Otherwise we can repeat the process, i.e., the table is not final.

	$v_1 = -x_1$	$v_2 = -x_2$	$w = 1$
u_1 $y_1 =$	2	−2	1
u_2 $y_2 =$	−2	2	−3
1 $z =$	−3	1	0

Here the problem of maximizing the linear form

$$z = 3x_1 - x_2$$

under the constraints

$$\begin{aligned} y_1 &= -2x_1 + 2x_2 + 1 \geqslant 0, \\ y_2 &= 2x_1 - 2x_2 - 3 \geqslant 0, \\ x_1 &\geqslant 0, \quad x_2 \geqslant 0 \end{aligned}$$

is inconsistent because $y_1 + y_2 = -2 < 0$. The dual problem of minimizing the linear form

$$w = u_1 - 3u_2$$

under the constraints

$$\begin{aligned} v_1 &= 2u_1 - 2u_2 - 3 \geqslant 0, \\ v_2 &= -2u_1 + 2u_2 + 1 \geqslant 0, \\ u_1 &\geqslant 0, \quad u_2 \geqslant 0 \end{aligned}$$

is also inconsistent, because $v_1 + v_2 = -2 < 0$.

Remark 2. It is not difficult to see that we obtain simultaneously the solutions of the two dual problems only when we maximize the linear form in the problem in which the left side of the constraints is less than the right $\left(\sum_{j=1}^{n} a_{ij}x_j \leqslant a_i\right)$ i.e., the linear form at the bottom of the combined table, and minimize the linear form of the problem in which the left side of the constraints is greater than the right $\left(\sum_{i=1}^{m} a_{ij}u_i \geqslant p_j\right)$ i.e., the linear form on the left of the combined table.

4. Equivalence of Pairs of Dual Problems to the Problem of Solving a System of Linear Inequalities

Consider a pair of dual linear programming problems with constraints combined into a table of the form (2.18).

The problem of finding optimal solutions for this pair of dual problems is equivalent to the problem of solving the system of linear inequalities

$$\left.\begin{aligned} &a_{i1}x_1 + \ldots + a_{in}x_n \leqslant a_i \quad (i = 1, \ldots, m), \\ &x_j \geqslant 0 \quad (j = 1, \ldots, n), \\ &a_{1j}u_1 + \ldots + a_{mj}u_m \geqslant p_j \quad (j = 1, \ldots, n), \\ &u_i \geqslant 0 \quad (i = 1, \ldots, m). \end{aligned}\right\} \tag{2.20}$$

$$p_1x_1 + \ldots + p_nx_n \geqslant a_1u_1 + \ldots + a_mu_m, \tag{2.21}$$

which consists of all constraints of both problems (including non-negativity of all variables) and the additional inequality (2.21), which replaces the optimization requirement.

Proof. Let $x^*(x_1^*, \ldots, x_n^*)$ and $u^*(u_1^*, \ldots, u_m^*)$ be corresponding optimal solutions for our pair of dual problems. Then, by the fundamental duality theorem, we have the equation

$$p_1x_1^* + \ldots + p_nx_n^* = a_1u_1^* + \ldots + a_mu_m^*, \tag{2.22}$$

i.e., in addition to system (2.20), these optimal solutions satisfy inequality (2.21), so that any pair of corresponding optimal solutions is also a solution of system (2.20)-(2.21).

Conversely, let $x(x_1, \ldots, x_n)$ and $u(u_1, \ldots, u_m)$ be a solution of system (2.20)-(2.21). Because x and u satisfy system (2.20), we have

$$\sum_{j=1}^{n} p_jx_j \leqslant \sum_{j=1}^{n}\left(\sum_{i=1}^{m} a_{ij}u_i\right)x_j \leqslant \sum_{i=1}^{m} a_iu_i,$$

i.e.,

$$p_1x_1 + \ldots + p_nx_n \leqslant a_1u_1 + \ldots + a_mu_m. \tag{2.23}$$

Thus, x and u satisfy inequalities (2.21) and (2.23), and so satisfy Eq. (2.22).

It is now sufficient to show that *if two solutions x and u of system (2.20) satisfy Eq. (2.22), then they are optimal.*

Indeed, if x, for example, were not optimal, then, by denoting optimal solutions by x^* and u^*, we would have

$$\sum_{j=1}^{n} p_jx_j^* > \sum_{j=1}^{n} p_jx_j = \sum_{i=1}^{m} a_iu_i \geqslant \sum_{i=1}^{m} a_iu_i^*,$$

i.e.,

$$\sum_{j=1}^{n} p_jx_j^* > \sum_{i=1}^{m} a_iu_i^*,$$

which contradicts the fundamental duality theorem.

5. The Second Duality Theorem

If at least one optimal solution of one of a pair of dual problems causes the ith constraint to become a strict inequality, then the ith component (i.e., x_i or u_i) of each optimal solution of the other dual problem is **equal** *to zero.*

If, however, the ith component of at least one optimal solution of one of a pair of dual problems is positive, then each optimal solution of the dual problems causes the ith constraint of this problem to become an equality.

In other words, *optimal solutions x^* and u^* of a pair of dual problems satisfy the conditions*

$$1)\quad x_j^*\left(\sum_{i=1}^{m} a_{ij}u_i^* - p_j\right) = 0 \qquad (j = 1, \ldots, n),$$

$$2)\quad u_i^*\left(\sum_{j=1}^{n} a_{ij}x_j^* - a_i\right) = 0 \qquad (i = 1, \ldots, m).$$

Proof. Let x^* and u^* be optimal solutions of a pair of dual problems, so that they satisfy system (2.20) and the following inequalities, which follow from system (2.20):

$$\sum_{j=1}^{n} p_j x_j^* \leqslant \sum_{i=1}^{m}\sum_{j=1}^{n} a_{ij}u_i^* x_j^* \leqslant \sum_{i=1}^{m} a_i u_i^*.$$

By the first duality theorem (Paragraph 3), we have the equation

$$\sum_{j=1}^{n} p_j x_j^* = \sum_{i=1}^{m} a_i u_i^*$$

for optimal solutions x^* and u^*; using the inequalities written above, we find that

$$\sum_{j=1}^{n} p_j x_j^* = \sum_{j=1}^{n}\sum_{i=1}^{m} a_{ij}u_i^* x_j^*,$$

$$\sum_{i=1}^{m} a_i u_i^* = \sum_{i=1}^{m}\sum_{j=1}^{n} a_{ij}u_i^* x_j^*.$$

It follows from the first equation that

$$\sum_{j=1}^{n} x_j^*\left(\sum_{i=1}^{m} a_{ij}u_i^* - p_j\right) = 0.$$

Since all the x_j^* and the expressions in parentheses are nonnegative, we have

$$x_j^*\left(\sum_{i=1}^{m} a_{ij}u_i^* - p_j\right) = 0 \qquad (j = 1, \ldots, n).$$

Conditions 2) can be proved analogously.

Converse theorem. If two basic solutions x^* and u^* of a pair of dual problems satisfy conditions 1)–2), they are optimal.

Proof. Summing condition 1) over j and condition 2) over i, we obtain the equations

$$\sum_{i=1}^{m}\sum_{j=1}^{n} a_{ij}u_i^*x_j^* = \sum_{j=1}^{n} p_jx_j^*,$$

$$\sum_{i=1}^{m}\sum_{j=1}^{n} a_{ij}u_i^*x_j^* = \sum_{i=1}^{m} a_iu_i^*,$$

so that the values of the functions z and w at the points x^* and u^* coincide. Because z and w are equal, it follows (Paragraph 4) that x^* and u^* are optimal solutions.

6. Economic Interpretations of the Basic and Dual Problems

Assume that the conditions of the basic and dual problems have been combined into a table of the form (2.18).

The basic linear programming problem can be given an economic interpretation in the following manner.

Assume that n different activities are required to produce a given product, and that m different ingredients (various forms of raw materials) are used. Let the jth activity use, per unit time, a_{ij} units of the ith ingredient, let there be a total cost of the ith ingredient, of which there is a total supply of a_i units, and let there be p_j units of product produced. Finally, let x_j be the time required for the jth activity. Then, for a "plan" $x=(x_1, \ldots, x_n)$ the production will be $z = p_1x_1 + \ldots + p_nx_n$ units of product and $a_{i1}x_1 + \ldots + a_{in}x_n$ units of the ith ingredient ($i=1, \ldots, m$) will be used. The following problem appears naturally: Find a policy (optimal) for which, with a given expenditure of ingredients, the maximum quantity of product will be produced. The mathematical model of this problem is a basic linear programming problem:

Maximize the linear form

$$z = p_1x_1 + \ldots + p_nx_n$$

under the constraints

$$a_{i1}x_1 + \ldots + a_{in}x_n \leqslant a_i \qquad (i=1, \ldots, m),$$
$$x_1 \geqslant 0, \ldots, x_n \geqslant 0.$$

To interpret the dual linear programming problem economically, it is desirable to take the cost per unit of product as the unit of measurement. Then the jth activity will produce goods at a cost of p_j units per unit time. This will require a_{1j} units of the first ingredient, a_{2j} of the second, ..., and a_{mj} of the mth ingredient.

If we denote the relative costs per unit of each ingredient by $u_1, \ldots, u_m$, respectively, we obtain, as an estimate of the quantity of ingredients required (in the cost scale that has been adopted), the sum $a_{1j}u_1 + \ldots + a_{mj}u_m$ and, clearly, it is no less than the cost p_j of the product obtained, i.e.,

$$a_{1j}u_1 + \ldots + a_{mj}u_m \geqslant p_j \qquad (j = 1, \ldots, n). \tag{2.24}$$

It is clear that $u_1 \geqslant 0, \ldots, u_m \geqslant 0$ and that, if we take $u_1, \ldots, u_m$ sufficiently large, all of conditions (2.24) will be satisfied. Since, of course, we don't want to increase the relative costs of the ingredients it is natural to minimize them, i.e., to choose them so that a further decrease is impossible, i.e., requires a change in conditions (2.24). It is clear that such minimal basic (optimal) relative costs will minimize the cost of the total quantity of ingredients required, i.e., will minimize the sum

$$a_1u_1 + \ldots + a_mu_m.$$

Thus, the following dual problem serves as a mathematical model of the economic problem of allocating ingredients so that their costs in a relative cost scale are minimal: Minimize the linear form

$$w = a_1u_1 + \ldots + a_mu_m$$

under the constraints

$$a_{1j}u_1 + \ldots + a_{mj}u_m \geqslant p_j \qquad (j = 1, \ldots, n)$$
$$u_1 \geqslant 0, \ldots, u_m \geqslant 0.$$

The fundamental duality theorem now has the following economic interpretation:

If an optimal policy for maximum production exists for problem (2.18), then there also exists an optimal policy for minimizing the relative cost of ingredients, and in this cost scale the cost z of the entire product produced according to an optimal policy coincides with the cost w of all of the ingredients.

The second duality theorem now reads as follows:

If consumption $\sum_{j=1}^{n} a_{ij}x_j$ of the ith ingredient is strictly less than the supply a_i in some optimal policy,

$$\sum_{j=1}^{n} a_{ij}x_j < a_i,$$

then the cost u_i of this ingredient is equal to zero in each optimal relative-cost policy. If, however, in some optimal relative-cost policy the cost u_i of the ith ingredient is greater than zero, then the consumption of this ingredient is exactly equal to its supply for each optimal policy:

$$\sum_{j=1}^{n} a_{ij}x_j = a_i.$$

Moreover, if, for some optimal relative-cost policy, the cost $\sum_{i=1}^{m} a_{ij}u_i$ of ingredients used in the jth activity is strictly greater than the cost p_j of the final product produced in this operation,

$$\sum_{i=1}^{m} a_{ij}u_i > p_j,$$

then the jth activity is not used in any optimal policy, i.e., $x_j = 0$. If, however, the jth activity is used ($x_j > 0$) in some optimal production policy, then the cost $\sum_{i=1}^{m} a_{ij}u_i$ of ingredients used in the jth activity in some optimal relative-cost policy is exactly equal to the cost p_j of the product produced by this activity:

$$\sum_{i=1}^{m} a_{ij}u_i = p_j.$$

Thus, optimal policies provided by dual problems agree in the sense that an optimal production policy corresponds to an optimal relative-cost plan, in which profitable activities are used and unprofitable operations are not, and vice versa.

7. Dual Problems with Mixed Systems of Constraints

In the pairs of dual problems considered above, both systems of constraints contained only inequalities. Such problems can be called *symmetrically dual problems* or *problems with constraints of the same type.*

But an asymmetric duality can also be established: Constraints can be given in the mixed form of inequalities and equations, or in the form of equations and inequalities only of the form $x_j \geqslant 0$ ($u_i \geqslant 0$).*

1) Mixed systems of constraints. We first consider the problem** of maximizing the linear form

$$z = p_1x_1 + \dots + p_nx_n$$

under the condition that the variables $x_1, \dots, x_n$ satisfy the mixed system of constraints

*It is not difficult to show that these problems, which, at first sight, appear to be more general, can be reduced to symmetric problems, so that the first duality theorem also holds for asymmetric problems, while the second holds, with the obvious change that its assertion pertains only to inequality-type constraints and to variables that are assumed to be nonnegative. We shall not discuss this in detail, and below we shall show how to solve such problems directly.

**Cf. Section 4.

$$
\begin{aligned}
y_1 &= -a_{11}x_1 - \dots - a_{1n}x_n + a_1 \geqslant 0, \\
&\dots\dots\dots\dots\dots\dots\dots \\
y_r &= -a_{r1}x_1 - \dots - a_{rn}x_n + a_r \geqslant 0, \\
0 &= -a_{r+1,1}x_1 - \dots - a_{r+1,n}x_n + a_{r+1}, \\
&\dots\dots\dots\dots\dots\dots\dots \\
0 &= -a_{m1}x_1 - \dots - a_{mn}x_n + a_m, \\
&x_1 \geqslant 0, \dots, x_s \geqslant 0, \ s \leqslant n.
\end{aligned}
$$

The dual of this problem is the problem of minimizing the linear form

$$w = a_1u_1 + \dots + a_mu_m$$

under the constraints

$$
\begin{aligned}
v_1 &= a_{11}u_1 + \dots + a_{m1}u_m - p_1 \geqslant 0, \\
&\dots\dots\dots\dots\dots\dots\dots \\
v_s &= a_{1s}u_1 + \dots + a_{ms}u_m - p_s \geqslant 0, \\
0 &= a_{1,s+1}u_1 + \dots + a_{m,s+1}u_m - p_{s+1}, \\
&\dots\dots\dots\dots\dots\dots\dots \\
0 &= a_{1n}u_1 + \dots + a_{mn}u_m - p_n, \\
&u_1 \geqslant 0, \dots, u_r \geqslant 0.
\end{aligned}
$$

As in the case of a symmetric problem, it is convenient to combine the constraints of this problem in a single table:

		$v_1 =$ $-x_1$	...	$v_s =$ $-x_s$	$0 =$ $-x_{s+1}$	...	$0 =$ $-x_n$	$w =$ 1
u_1	$y_1 =$	a_{11}	...	a_{1s}	$a_{1,s+1}$	...	a_{1n}	a_1
...	...	...	...	...	...	...	...	...
u_r	$y_r =$	a_{r1}	...	a_{rs}	$a_{r,s+1}$	...	a_{rn}	a_r
u_{r+1}	$0 =$	$a_{r+1,1}$	...	$a_{r+1,s}$	$a_{r+1,s+1}$	...	$a_{r+1,n}$	a_{r+1}
...	...	...	...	...	...	...	...	...
u_m	$0 =$	a_{m1}	...	a_{ms}	$a_{m,s+1}$	...	a_{mn}	a_m
1	$z =$	$-p_1$	...	$-p_s$	$-p_{s+1}$	...	$-p_n$	0

(2.25)

We should note that nonnegativity conditions are imposed only on those independent variables u_i (x_j) that, in combined table (2.25), are located in rows (columns) corresponding to the inequality constraints of the basic (dual) problem. No constraints are imposed on the variables u_i (x_j) corresponding to equation constraints in the basic (dual) problem.

Table (2.25) can be used, as usual (see Section 4), to solve the basic problem, which automatically yields a solution to the dual problem.

Example. Consider the problem dual to the problem of maximizing the linear form

$$z = 10x_1 - x_2 - 9x_3 - 8x_4$$

under the mixed system of constraints

$$\begin{aligned}
2x_1 - x_2 - 3x_3 - x_4 + 2 &= 0,\\
5x_1 - 2x_2 - 3x_4 + 5 &= 0,\\
y_1 = -7x_1 + 4x_2 - x_3 - 4x_4 + 1 &\geqslant 0,\\
y_2 = -3x_1 - 2x_2 - 5x_3 - 6x_4 + 10 &\geqslant 0,\\
x_1 \geqslant 0,\ x_2 \geqslant 0,\ x_3 \geqslant 0,\ x_4 &\geqslant 0.
\end{aligned}$$

By definition, we must minimize the linear form

$$w = 2u_1 + 5u_2 + u_3 + 10u_4$$

under the constraints

$$\begin{aligned}
v_1 &= -2u_1 - 5u_2 + 7u_3 + 3u_4 - 10 \geqslant 0,\\
v_2 &= u_1 + 2u_2 - 4u_3 + 2u_4 + 1 \geqslant 0,\\
v_3 &= 3u_1 + u_3 + 5u_4 + 9 \geqslant 0,\\
v_4 &= u_1 + 3u_2 + 4u_3 + 6u_4 + 8 \geqslant 0,\\
&u_3 \geqslant 0, \quad u_4 \geqslant 0.
\end{aligned}$$

The basic problem was solved on pp. 44-45, and we found that

$$\max z = -\frac{62}{7}.$$

As a result,

$$\min w = -\frac{62}{7}.$$

To determine the values of the u_i on which this minimum is achieved, we combine the tables obtained above, during solution of the maximization problem, with the dual tables, and separately write expressions for the eliminated independent variables of the dual problem, i.e., for the variables on which no constraints are imposed, since they are required for expression of the solution in terms of the old coordinates only after the problem is solved. We have

	$v_1 =$ $-x_1$	$v_2 =$ $-x_2$	$v_3 =$ $-x_3$	$v_4 =$ $-x_4$	$w =$ 1	
u_1 $0 =$	−2	$\boxed{1}$	3	1	2	
u_2 $0 =$	−5	2	0	3	5	
u_3 $y_1 =$	7	−4	1	4	1	→
u_4 $y_2 =$	3	2	5	6	10	
1 $z =$	−10	1	9	8	0	

	$v_1 = -x_1$	$u_1 = 0$	$v_3 = -x_3$	$v_4 = -x_4$	$w = 1$
v_2 $x_2 =$	-2	1	3	1	2
u_2 $0 =$	-1	-2	-6	$\boxed{1}$	1
→ u_3 $y_1 =$	-1	4	13	8	9
u_4 $y_2 =$	7	-2	-1	4	6
1 $z =$	-8	-1	6	7	-2

,

$$u_1 = v_2 - 2u_2 + 4u_3 - 2u_4 - 1.$$

We eliminate the second column (under u_1) and, after modified Jordan elimination, we obtain the table

	$v_1 = -x_1$	$v_3 = -x_3$	$u_2 = 0$	$w = 1$
v_2 $x_2 =$	-1	9	-1	1
v_4 $x_4 =$	-1	-6	1	1
u_3 $y_1 =$	$\boxed{7}$	61	-8	1
u_4 $y_2 =$	11	23	-4	2
1 $z =$	-1	48	-7	-9

,

$$u_2 = -v_2 + v_4 - 8u_3 - 4u_4 - 7.$$

We eliminate the third column and execute the next step, after which we obtain the table

	$u_3 = -y_1$	$v_3 = -x_3$	$w = 1$
v_2 $x_2 =$			$\frac{8}{7}$
v_4 $x_4 =$			$\frac{8}{7}$
v_1 $x_1 =$			$\frac{1}{7}$
u_4 $y_2 =$			$\frac{3}{7}$
1 $z =$	$\frac{1}{7}$	$\frac{397}{7}$	$-\frac{62}{7}$

.

The last table is final, since all the constant terms of the basic problem and the coefficients of the z-row are nonnegative. Thus,

$$\min w = -\frac{62}{7}$$

and is achieved when

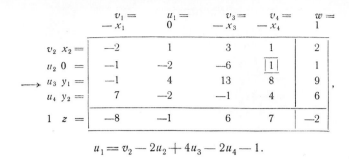

$$v_2=v_4=v_1=u_4=0, \quad u_3=\frac{1}{7}, \quad v_3=\frac{397}{7},$$

i.e., when

$$u_1=\frac{111}{7}, \quad u_2=-\frac{57}{7}, \quad u_3=\frac{1}{7}, \quad u_4=0.$$

2) *Equation constraints (and inequality constraints of the form* $x_j \geqslant 0$*).* We shall consider the problem of maximizing the linear form

$$z=p_1x_1+\ldots+p_nx_n$$

under constraints of the form

$$\begin{gathered} 0=-a_{11}x_1-\ldots-a_{1n}x_n+a_1, \\ \cdots\cdots\cdots\cdots \\ 0=-a_{m1}x_1-\ldots-a_{mn}x_n+a_m, \\ x_1\geqslant 0, \ldots, x_n\geqslant 0. \end{gathered}$$

This problem is the special case to which the mixed problem discussed above reduces when $r=0$, $s=n$. It is assumed that the number of equations in the problem is less then the number of unknowns.

The dual problem consists in minimizing the linear form

$$w=a_1u_1+\ldots+a_mu_m$$

under the constraints

$$\begin{gathered} v_1=a_{11}u_1+\ldots+a_{m1}u_m-p_1\geqslant 0, \\ \cdots\cdots\cdots\cdots \\ v_n=a_{1n}u_1+\ldots+a_{mn}u_m-p_n\geqslant 0. \end{gathered}$$

Since $r=0$, no constraints are imposed on the variables u_i.

As above, it is convenient to combine the conditions of this pair of dual problems in a single table:

<table>
<tr><td></td><td></td><td>$v_1=$
$-x_1$</td><td>...
...</td><td>$v_n=$
$-x_n$</td><td>$w=$
1</td></tr>
<tr><td>u_1</td><td>$0=$</td><td>a_{11}</td><td>...</td><td>a_{1n}</td><td>a_1</td></tr>
<tr><td>...</td><td>...</td><td>...</td><td>...</td><td>...</td><td>...</td></tr>
<tr><td>u_m</td><td>$0=$</td><td>a_{m1}</td><td>...</td><td>a_{mn}</td><td>a_m</td></tr>
<tr><td>1</td><td>$z=$</td><td>$-p_1$</td><td>...</td><td>$-p_n$</td><td>0</td></tr>
</table>

We solve the basic problem, which will lead simultaneously to a solution of both dual problems.

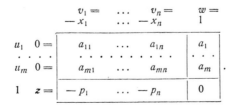

Example. The problem dual to the problem of maximizing the linear form

$$z = -5x_1 + 10x_2 - 7x_3 + 3x_4$$

under the constraints

$$\begin{aligned} 0 &= -\ x_1 - \ x_2 - 7x_3 - 2x_4 + \tfrac{7}{2}, \\ 0 &= \ \ 2x_1 + \ x_2 - 3x_3 - 3x_4 + \tfrac{3}{2}, \\ 0 &= -2x_1 - 2x_2 - 8x_3 - \ x_4 + 4, \\ & x_1 \geqslant 0, \quad x_2 \geqslant 0, \quad x_3 \geqslant 0, \quad x_4 \geqslant 0, \end{aligned}$$

which was solved in Example 1 of Paragraph 3, Section 4, is the problem of minimizing the form

$$w = \frac{7}{2}u_1 + \frac{3}{2}u_2 + 4u_3$$

under the constraints

$$\begin{aligned} v_1 &= u_1 - 2u_2 + 2u_3 + \ 5 \geqslant 0, \\ v_2 &= \ u_1 - \ u_2 + 2u_3 - 10 \geqslant 0, \\ v_3 &= 7u_1 + 3u_2 + 8u_3 + \ 7 \geqslant 0, \\ v_4 &= 2u_1 + 3u_2 + \ u_3 - \ 3 \geqslant 0. \end{aligned}$$

As the solution of the basic problem implies,

$$\min w = \max z = 18.$$

To determine values of the independent variables u_1, u_2, u_3 for which min w is achieved, we write expressions for them by using the dual tables obtained in the process of solving the basic problem.

The combined table for the basic and dual problems is

	$v_1 = -x_1$	$v_2 = -x_2$	$v_3 = -x_3$	$v_4 = -x_4$	$w = 1$
u_1 $0 =$	1	1	7	2	$\frac{7}{2}$
u_2 $0 =$	−2	−1	3	3	$\frac{3}{2}$
u_3 $0 =$	$\boxed{2}$	2	8	1	4
1 $z =$	5	−10	7	−3	0

.

Modified Jordan elimination over the entry 2 yields the table

	$u_3 = 0$	$v_2 = -x_2$	$v_3 = -x_3$	$v_4 = -x_4$	$w = 1$
u_1 $0 =$	$-\frac{1}{2}$	0	$\boxed{3}$	$\frac{3}{2}$	$\frac{3}{2}$
u_2 $0 =$	1	1	11	4	$\frac{11}{2}$
v_1 $x_1 =$	$\frac{1}{2}$	1	4	$\frac{1}{2}$	2
1 $z =$	$-\frac{5}{2}$	-15	-13	$-\frac{11}{2}$	-10

,

in which we eliminate the column under the zero carried to the top. This table gives us an expression for u_3:

$$u_3 = -\frac{1}{2}u_1 + u_2 + \frac{1}{2}v_1 - \frac{5}{2}.$$

The next resolvent element is 3, and we obtain the table

	$v_2 = -x_2$	$u_1 = 0$	$v_4 = -x_4$	$w = 1$
v_3 $x_3 =$	0	$\frac{1}{3}$	$\frac{1}{2}$	$\frac{1}{2}$
u_2 $0 =$	$\boxed{1}$	$-\frac{11}{3}$	$-\frac{3}{2}$	0
v_1 $x_1 =$	1	$-\frac{4}{3}$	$-\frac{3}{2}$	0
1 $z =$	-15	$\frac{13}{3}$	1	$-\frac{7}{2}$

,

from which it follows that

$$u_1 = \frac{1}{3}v_3 - \frac{11}{3}u_2 - \frac{4}{3}v_1 + \frac{13}{3}.$$

We now eliminate the second column, and the table takes the form

	$u_2 = 0$	$v_4 = -x_4$	$w = 1$
v_3 $x_3 =$	0	$\boxed{\frac{1}{2}}$	$\frac{1}{2}$
v_2 $x_2 =$	1	$-\frac{3}{2}$	0
v_1 $x_1 =$	-1	0	0
1 $z =$	15	$-\frac{43}{2}$	$-\frac{7}{2}$

,

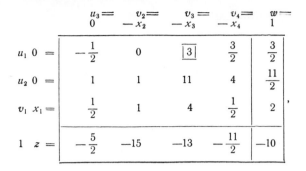

from which it follows that

$$u_2 = v_2 - v_1 + 15.$$

We now eliminate the first column, which yields

	$v_3 = -x_3$	$w = 1$
$v_4\ x_4 =$		1
$v_2\ x_2 =$		$\frac{3}{2}$
$v_1\ x_1 =$		0
$1\ z =$	43	18

so that

$$\min w = \max z = 18$$

and this is achieved when

$$v_4 = v_2 = v_1 = 0, \quad v_3 = 43,$$

i.e., when

$$u_2 = 15, \quad u_1 = -\frac{109}{3}, \quad u_3 = \frac{92}{3}.$$

8. The Dual Simplex Method

Assume that the conditions for a pair of dual problems have been combined in a single table

	$v_1 = -x_1$	$\ldots$	$v_s = -x_s$	$\ldots$	$v_n = -x_n$	$w = 1$
$u_1\ y_1 =$	a_{11}	$\ldots$	a_{1s}	$\ldots$	a_{1n}	a_1
$\ldots$	$\ldots$	$\ldots$	$\ldots$	$\ldots$	$\ldots$	$\ldots$
$u_r\ y_r =$	a_{r1}	$\ldots$	a_{rs}	$\ldots$	a_{rn}	a_r
$\ldots$	$\ldots$	$\ldots$	$\ldots$	$\ldots$	$\ldots$	$\ldots$
$u_m\ y_m =$	a_{m1}	$\ldots$	a_{ms}	$\ldots$	a_{mn}	a_m
$1\ z =$	$-p_1$	$\ldots$	$-p_s$	$\ldots$	$-p_n$	0

(2.26)

Then, as we showed above, the solution of the problem of maximizing z simultaneously yields a solution to the problem of minimizing w.

If we follow the transformations of the table and variables u_i and v_j, which can be done more easily by writing the table in the usual form

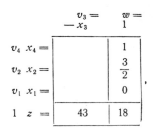

$$
\begin{array}{r|ccccc|c|}
 & u_1 & \dots & u_r & \dots & u_m & 1 \\
\hline
v_1 = & a_{11} & \dots & a_{r1} & \dots & a_{m1} & -p_1 \\
\dots & \dots & \dots & \dots & \dots & \dots & \dots \\
v_s = & a_{1s} & \dots & a_{rs} & \dots & a_{ms} & -p_s \\
\dots & \dots & \dots & \dots & \dots & \dots & \dots \\
v_n = & a_{1n} & \dots & a_{rn} & \dots & a_{mn} & -p_n \\
\hline
w = & a_1 & \dots & a_r & \dots & a_m & 0 \\
\hline
\end{array}, \qquad (2.27)
$$

we obtain a description of a new method of solving the problem of minimizing w; this method was developed by Lemke [31] and is called the *dual simplex method.*

Below, the rules established above for the simplex method of solving problems of maximizing z, transforming table (2.26), and the consequent rules developed for the dual simplex method for solving the problem of minimizing w by appropriate transformation on table (2.27) are described in parallel.

Simplex Method for Solving the Problem of Maximizing z

I. Rule for choosing resolvent elements for finding basic solutions.

1. We consider a row with negative slack term, say, $a_r < 0$. If, however, all the slack terms are nonnegative, a basic solution has been found and we proceed to find an optimal solution.

2. In the rth row we find a negative coefficient, say, $a_{rs} < 0$; the column containing this coefficient will be the resolvent column.

If all the coefficients in the rth row are nonnegative, the problem is inconsistent.

3. We find the nonnegative ratios of the slack terms to the coefficients of the resolvent (sth) column. For the resolvent element we choose the

Dual Simplex Method for Minimizing w

I. Rule for choosing resolvent elements for eliminating negativity in the w-row.

1. We consider a column with the negative coefficient in the w-row, say, $a_r < 0$. If, however, all the coefficients of the w-row are nonnegative, then 0 provides an upper bound for w and we proceed to find an optimal solution.

2. In the rth column we find a negative coefficient, say, $a_{rs} < 0$; we take the row containing this coefficient as the resolvent row.

If all of the coefficients of the rth column are nonnegative, then the form w is either unbounded below or the problem is inconsistent.

3. We find the nonnegative ratios of the coefficients of the w-row to the coefficients of the resolvent (sth) row, and, for the resolvent element, we choose

coefficient in the sth column for which the ratio is smallest.

If the smallest ratio is zero, we take its denominator as the resolvent element only when it is positive.

We execute a modified Jordan elimination over the resolvent element that is found.

If application of the preceding rules yields a table of the form (2.28a)

the coefficient in the sth row for which this ratio is smallest.

If the smallest ratio is zero, then its denominator will be the resolvent element only when it is positive.

After a resolvent element is chosen, we execute a modified Jordan elimination over it.

If application of the above rules yields a table of the form (2.28b)

	$-y_1$	$\dots$	$-y_s$	$-x_{s+1}$	$\dots$	$-x_n$	1
$x_1 =$	b_{11}	$\dots$	b_{1s}	$b_{1,s+1}$	$\dots$	b_{1n}	b_1
$\dots$	$\dots$	$\dots$	$\dots$	$\dots$	$\dots$	$\dots$	$\dots$
$x_s =$	b_{s1}	$\dots$	b_{ss}	$b_{s,s+1}$	$\dots$	b_{sn}	b_s
$y_{s+1} =$	$b_{s+1,1}$	$\dots$	$b_{s+1,s}$	$b_{s+1,s+1}$	$\dots$	$b_{s+1,n}$	b_{s+1}
$\dots$	$\dots$	$\dots$	$\dots$	$\dots$	$\dots$	$\dots$	$\dots$
$y_m =$	b_{m1}	$\dots$	b_{ms}	$b_{m,s+1}$		b_{mn}	b_m
$z =$	q_1	$\dots$	q_s	q_{s+1}	$\dots$	q_n	Q

(2.28a)

	v_1	$\dots$	v_s	u_{s+1}	$\dots$	u_m	1
$u_1 =$	b_{11}	$\dots$	b_{s1}	$b_{s+1,1}$	$\dots$	b_{m1}	q_1
$\dots$	$\dots$	$\dots$	$\dots$	$\dots$	$\dots$	$\dots$	$\dots$
$u_s =$	b_{1s}	$\dots$	b_{ss}	$b_{s+1,s}$	$\dots$	b_{ms}	q_s
$v_{s+1} =$	$b_{1,s+1}$	$\dots$	$b_{s,s+1}$	$b_{s+1,s+1}$	$\dots$	$b_{m,s+1}$	q_{s+1}
$\dots$	$\dots$	$\dots$	$\dots$	$\dots$	$\dots$	$\dots$	$\dots$
$v_n =$	b_{1n}	$\dots$	b_{sn}	$b_{s+1,n}$	$\dots$	b_{mn}	q_n
$w =$	b_1	$\dots$	b_s	b_{s+1}	$\dots$	b_m	Q

(2.28b)

in which all the slack terms b_1, $b_2, \dots, b_m$ are nonnegative and there are negative coefficients in the z-row, say, $q_s < 0$, an optimal solution has not yet been found and we proceed to find one. The quantity Q yields an estimate of z from below.

II. Rule for choosing resolvent elements for finding optimal solutions with the simplex method.

1. For the resolvent column we choose a column containing a negative coefficient in the z-row, say, the sth column ($q_s < 0$).

in which all of the coefficients $b_1, \dots, b_m$ of the w-row are nonnegative and there is still a negative term, say, $q_s < 0$, in the column of slack terms, an optimal solution has not yet been found and we proceed to find it. The quantity Q provides a lower bound for w.

II. Rule for choosing resolvent elements for finding optimal solutions with the dual simplex method.

1. For the resolvent row we choose a row with a negative constant term, say, the sth row ($q_s < 0$).

2. We find all the positive coefficients in this row, divide them by the corresponding slack terms, and, for the resolvent element, we choose the coefficient of the sth column for which the ratio is smallest.

If the sth column contains no positive coefficients, the function z is unbounded.

A finite number of modified Jordan eliminations will either maximize z or show that z is unbounded.

2. We find all the positive coefficients of this row, divide them by the corresponding coefficients of the w-row, and, for the resolvent element, choose the coefficient in the sth row for which this ratio is smallest.

If the sth row contains no positive coefficient, the problem is inconsistent.

A finite number of modified Jordan eliminations either minimizes the function w or demonstrates that the problem is inconsistent.

*Example 1.** Minimize the function

$$z = 4x_1 - x_2$$

under the constraints

$$\begin{aligned} y_1 &= \quad\quad\;\; x_2 - 2 \geqslant 0, \\ y_2 &= -x_1 + x_2 + 1 \geqslant 0, \\ y_3 &= \;\;\; x_1 - x_2 + 1 \geqslant 0, \\ y_4 &= \;\;\; x_1 - \frac{3}{2} \geqslant 0, \end{aligned}$$

$$x_1 \geqslant 0, \quad x_2 \geqslant 0.$$

The table for the problem is

	x_1	x_2	1
$y_1 =$	0	1	-2
$y_2 =$	-1	1	1
$y_3 =$	1	$\boxed{-1}$	1
$y_4 =$	1	0	$-\frac{3}{2}$
$z =$	4	-1	0

Over the negative coefficients in the z-row, there is a negative coefficient, -1, in the third row, which we take as the resolvent row.

Inspection of the nonnegative ratios $\frac{4}{1}$ and $\frac{-1}{-1}$ indicates that the resolvent element must be -1, and ordinary Jordan elimination yields the table

* Instead of denoting the variables by u_i and v_j, we shall, as usual, denote them by x_i and y_j.

	x_1	y_3	1
$y_1 =$	1	-1	-1
$y_2 =$	0	-1	2
$x_2 =$	1	-1	1
$y_4 =$	$\boxed{1}$	0	$-\frac{3}{2}$
$z =$	3	1	-1

which has positive coefficients in the z-row.

We now search for an optimal solution. For the resolvent row we take the fourth row, which contains the negative constant term $-\frac{3}{2}$. For the resolvent element, we use the 1 in this row. Ordinary Jordan elimination yields the table

	y_4	y_3	1
$y_1 =$			$\frac{1}{2}$
$y_2 =$			2
$x_2 =$			$\frac{5}{2}$
$x_1 =$			$\frac{3}{2}$
$z =$	3	1	$\frac{7}{2}$

in which all the slack terms are positive. As a result, an optimal solution has been found:

$$\min z = \frac{7}{2},$$

which is achieved at

$$x_1 = \frac{3}{2}, \quad x_2 = \frac{5}{2}.$$

Remark 1. To use the dual simplex method to maximize w, using the above rules, we need find only the minimum of $-w$, and then change the sign of the result, which will immediately provide the maximum of w. In this case it is necessary to change the above rules so that all the coefficients in the w-row become nonpositive.

Example 2. Maximize the function

$$z = 4x_1 - x_2$$

under the constraints

$$\begin{aligned}
y_1 &= \phantom{-x_1+{}} x_2 - 2 \geqslant 0,\\
y_2 &= -x_1 + x_2 + 1 \geqslant 0,\\
y_3 &= x_1 - x_2 + 1 \geqslant 0,\\
y_4 &= -x_1 \phantom{{}+x_2} + 4 \geqslant 0,\\
&x_1 \geqslant 0, \quad x_2 \geqslant 0.
\end{aligned}$$

The table for the problem is

	x_1	x_2	1
$y_1 =$	0	1	—2
$y_2 =$	—1	1	1
$y_3 =$	1	—1	1
$y_4 =$	[—1]	0	4
$z =$	4	—1	0

.

We consider the column with the positive coefficient in the z-row, find the negative coefficients in it, and find a row, say, the fourth, containing a negative coefficient to be the resolvent row. We find the nonpositive ratios of the coefficients of the z-row to the corresponding coefficients in the resolvent row, and the coefficients for which this ratio is largest (smallest in absolute value); we choose one of these coefficients as the resolvent element. In our example this ratio is unique, $\frac{4}{-1}$, so that the resolvent element is -1.

Ordinary Jordan elimination yields the table

	y_4	x_2	1
$y_1 =$	0	1	—2
$y_2 =$	1	[1]	—3
$y_3 =$	—1	—1	5
$x_1 =$	—1	0	4
$z =$	—4	—1	16

,

in which all of the coefficients of the z-row are negative, and we can turn to finding an optimal solution.

For the resolvent row we choose a row, say, the second, containing a negative slack term. To determine the resolvent element, we consider the nonpositive ratios of the coefficients of the z-row to the (positive) coefficients in the resolvent row, and we choose the coefficient for which this ratio is largest (smallest in absolute value) as the resolvent element.

In our example it is clear from the ratios $\left|\frac{-4}{1}\right|$ and $\left|\frac{-1}{1}\right|$ that the resolvent element must be the 1 in the second column. Ordinary Jordan elimination leads to the table

	y_4	y_2	1
$y_1 =$			1
$x_2 =$			3
$y_3 =$			2
$x_1 =$			4
$z =$	—3	—1	13

in which all of the constant terms are nonnegative, so that an optimal solution has been found:

$$\max z = 13;$$

this optimum is achieved at $x_1 = 4$, $x_2 = 3$.

Remark 2. In the dual simplex method, modified Jordan elimination can be used instead of ordinary Jordan elimination. Since, in this case, variables in the upper row of the table are written with minus signs, during selection of a resolvent element we must recall that the signs of all of the entries in the table, except for the slack terms, have signs opposite to those in the coefficients of the ordinary table, for which the rules have been formulated.

As a result, we attempt to minimize w only when all the coefficients of the w-row are nonpositive (as in the ordinary simplex method), and for the resolvent elements we take only those negative coefficients in the resolvent rows (i.e., those containing negative slack terms) for which the ratios of the coefficients in the w-row to the corresponding negative coefficients in the resolvent rows are smallest.

We attempt to maximize w when all the coefficients in the w-row are nonnegative (as in the usual simplex method), and for the resolvent elements we take only the negative coefficients in the resolvent rows for which the ratios of the coefficients in the w-row to the corresponding negative coefficients in the resolvent rows are smallest.

Remark 3. Assume that when z is minimized (maximized) by means of the simplex method, all the coefficients in the z-row are nonpositive (nonnegative) when a basic solution is sought, or in the initial table. Then, of course, it is desirable to solve the problem with the dual simplex method, since, to find an optimal solution, it is necessary only to make the slack terms nonnegative. Thus, for minimizing z in the example with the table

	$-x_1$	$-x_2$	$-x_3$	1
$y_1 =$	1	—1	1	5
$y_2 =$	—1	[—3]	3	—3
$y_3 =$	—2	1	—2	2
$z =$	—3	—1	—4	0

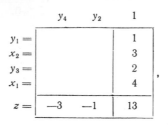

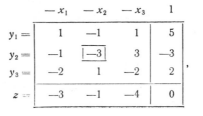

it is desirable to use the dual simplex method (since the coefficients of the z-row are already nonpositive).

Modified Jordan elimination over the entry -3 (since $\frac{-1}{-3} < \frac{-3}{-1}$) immediately yields an optimal solution

	$-x_1$	$-y_2$	$-x_3$	1
$y_1 =$				6
$x_2 =$				1
$y_3 =$				1
$z =$	$\frac{-8}{3}$	$-\frac{1}{3}$	-5	1

;

min $z=1$ and is achieved when $x_1 = x_3 = 0$, $x_2 = 1$.

Remark 4. As in the usual simplex method, the computational procedure for the dual simplex method reduces to successive transformation of tables according to the special rules given above. It is impossible to predict the difficulty presented by either of the methods.

We note that while a maximal (minimal) solution is approached from below (from above) through basic solutions in the ordinary simplex method, in the dual simplex method we approach a maximal (minimal) solution from above (from below), and the intermediate solutions are not basic solutions. Indeed, if the variables located at the top of intermediate table (2.28b) are set equal to zero, then, because there are negative slack terms, some of the variables on the side will also be negative.

Sometimes, when there is a large number of variables and constraints, it is desirable to use both methods for solving the same problem, since, in this case, it is possible to approach an optimal value of the linear form simultaneously from both sides—from above and from below—and if the difference between corresponding values of the linear forms is sufficiently small, the computation can be terminated and the basic solution can be taken as an approximate solution for the basic problem.

8. INTEGER PROGRAMMING

1. Statement of the Problem. Geometric Interpretation

Frequently, a linear programming problem, i.e., a problem of maximizing a linear form

$$z = p_1 x_1 + \dots + p_n x_n \tag{2.29}$$

under constraints

$$\left.\begin{array}{ll} a_{i1}x_1 + \dots + a_{in}x_n \leqslant a_i & (i = 1, \dots, m), \\ x_j \geqslant 0 \quad (j = 1, \dots, n), & \end{array}\right\} \tag{2.30}$$

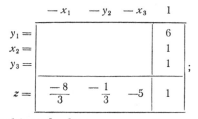

defining a polyhedron Ω, requires that the solution be integral where a_{ij} and a_i ($i = 1, \ldots, m; j = 1, \ldots, n$) are assumed to be integers.

The simplex method, however, leads directly to an integral solution only for a few problems. In the general case special methods are required to find an optimal integer solution for problem (2.29)-(2.30). These methods consist in choosing linear constraints that must be added to (2.30) to insure an integral solution.

R.E. Gomory [27-29b] had proposed a method that leads to an integral solution in a finite number of steps. It is easy to explain the method geometrically.

Consider the set of integer points in the polyhedron of constraints Ω. If the polyhedron Ω is replaced by the convex hull of integer points, the solution obtained with the simplex method for this variation of the problem is clearly an integer solution and provides an optimal integer solution for the initial problem.

Because it is difficult to construct this convex hull, intermediate polyhedrons including it and contained in Ω are constructed. In the method under discussion, this is accomplished by introduction of additional constraints that, in each step, decrease the polyhedron Ω (eliminate part of it) without eliminating any integer points, and the plane of the additional linear constraint passes through only one integer point. After a finite number of steps, a problem whose optimal solutions are simultaneously optimal integer solutions of the initial problem is obtained.

2. Description of the Algorithm. Preliminary Step

Solution of problem (2.29)-(2.30) with the simplex method leads, after a finite number of steps, to the table

	$-y_1$	$\ldots$	$-y_s$	$-x_{s+1}$	$\ldots$	$-x_n$	1
$x_1 =$	b_{11}	$\ldots$	b_{1s}	$b_{1,s+1}$	$\ldots$	b_{1n}	b_1
$\ldots$	$\ldots$	$\ldots$	$\ldots$	$\ldots$	$\ldots$	$\ldots$	$\ldots$
$x_s =$	b_{s1}	$\ldots$	b_{ss}	$b_{s,s+1}$	$\ldots$	b_{sn}	b_s
$y_{s+1} =$	$b_{s+1,1}$	$\ldots$	$b_{s+1,s}$	$b_{s+1,s+1}$	$\ldots$	$b_{s+1,n}$	b_{s+1}
$\ldots$	$\ldots$	$\ldots$	$\ldots$	$\ldots$	$\ldots$	$\ldots$	$\ldots$
$y_m =$	b_{m1}	$\ldots$	b_{ms}	$b_{m,s+1}$	$\ldots$	b_{mn}	b_m
$z =$	q_1	$\ldots$	q_s	q_{s+1}	$\ldots$	q_n	Q

,

in which all of the slack terms $b_1, \ldots, b_m$ and coefficients $q_1, \ldots, q_n$ of the z-row are nonnegative, so that

$$y_1 = \ldots = y_s = x_{s+1} = \ldots = x_n = 0, \quad x_1 = b_1, \ldots, x_s = b_s$$

provides an optimal solution of the problem. If not all the slack terms are integers, the solution is not an integer solution and we proceed to the general step.

For convenience, we rewrite the last table in the form

$$
\begin{array}{r|ccccc|c|}
 & -\xi_1 & \dots & -\xi_j & \dots & -\xi_n & 1 \\
\hline
\eta_1 = & b_{11} & \dots & b_{1j} & \dots & b_{1n} & b_1 \\
\dots & \dots & \dots & \dots & \dots & \dots & \dots \\
\eta_i = & b_{i1} & \dots & b_{ij} & \dots & b_{in} & b_i \\
\dots & \dots & \dots & \dots & \dots & \dots & \dots \\
\eta_m = & b_{m1} & \dots & b_{mj} & \dots & b_{mn} & b_m \\
\hline
z = & q_1 & \dots & q_j & \dots & q_n & Q \\
\hline
\end{array}
\qquad (2.31)
$$

General step. 1) Construction of the additional constraint. Assume that b_i is not an integer. We set

$$\beta_{ij} = b_{ij} - [b_{ij}] = b_{ij} - n_{ij}\text{*},$$
$$\beta_i = b_i - [b_i] = b_i - n_i$$

(so that $n_{ij} \leqslant b_{ij} < n_{ij} + 1$, $n_i < b_i < n_i + 1$, and $0 \leqslant \beta_{ij} < 1$, $0 < \beta_i < 1$), and we write the additional constraint

$$s_i = -\beta_{i1}(-\xi_1) - \beta_{i2}(-\xi_2) - \dots - \beta_{in}(-\xi_n) - \beta_i \geqslant 0. \qquad (2.32)$$

The s_i obtained in this manner is a nonnegative integer when ξ_j and η_i are nonnegative integers.

Indeed,

$$s_i = -\sum_{j=1}^{n} \beta_{ij}(-\xi_j) - \beta_i = \sum_{j=1}^{n} n_{ij}(-\xi_j) + n_i - \eta_i,$$

from which it follows (from the last expression) that s_i is integral, and it follows from the foregoing discussion and the fact that β_{ij} and ξ_j are nonnegative that $s_i \geqslant -\beta_i > -1$, which, in conjunction with the fact that s_i is integral, proves that it is nonnegative.

If, as in the case under discussion, the optimal solutions of initial problem (2.29)-(2.30) are not integral (since $\eta_i = b_i$ is not integral), they do not satisfy the additional constraint (2.32), so that when $\xi_1 = \dots = \xi_n = 0$ we have

$$s_i = -\beta_i < 0.$$

Hence the additional constraint (2.32) eliminates the part of Ω that contains nonintegral optimal solutions without disturbing the integer solutions.

It is not difficult to see that the plane $s_i = 0$ passes through some integer point (it is also possible that it does not belong to Ω).

2) Solution of the transformed problem. We introduce the constraint $s_i \geqslant 0$ into the last table:

* The notation $[a]$ indicates the integral part of a, i.e., the largest integer not greater than a.

	$-\xi_1$	…	$-\xi_j$	…	$-\xi_n$	1
$\eta_1 =$	b_{11}	…	b_{1j}	…	b_{1n}	b_1
…	…	…	…	…	…	…
$\eta_i =$	b_{i1}	…	b_{ij}	…	b_{in}	b_i
…	…	…	…	…	…	…
$\eta_m =$	b_{m1}	…	b_{mj}	…	b_{mn}	b_m
$s_i =$	$-\beta_{i1}$	…	$-\beta_{ij}$	…	$-\beta_{in}$	$-\beta_i$
$z =$	q_1	…	q_j	…	q_n	Q

Now we solve the new problem of maximizing z under constraints (2.30) and (2.32).

To preserve the signs of the nonnegative coefficients of the z-row, we use the dual simplex method (Section 7, Paragraph 8) to find an optimal solution. If the optimal solution obtained in this manner is not an integer solution, we repeat the general step, and, after a finite number of repetitions [28], we obtain an optimal integer solution of the new problem and of the initial problem, if such a solution exists.*

Example [29a]. Find a nonnegative integral solution of the system

$$\begin{aligned} 3x_1 + 2x_2 \qquad &\leqslant 10, \\ x_1 + 4x_2 \qquad &\leqslant 11, \\ 3x_1 + 3x_2 + x_3 &\leqslant 13, \end{aligned}$$

that will maximize the linear form

$$z = 4x_1 + 5x_2 + x_3.$$

We rewrite the constraints in the form

$$\begin{aligned} y_1 &= -3x_1 - 2x_2 \qquad + 10 \geqslant 0, \\ y_2 &= -\ \ x_1 - 4x_2 \qquad + 11 \geqslant 0, \\ y_3 &= -3x_1 - 3x_2 - x_3 + 13 \geqslant 0 \end{aligned}$$

and consider the table

	$-x_1$	$-x_2$	$-x_3$	1
$y_1 =$	3	2	0	10
$y_2 =$	1	$\boxed{4}$	0	11
$y_3 =$	3	3	1	13
$z =$	−4	−5	−1	0

Three modified Jordan eliminations

* A test for the absence of an integer-valued solution is the appearance of at least one row with fractional slack term and integral coefficients, since in this case the corresponding equation has no integral solution.

	$-x_1$	$-y_2$	$-x_3$	1
$y_1=$	$\boxed{\frac{10}{4}}$	$-\frac{2}{4}$	0	$\frac{18}{4}$
$x_2=$	$\frac{1}{4}$	$\frac{1}{4}$	0	$\frac{11}{4}$
$y_3=$	$\frac{9}{4}$	$-\frac{3}{4}$	1	$\frac{19}{4}$
$z=$	$-\frac{11}{4}$	$\frac{5}{4}$	-1	$\frac{55}{4}$

$\rightarrow$

	$-y_1$	$-y_2$	$-x_3$	1
$x_1=$	$\frac{4}{10}$	$-\frac{2}{10}$	0	$\frac{18}{10}$
$x_2=$	$-\frac{1}{10}$	$\frac{3}{10}$	0	$\frac{23}{10}$
$y_3=$	$-\frac{9}{10}$	$-\frac{3}{10}$	$\boxed{1}$	$\frac{7}{10}$
$z=$	$\frac{11}{10}$	$\frac{7}{10}$	-1	$\frac{187}{10}$

,

yield the table

	$-y_1$	$-y_2$	$-y_3$	1
$x_1=$	$\frac{4}{10}$	$-\frac{2}{10}$	0	$\frac{18}{10}$
$x_2=$	$-\frac{1}{10}$	$\frac{3}{10}$	0	$\frac{23}{10}$
$x_3=$	$-\frac{9}{10}$	$-\frac{3}{10}$	1	$\frac{7}{10}$
$z=$	$\frac{2}{10}$	$\frac{4}{10}$	1	$\frac{194}{10}$

,

which provides an optimal solution that is not integral:

$$x_1=\frac{18}{10}, \quad x_2=\frac{23}{10}, \quad x_3=\frac{7}{10}, \quad \max z=\frac{194}{10}.$$

To find an integral solution, we introduce, in accordance with the foregoing discussion, the additional constraint

$$s_3=\frac{1}{10}y_1+\frac{7}{10}y_2-\frac{7}{10}\geqslant 0.$$

The table now takes the form

	$-y_1$	$-y_2$	$-y_3$	1
$x_1=$	$\frac{4}{10}$	$-\frac{2}{10}$	0	$\frac{18}{10}$
$x_2=$	$-\frac{1}{10}$	$\frac{3}{10}$	0	$\frac{23}{10}$
$x_3=$	$-\frac{9}{10}$	$-\frac{3}{10}$	1	$\frac{7}{10}$
$s_3=$	$-\frac{1}{10}$	$\boxed{-\frac{7}{10}}$	0	$-\frac{7}{10}$
$z=$	$\frac{2}{10}$	$\frac{4}{10}$	1	$\frac{194}{10}$

.

To preserve the signs in the z-row, we apply the dual simplex method.

The rule appropriate to this case leads to selection of $-\frac{7}{10}$ as the resolvent element in the last row, because

$$\left|\frac{4}{10} : -\frac{7}{10}\right| < \left|\frac{2}{10} : -\frac{1}{10}\right|.$$

After modified Jordan elimination, the table

	$-y_1$	$-s_3$	$-y_3$	1
$x_1 =$				2
$x_2 =$				2
$x_3 =$				1
$y_2 =$				1
$z =$	$\frac{1}{7}$	$\frac{4}{7}$	1	19

yields the optimal integral solution

$$\max z = 19,$$

which is achieved when

$$x_1 = 2, \quad x_2 = 2, \quad x_3 = 1.$$

3. Another Method for Constructing Additional Constraints [24]

Assume that in solving problem (2.29)-(2.30) we have obtained a table (2.31) defining a nonintegral optimal solution

$$\xi_1 = \ldots = \xi_n = 0, \quad \eta_1 = b_1 \geqslant 0, \ \ldots, \ \eta_m = b_m \geqslant 0.$$

We introduce the additional constraint

$$\xi_1 + \xi_2 + \ldots + \xi_n \geqslant 1, \tag{2.33}$$

which is clearly satisfied by an optimal integral solution. Indeed, since the solution $\xi_1 = \ldots = \xi_n = 0$ is not integral, then for any optimal integral solution at least one of the ξ_j must be a natural number and $\xi_1 + \ldots + \xi_n \geqslant 1$.

We should note that our nonintegral optimal solution does not satisfy constraint (2.33) and is eliminated by it from the polyhedron Ω.

If the optimal solution provided by the modified problem at this point is not integral, we continue the process.*

---

* Necessary conditions for convergence are given in [29b].

We shall illustrate this method by solving the example of the preceding paragraph. The result of solution without the integer requirement yields the table

	$-y_1$	$-y_2$	$-y_3$	1
$x_1 =$	$\frac{4}{10}$	$-\frac{2}{10}$	0	$\frac{18}{10}$
$x_2 =$	$-\frac{1}{10}$	$\frac{3}{10}$	0	$\frac{23}{10}$
$x_3 =$	$-\frac{9}{10}$	$-\frac{3}{10}$	1	$\frac{7}{10}$
$z =$	$\frac{2}{10}$	$\frac{4}{10}$	1	$\frac{194}{10}$

To find an integral solution, we introduce the additional constraint

$$y_1 + y_2 + y_3 \geqslant 1$$

or

$$y_4 = y_1 + y_2 + y_3 - 1 \geqslant 0;$$

into the table

	$-y_1$	$-y_2$	$-y_3$	1
$x_1 =$	$\frac{4}{10}$	$-\frac{2}{10}$	0	$\frac{18}{10}$
$x_2 =$	$-\frac{1}{10}$	$\frac{3}{10}$	0	$\frac{23}{10}$
$x_3 =$	$-\frac{9}{10}$	$-\frac{3}{10}$	1	$\frac{7}{10}$
$y_4 =$	$\boxed{-1}$	-1	-1	-1
$z =$	$\frac{2}{10}$	$\frac{4}{10}$	1	$\frac{194}{10}$

and execute a modified Jordan elimination over the element -1, which is selected in accordance with the rules of the dual simplex method. We thus obtain the table

	$-y_4$	$-y_2$	$-y_3$	1
$x_1 =$	$\frac{4}{10}$	$-\frac{6}{10}$	$-\frac{4}{10}$	$\frac{14}{10}$
$x_2 =$	$-\frac{1}{10}$	$\frac{4}{10}$	$\frac{1}{10}$	$\frac{24}{10}$
$x_3 =$	$-\frac{9}{10}$	$\frac{6}{10}$	$\frac{19}{10}$	$\frac{16}{10}$
$y_1 =$	-1	1	1	1
$z =$	$\frac{2}{10}$	$\frac{2}{10}$	$\frac{8}{10}$	$\frac{192}{10}$

The solution given by this table is again not integral, so we introduce the additional constraint $y_4+y_2+y_3\geqslant 1$ or $y_5=y_4+y_2+y_3-1\geqslant 0$ into the table

	$-y_4$	$-y_2$	$-y_3$	1
$x_1=$	$\frac{4}{10}$	$-\frac{6}{10}$	$-\frac{4}{10}$	$\frac{14}{10}$
$x_2=$	$-\frac{1}{10}$	$\frac{4}{10}$	$\frac{1}{10}$	$\frac{24}{10}$
$x_3=$	$-\frac{9}{10}$	$\frac{6}{10}$	$\frac{19}{10}$	$\frac{16}{10}$
$y_1=$	-1	1	1	1
$y_5=$	-1	$\boxed{-1}$	-1	-1
$z=$	$\frac{2}{10}$	$\frac{2}{10}$	$\frac{8}{10}$	$\frac{192}{10}$

and execute a modified Jordan elimination over the resolvent element given by the rules of the dual simplex method. We thus obtain the table

	$-y_4$	$-y_5$	$-y_3$	1
$x_1=$				2
$x_2=$				2
$x_3=$				1
$y_1=$				0
$y_2=$				1
$z=$	0	$\frac{2}{10}$	$\frac{6}{10}$	19

,

which yields an optimal integral solution:

$$\max z = 19;$$

this optimum is achieved at

$$x_1 = 2, \quad x_2 = 2, \quad x_3 = 1.$$

9. PARAMETRIC PROGRAMMING [2]

1. Statement of the Problem

We now consider a generalization of the linear programming problem in which the coefficients of the linear form, instead of being constants, are linear functions of some parameter t.

The precise statement of the parametric programming problem is as follows:

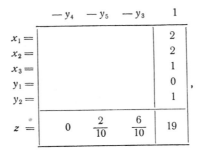

Given a function

$$z_t = \sum_{j=1}^{n} (p_j + tq_j)(-x_j) \qquad (2.34)$$

that is linear for all $t \in [\alpha, \beta]$ and a system of constraints

$$\sum_{j=1}^{n} a_{ij}x_j \leqslant a_i \qquad (i = 1, \ldots, m) \qquad (2.35)$$

defining some nonempty polyhedron Ω, partition the segment $[\alpha, \beta]$ into a finite number of subsets such that for all t in each subset the maximal value of z_t is achieved at the same vertex of the polyhedron Ω. We have placed a minus sign in front of all the variables for convenience in computation.

2. Algorithm for Solution of the Problem

Each step in the algorithm consists of two operations:

1) solution of the linear programming problem with constraints (2.35) and the linear form obtained from (2.34) by fixing t (i.e., finding the vertex of the polyhedron Ω at which max z_t is achieved);

2) determination of the subsets of values of t for which z_t is maximal at the vertex obtained.

1) Setting $t = \alpha$, we obtain a target function

$$z_\alpha = \sum_{j=1}^{n} (p_j + \alpha q_j)(-x_j)$$

with constant coefficients; we now solve the ordinary problem of maximizing the linear form z_α under constraints (2.35), which, by assumption, are consistent.

To solve this problem, we write the usual table, to which we add two rows at the bottom. In the first of these rows we place the numbers p_j, and in the second, we place the q_j. To obtain the coefficients of the linear form z_t, we must multiply the coefficients of the last row by t and add them to the coefficients in the next-to-last:

	$-x_1$	...	$-x_j$	...	$-x_n$	1
$y_1 =$	a_{11}	...	a_{1j}	...	a_{1n}	a_1
...	...	...	...	...	...	...
$y_i =$	a_{i1}	...	a_{ij}	...	a_{in}	a_i
...	...	...	...	...	...	...
$y_m =$	a_{m1}	...	a_{mj}	...	a_{mn}	a_m
$z_\alpha =$	$(p_1 + \alpha q_1)$	...	$(p_j + \alpha q_j)$	...	$(p_n + \alpha q_n)$	0
$z_t =$	p_1	...	p_j	...	p_n	0
	q_1	...	q_j	...	q_n	0

Transformation of the table according to the rules of the simplex method raises the following two possibilities: a) either z_α has a *finite maximum*, or b) it is unbounded. We shall consider both cases below.

a) Assume that it has been proved that $\max z_\alpha < \infty$, i.e., we have obtained a table in which all the coefficients of the z_α - row (and the slack terms) are nonnegative. We then proceed to the second operation.

2) Here we find the set of all values of t for which $\max z_t$ is achieved at the same vertex of the polyhedron Ω as $\max z_\alpha$. It is clear that it consists of those and only those values of t for which all coefficients of the z_t-row in the last table are nonnegative, i.e., for which the system

$$p'_j + tq'_j \geqslant 0 \qquad (j = 1, \ldots, n) \tag{2.36}$$

($t = \alpha$ is one of these values) is consistent.

Elementary analysis of system (2.36) shows that the desired set of parameter values for t satisfies the inequalities

$$\alpha_1 \leqslant t \leqslant \alpha_2,$$

where

$$\alpha_1 = \begin{cases} \max\limits_{q'_j > 0}\left(-\dfrac{p'_j}{q'_j}\right), & \text{if there exist } q'_j > 0, \\ -\infty, & \text{if all } q'_j \leqslant 0; \end{cases}$$

$$\alpha_2 = \begin{cases} \min\limits_{q'_j < 0}\left(-\dfrac{p'_j}{q'_j}\right), & \text{if there exist } q'_j < 0, \\ +\infty, & \text{if all } q'_j \geqslant 0. \end{cases}$$

Indeed, if there are both positive and negative coefficients q'_j ($j = 1, \ldots, n$), then, by first solving the system of inequalities in (2.36) for which $q'_j > 0$, we find that

$$t \geqslant -\frac{p'_j}{q'_j} \qquad (q'_j > 0)$$

and, therefore,

$$\alpha_1 = \max_{q'_j > 0}\left(-\frac{p'_j}{q'_j}\right).$$

If we now solve the system of those inequalities in (2.36) for which $q'_j < 0$, we find that

$$t \leqslant -\frac{p_j'}{q_j'} \qquad (q_j' < 0)$$

and, therefore, that

$$\alpha_2 = \min\left(-\frac{p_j'}{q_j'}\right).$$

If all of the q_j' have the same sign, then, if $q_j' \leqslant 0$ $(j=1, \ldots, n)$, all the t for which system (2.36) is consistent have no lower bound and $\alpha_1 = -\infty$.

If, however, all the $q_j' \geqslant 0$ $(j=1, \ldots, n)$, then the values of t are not bounded above and $\alpha_2 = +\infty$.

We, of course, are interested in only those values of t that belong to the interval $[\alpha, \beta]$.

If $\alpha_2 \geqslant \beta$, the problem is solved: for all $t \in [\alpha, \beta]$ the function z_t is maximal at the vertex of the polyhedron Ω on which max z_α is achieved.

If, however,

$$\alpha_2 = -\frac{p_{j_0}'}{q_{j_0}'} < \beta$$

and all the coefficients in the j_0th column of the last table are *non-positive*, then the coefficient $p_{j_0}' + tq_{j_0}'$ for $t > \alpha_2$ will be negative, the function z_t will be unbounded above, and the problem will again have been solved: for all $t \in [\alpha, \alpha_2]$] the function z_t is maximal on the same vertex as z_α, while for $t \in (\alpha_2, \beta]$ it is unbounded.

Again assume that $\alpha_2 < \beta$ and is achieved only when $j = j_0$,

$$\alpha_2 = -\frac{p_{j_0}'}{q_{j_0}'},$$

but that there are positive coefficients among the coefficients of the j_0th column. In this case we repeat the algorithm, executing operation 1), but using the function z_{α_2} instead of z_α, i.e., we execute a modified Jordan elimination over the j_0th resolvent column and proceed to an adjacent vertex of the polyhedron Ω. It is clear that in this case the z_{α_2}-row will not change, so that z_{α_2} will achieve a maximum at the new vertex.

If, however, system (2.36) is also consistent when $t \neq \alpha_2$, then $t > \alpha_2$, for if $t < \alpha_2$ then

$$-\frac{p_{j_0}' + tq_{j_0}'}{a_{kj_0}} < 0$$

where a_{kj_0} is the resolvent element, i.e., the corresponding system (2.36) is inconsistent.

If α_2 is achieved for several values of j, say, for $j = j_0, j_1, \ldots, j_{\nu_1}$, then, when operation 1) is executed, the resolvent column must be one of the columns numbered $j_0, \ldots, j_{\nu_1}$ for which the inequality

$$p_{j_\nu} + (\alpha_2 + \varepsilon) q_{j_\nu} < 0$$

holds for a sufficiently small $\varepsilon > 0$, i.e., the resolvent column must be one of those for which $q_{j_\nu} < 0$. In other words, we must solve the problem of maximizing $z_{\alpha_2+\varepsilon}$ under constraints (2.35).

After a finite number of modified Jordan eliminations, either all the negative q_{j_ν} have been eliminated or we obtain a vertex at which the function $z_{\alpha_2+\varepsilon}$ is maximal, i.e., we are led to case a), or it has become clear that $z_{\alpha_2+\varepsilon}$ is unbounded, i.e., we have been led to case b).

b) It remains to consider case b), when, as a result of operation 1), it turns out that the function z_α is unbounded above, i.e., the z_α-row of the table contains a negative coefficient, say, $p'_{j_0} + \alpha q'_{j_0} < 0$ and all the coefficients in the corresponding j_0th column are nonpositive.

If $q'_{j_0} \leqslant 0$ here, then the coefficient $p'_{j_0} + t q'_{j_0}$ is negative for all $t \geqslant \alpha$ and the function z_t is unbounded above for all $t \in [\alpha, \beta]$. The problem is therefore solved.

If, however, $q'_{j_0} > 0$, then for $t \in \left[\alpha, -\frac{p'_{j_0}}{q'_{j_0}}\right)$ the coefficient $p'_{j_0} + t q'_{j_0}$ is negative and, therefore, the function z_t is unbounded. For $t \geqslant -\frac{p'_{j_0}}{q'_{j_0}}$ the problem requires a new investigation, i.e., we must apply the algorithm to the segment $\left[-\frac{p'_{j_0}}{q'_{j_0}}, \beta\right]$ instead of $[\alpha, \beta]$.

Finally, we should note that after a finite number of steps the problem will be solved, since, in each step, we determine either an interval for which the vertex obtained is optimal (there is a finite number of such vertices and they cannot repeat) or an interval for which the linear function is not bounded, which corresponds to an edge (face) of the polyhedron Ω, and there are also only a finite number of such edges and they also cannot repeat (it is assumed that degeneracy occurs in neither case).

3. Example

Solve the parametric programming problem for the function

$$z_t = (2 - t) x_1 + x_2,$$

in the interval [1, 10] with the constraints

$$\begin{aligned} y_1 &= -2x_1 - x_2 + 8 \geqslant 0, \\ y_2 &= x_1 + x_2 - 1 \geqslant 0, \\ y_3 &= 3x_1 - 2x_2 + 3 \geqslant 0, \\ y_4 &= -x_1 + x_2 + 4 \geqslant 0. \end{aligned}$$

First step. 1) For $t=1$ we have

$$z_1 = x_1 + x_2.$$

We now construct the table

	$-x_1$	$-x_2$	1
$y_1 =$	2	1	8
$y_2 =$	$\boxed{-1}$	-1	-1
$y_3 =$	-3	2	3
$y_4 =$	1	-1	4
$z_1 =$	-1	-1	0
$z_t =$	-2	-1	0
	1	0	0

and maximize z_1.

Eliminating the coordinates x_1 and x_2, we obtain the table

	$-y_2$	$-y_1$	1
$y_3 =$	7	5	36
$y_4 =$	$\boxed{-3}$	-2	-9
$z_1 =$	-1	0	-1
$z_t =$	0	1	8
	-1	-1	7

and the following expressions for x_1 and x_2:

$$x_1 = y_2 - x_2 + 1,$$

$$x_2 = 2y_2 + y_1 - 6.$$

To find a basic solution, we execute a modified Jordan elimination over the entry -3, which yields

	$-y_4$	$-y_1$	1
$y_3 =$	$\boxed{\frac{7}{3}}$	$\frac{1}{3}$	15
$y_2 =$	$-\frac{1}{3}$	$\frac{2}{3}$	3
$z_1 =$	$-\frac{1}{3}$	$\frac{2}{3}$	4
$z_t =$	0	1	8
	$-\frac{1}{3}$	$-\frac{1}{3}$	-4

.

Modified Jordan elimination over the entry $\frac{7}{3}$ yields the table

	$-y_3$	$-y_1$	1
$y_4 =$	$\frac{3}{7}$	$\frac{1}{7}$	$\frac{45}{7}$
$y_2 =$	$\frac{1}{7}$	$\frac{5}{7}$	$\frac{36}{7}$
$z_1 =$	$\frac{1}{7}$	$\frac{5}{7}$	$\frac{43}{7}$
$z_t =$	0	1	8
	$\frac{1}{7}$	$-\frac{2}{7}$	$-\frac{13}{7}$

,

from which it follows that

$$\max z_1 = \frac{43}{7},$$

which is achieved when

$$y_3 = y_1 = 0, \quad y_4 = \frac{45}{7}, \quad y_2 = \frac{36}{7},$$

i.e., when

$$x_1 = \frac{13}{7}, \quad x_2 = \frac{30}{7}.$$

2) We now determine the set of all values of t for which $\max z_t$ is achieved at the vertex $x_1 = \frac{13}{7}$, $x_2 = \frac{30}{7}$. Since there are both positive and negative entries in the last row of the last table, we have

$$\alpha_1 = \max_{q_j > 0} \left(-\frac{p_j}{q_j}\right) = 0, \quad \alpha_2 = \min_{q_j < 0} \left(-\frac{p_j}{q_j}\right) = \frac{7}{2},$$

i.e., this vertex is optimal for $t \in \left[0, \frac{7}{2}\right]$.

For $\max z_t$ we have

$$\max z_t = 8 - \frac{13}{7} t.$$

Second step. Since $\alpha_2 = \frac{7}{2} < 10 = \beta$, we determine the coefficients of the $z_{\frac{7}{2}}$-row, and substitute the $z_{\frac{7}{2}}$-row for the z_1-row in the last table:

	$-y_3$	$-y_1$	1
$y_4 =$	$\frac{3}{7}$	$\frac{1}{7}$	$\frac{45}{7}$
$y_2 =$	$\frac{1}{7}$	$\boxed{\frac{5}{7}}$	$\frac{36}{7}$
$z_{\frac{7}{2}} =$	$\frac{1}{2}$	0	$\frac{3}{2}$
$z_t =$	0	1	8
	$\frac{1}{7}$	$-\frac{2}{7}$	$-\frac{13}{7}$

We now execute a modified Jordan elimination over the entry $\frac{5}{7}$, which yields

	$-y_3$	$-y_2$	1
$y_4 =$			$\frac{27}{5}$
$y_1 =$			$\frac{36}{5}$
$z_{\frac{7}{2}} =$	$\frac{1}{2}$	0	$\frac{3}{2}$
$z_t =$	$-\frac{1}{5}$	$-\frac{7}{5}$	$\frac{4}{5}$
	$\frac{1}{5}$	$\frac{2}{5}$	$\frac{1}{5}$

We now repeat operation 2): We find all values of t for which

$$\max z_t = \frac{4}{5} + \frac{1}{5} t$$

is achieved when

$$y_3 = y_2 = 0, \quad y_4 = \frac{27}{5}, \quad y_1 = \frac{36}{5},$$

i.e., at the vertex

$$x_1 = -\frac{1}{5}, \quad x_2 = \frac{6}{5}.$$

Since all of the $q_j > 0$, we have $\alpha_2 = +\infty$ and

$$\alpha_1 = \max_{q_j > 0} \left(-\frac{p_j}{q_j} \right) = \frac{7}{2},$$

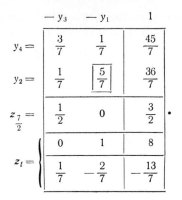

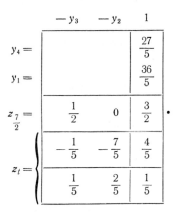

from which it follows that the vertex is optimal for $\frac{7}{2} \leqslant t < +\infty$, and the problem is solved: The interval [1, 10] must be partitioned into two intervals, $\left[1, \frac{7}{2}\right]$ and $\left[\frac{7}{2}, 10\right]$. At the vertex

$$x_1 = \frac{13}{7}, \quad x_2 = \frac{30}{7}$$

max z_t is achieved for all $t \in \left[1, \frac{7}{2}\right]$, while at the vertex

$$x_1 = -\frac{1}{5}, \quad x_2 = \frac{6}{5}$$

max z_t is achieved for all $t \in \left[\frac{7}{2}, 10\right]$.

4. The Dual Parametric Programming Problem

We now consider the problem dual to the parametric programming problem. This dual problem has the following statement: Given a linear function

$$w = \sum_{i=1}^{m} a_i u_i \tag{2.37}$$

and a system of linear constraints

$$\sum_{i=1}^{m} a_{ij} u_i \geqslant p_j + t q_j \qquad (j = 1, \ldots, n), \tag{2.38}$$

where $\alpha \leqslant t \leqslant \beta$, partition the segment $[\alpha, \beta]$ into a finite number of subsets so that for all values of t in each subset the minimal value of the function w is achieved at the vertices defined by a single subsystem of the system

$$\sum_{i=1}^{m} a_{ij} u_i = p_j + t q_j \qquad (j = 1, \ldots, n),$$

i.e., is achieved at vertices differing only by parallel translation of the planes determining them.

According to the general theory of duality presented in Section 7, by solving one of a pair of dual problems, say, problem (2.34)-(2.35), we simultaneously solve the second problem(2.37)-(2.38).

5. Geometric Interpretation

The system of constraints (2.35) defines some nonempty polyhedron Ω, while the equation $z_\alpha = 0$ defines some plane passing through the coordinate origin.

By solving the linear programming problem for $t=\alpha$ we find the vertex P_1 of the polyhedron Ω whose deviation from the plane $z_\alpha=0$ is maximal.

By changing the value of the parameter t, we change the coefficients of the equation $z_\alpha=0$, i.e., we rotate the plane $z_\alpha=0$ about the coordinate origin. Here the maximal deviation from the new plane $z_t=0$ will be achieved at the same vertex P_1 as that where the maximal deviation from the plane $z_\alpha=0$ is achieved, as long as the plane $z_t=0$, as it rotates about the coordinate origin, does not become parallel to some edge or face of the polyhedron Ω passing through the vertex P_1. In Fig. 9 max z_t is achieved at the vertex P_1 as long as the line $z_t=0$ is not parallel to the edge P_1P_2. Assume that this occurs at $t=\alpha_2$. Then the values of the parameter t for the linear programming problem (finding the point of the polyhedron Ω at which the form z_{α_2} is maximal) has an infinite set of solutions (in Fig. 9, all the points on the edge P_1P_2).

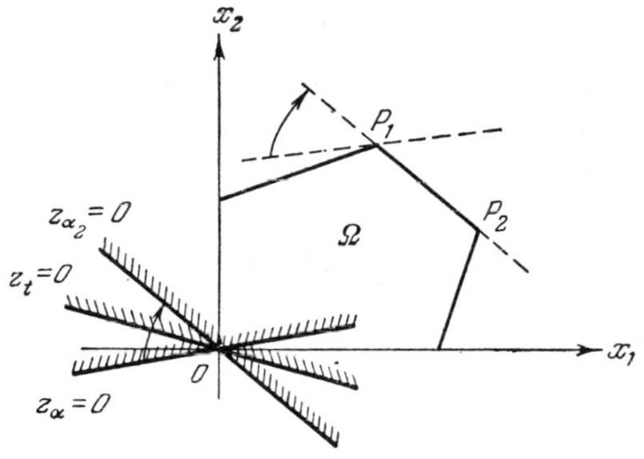

Fig. 9

Modified Jordan elimination makes it possible for us to pass along an edge parallel to the plane $z_{\alpha_2}=0$ to a vertex P_2 adjacent to P_1 in the polyhedron Ω.

If we now rotate the plane $z_{\alpha_2}=0$, we obtain a new set of values of t for which the linear form z_t is maximal at the vertex P_2, etc.

If the polyhedron Ω is unbounded, then, for certain values of the parameter t, the plane $z_t=0$ can clearly take any position for which the value of the form z_t is unbounded.

3

Applications of Linear Programming

The present chapter deals with applications of the theory discussed in Chapter 2 to a number of practical problems for which the mathematical model is a linear programming problem. Of the large group of such problems, we present only the most common, and numerical examples are solved by the simplex method. Very effective methods for solving the extremely important transportation problem are discussed in Chapter 4.

1. OPTIMAL PRODUCTION PLANNING*

1. The Maximum Profit Problem

In Section 7 of Chapter 2, in economically interpreting the basic linear programming problem, we presented one problem on optimal planning of production. In this problem we attempted to maximize the output of one type of manufacture with a given supply of raw materials and several activities. An example of another type of common problem on optimal production planning that also reduces to a linear programming problem is the problem of maximizing profit from the production of ***different types*** of products with a fixed supply of raw materials. This problem is stated as follows.

Assume that m types of raw materials are required for n products, where a unit of the jth product requires a_{ij} units of the ith type of raw material. Moreover, assume that each unit of the jth product yields a profit of p_j dollars.

It is required to determine quantities $x_1, \ldots, x_n$ of each type of product so as to maximize profits under the assumption that a_i units of the ith raw material are available ($i = 1, \ldots, m$).

Since a production plan $x(x_1, \ldots, x_n)$ calls for $a_{i1}x_1 + \ldots + a_{in}x_n$ units of the ith raw material to be used from the supply a_i, and the

*We shall attempt to find integral solutions for all problems discussed in this section; see also the footnote on p. 100.

profit under this plane is $p_1x_1 + \ldots + p_nx_n$ dollars, the mathematical model for this problem is the following linear programming problem:

Find $x_1, \ldots, x_n$ that maximize the linear form

$$z = p_1x_1 + \ldots + p_nx_n$$

under the constraints

$$a_{i1}x_1 + \ldots + a_{in}x_n \leqslant a_i \qquad (i = 1, \ldots, m),$$
$$x_1 \geqslant 0, \ldots, \quad x_n \geqslant 0.$$

2. The General Production Planning Problem [9]

Here we shall discuss the so-called general production planning problem, which is stated as follows:

We are given n different activities (or enterprises) each of which produces a complete product (say, a machine). Each product consists of k_1 parts No. 1, of k_2 parts No. 2, ..., and k_s parts No. s. Their production requires m different ingredients (say, different types of raw materials, labor, etc.), of which $a_1, \ldots, a_m$ units are available, where the ith activity requires a_{ik} units ($i = 1, \ldots, n$; $k = 1, \ldots, m$) of the kth ingredient in each production cycle, and b_{ij} units ($i = 1, \ldots, n$; $j = 1, \ldots, s$) of the jth part will be produced by the ith technology. The production plan $x\,(x_1, \ldots, x_n)$ reflects the production of each activity, so that x_i is the number of production cycles in the ith activity ($i = 1, \ldots, n$).

It is convenient to represent all this in tabular form:

Ingredient number / Activity number	$1 \ldots k \ldots m$	Part number	$1 \ldots j \ldots s$	Plan x
1	$a_{11} \ldots a_{1k} \ldots a_{1m}$		$b_{11} \ldots b_{1j} \ldots b_{1s}$	x_1
. . .	. . . .		. . . .	. . .
i	$a_{i1} \ldots a_{ik} \ldots a_{im}$		$b_{i1} \ldots b_{ij} \ldots b_{is}$	x_i
. . .	. . . .		. . . .	. . .
n	$a_{n1} \ldots a_{nk} \ldots a_{nm}$		$b_{n1} \ldots b_{nj} \ldots b_{ns}$	x_n

According to a given plan $x\,(x_1, \ldots, x_n)$, the consumption of the kth ingredient is $a_{1k}x_1 + \ldots + a_{nk}x_n$ ($k = 1, \ldots, m$), while the output of the jth part is $b_{1j}x_1 + \ldots + b_{nj}x_n$ ($j = 1, \ldots, s$). Since each finished product must contain k_j copies of the jth part, an output of $b_{1j}x_1 + \ldots + b_{nj}x_n$ copies of this part makes it possible to produce

$$\frac{b_{1j}x_1 + \ldots + b_{nj}x_n}{k_j}$$

completed units, and, therefore, the total number of complete units that can be produced under a given policy is equal to the smallest of the fractions

$$\frac{b_{11}x_1 + \dots + b_{n1}x_n}{k_1}, \dots, \frac{b_{1s}x_1 + \dots + b_{ns}x_n}{k_s}.$$

The problem consists in choosing a (optimal) policy that will provide the largest number of complete units with the available supplies $a_1, \dots, a_m$ of ingredients.

The mathematical model of this problem takes the following form:

Among the nonnegative solutions of the system of linear inequalities

$$\left.\begin{array}{l} a_{11}x_1 + \dots + a_{n1}x_n \leqslant a_1, \\ \dots\dots\dots\dots\dots \\ a_{1m}x_1 + \dots + a_{nm}x_n \leqslant a_m \end{array}\right\} \qquad (3.1)$$

find one for which the quantity

$$\min_{1 \leqslant j \leqslant s} \frac{b_{1j}x_1 + \dots + b_{nj}x_n}{k_j}$$

is maximal, i.e., find a solution for which the following "maximin" is achieved:

$$\max_x \min_{1 \leqslant j \leqslant s} \frac{b_{1j}x_1 + \dots + b_{nj}x_n}{k_j}.$$

When $s = 1$ the problem is a typical linear programming problem—the problem of maximizing the linear form

$$z = \frac{b_{11}x_1 + \dots + b_{n1}x_n}{k_1}$$

under the constraints (3.1) and $x_i \geqslant 0$ $(i = 1, \dots, n)$.

We introduce an auxiliary variable ξ to reduce the general problem to the following linear programming problem:

Maximize the linear form

$$z = \xi \qquad (3.2)$$

under the constraints (3.1) and

$$\left.\begin{array}{l} \dfrac{b_{11}x_1 + \dots + b_{n1}x_n}{k_1} \geqslant \xi, \\ \dots\dots\dots\dots\dots \\ \dfrac{b_{1s}x_1 + \dots + b_{ns}x_n}{k_s} \geqslant \xi, \\ x_i \geqslant 0 \quad (i = 1, \dots, n), \\ \xi \geqslant 0. \end{array}\right\} \qquad (3.3)$$

Remark. It is easy to prove that the problem under discussion is equivalent to the linear programming problem obtained above. A similar problem is discussed in detail in Section 1 of Chapter 5.

3. An Optimal Assignment Problem (9)

Frequently it is necessary to solve the following somewhat simplified variant of the general production planning problem.

Assume that each of n types of parts used to produce a final product can be constructed at each of m types of enterprises (factories), where there are c_i enterprises of the ith type ($i = 1, \ldots, m$) each of which can produce a_{ij} copies of the jth part per month, and that each unit of the final product requires k_j units of the jth type ($j = 1, \ldots, n$). The production plan must assign each enterprise production of only one type.

This is the problem of optimally distributing production among enterprises, i.e., determining the numbers x_{ij} ($i = 1, \ldots, m$; $j = 1, \ldots, n$) of enterprises of the ith that must be specialized for production of the jth part to guarantee a maximal output of the finished product.

It is clear that the problem stated above reduces to the general production planning problem (Paragraph 2) if we consider different enterprises instead of different activities and we do not consider available supplies of ingredients.

Indeed, under the plan $x_{11}, \ldots, x_{ij}, \ldots, x_{mn}$

$$a_{1j}x_{1j} + \ldots + a_{mj}x_{mj} \qquad (j = 1, \ldots, n)$$

units of the jth part will be produced, and the number of complete units that can be constructed is the smallest of the numbers

$$\frac{a_{11}x_{11} + \ldots + a_{m1}x_{m1}}{k_1}, \ \ldots, \ \frac{a_{1n}x_{1n} + \ldots + a_{mn}x_{mn}}{k_n},$$

i.e.,

$$\min_{1 \leqslant j \leqslant n} \frac{a_{1j}x_{1j} + \ldots + a_{mj}x_{mj}}{k_j}.$$

Introduction of an auxiliary variable ξ such that

$$\frac{a_{1j}x_{1j} + \ldots + a_{mj}x_{mj}}{k_j} \geqslant \xi \qquad (j = 1, \ldots, n)$$

reduces the problem to a linear programming problem*—maximization of the form

$$z = \xi$$

---

* See the Remark above.

under the constraints

$$\frac{a_{1j}x_{1j} + \ldots + a_{mj}x_{mj}}{k_j} \geqslant \xi \qquad (j = 1, \ldots, n),$$
$$x_{i1} + \ldots + x_{in} = c_i \qquad (i = 1, \ldots, m),$$
$$\xi \geqslant 0, \quad x_{ij} \geqslant 0 \qquad (i = 1, \ldots, m; \ j = 1, \ldots, n).$$

4. Example [9]

Two types of parts are required for production of a particular device. Each of five types of enterprises can be used to produce the two parts. The capacities of the enterprises for production of these parts and the numbers of enterprises of each type are shown in the following table:

Type of enterprise	Number of enterprises	Production capacity of enterprises	
		For part No. 1	For part No. 2
№ 1	5	100 thous.	15 thous.
№ 2	3	400 ,,	200 ,,
№ 3	40	20 ,,	2.5 ,,
№ 4	9	200 ,,	50 ,,
№ 5	2	600 ,,	250 ,,

It is required to determine how many enterprises of each type must be assigned production of the first part, and how many must be assigned production of the second part, so as to ensure a maximal output of units if each complete unit requires two parts of the first type and one of the second.

Let x_{ij} denote the number of enterprises of the ith type (i = 1, 2, 3, 4, 5) that are assigned production of the jth (j = 1, 2) part. The problem now reduces to the problem of maximizing the linear form

$$z = \xi$$

under the constraints

$$\frac{100x_{11} + 400x_{21} + 20x_{31} + 200x_{41} + 600x_{51}}{2} \geqslant \xi,$$
$$15x_{12} + 200x_{22} + 2{,}5x_{32} + 50x_{42} + 250x_{52} \geqslant \xi,$$
$$x_{11} + x_{12} = 5,$$
$$x_{21} + x_{22} = 3,$$
$$x_{31} + x_{32} = 40,$$
$$x_{41} + x_{42} = 9,$$
$$x_{51} + x_{52} = 2,$$
$$x_{ij} \geqslant 0 \qquad (i = 1, \ldots, 5; \quad j = 1, 2).$$

We rewrite the constraints of the problem in the form

$$\begin{aligned}
0 &= -x_{11} - x_{12} + 5,\\
0 &= -x_{21} - x_{22} + 3,\\
0 &= -x_{31} - x_{32} + 40,\\
0 &= -x_{41} - x_{42} + 9,\\
0 &= -x_{51} - x_{52} + 2,
\end{aligned}$$

$$y_1 = 100x_{11} + 400x_{21} + 20x_{31} + 200x_{41} + 600x_{51} - 2\xi \geqslant 0,$$
$$y_2 = 15x_{12} + 200x_{22} + 2{,}5x_{32} + 50x_{42} + 250x_{52} - \xi \geqslant 0.$$

Writing the conditions, as usual, in the form of a table and eliminating 0-equations, we obtain the table

	$-x_{12}$	$-x_{22}$	$-x_{32}$	$-x_{42}$	$-x_{52}$	$-y_2$	1
$x_{11} =$	1	0	0	0	0	0	5
$x_{21} =$	0	$\boxed{1}$	0	0	0	0	3
$x_{31} =$	0	0	1	0	0	0	40
$x_{41} =$	0	0	0	1	0	0	9
$x_{51} =$	0	0	0	0	1	0	2
$y_1 =$	130	800	25	300	1100	—2	5500
$\xi =$	—15	—200	—2.5	—50	—250	1	0
$z =$	—15	—200	—2.5	—50	—250	1	0

Since all the slack terms are nonnegative, we can immediately turn to finding an optimal solution. We obtain a sequence of three tables, of which the third is of the form

	$-x_{12}$	$-x_{21}$	$-x_{32}$	$-y_1$	$-x_{51}$	$-y_2$	1
$x_{11} =$							5
$x_{22} =$							3
$x_{31} =$							40
$x_{41} =$							6
$x_{52} =$							2
$x_{42} =$							3
$\xi =$							1250
$z =$	$\frac{20}{3}$	$\frac{200}{3}$	$\frac{5}{3}$	$\frac{1}{6}$	$\frac{200}{3}$	$\frac{2}{3}$	1250

All the coefficients of the z-row are positive, so we have the optimal solution

$$x_{12} = x_{21} = x_{32} = x_{51} = 0, \quad x_{11} = 5, \quad x_{22} = 3,$$
$$x_{31} = 40, \quad x_{41} = 6, \quad x_{52} = 2, \quad x_{42} = 3;$$

in this case

$$\max z = 1250 \text{ units.}$$

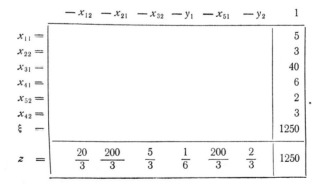

2. THE OPTIMAL TRIMMING PROBLEM (MINIMIZATION OF WASTE)

1. Statement of the Problem

Assume that some semifinished product (for example, a sheet of plywood) is sent to an enterprise in the form of m different lots respectively containing $a_1, \ldots, a_m$ units of the semifinished product, where the dimensions of the material in each lot are the same. The semifinished product must be cut so as to maximize the number of finished units, each of which contains k_1 parts of the first type, k_2 parts of the second, ..., k_l parts of the lth type. Assume that each unit of semifinished product can be cut into parts in n different ways, where the jth method of cutting a unit in the ith lot yields a_{ijs} parts of the sth type.

Let x_{ij} denote the number of units of the ith lot of semifinished products that have been allocated for cutting by the jth method, so that it is possible to obtain $a_{ijs}x_{ij}$ parts of the sth type from the ith lot with the jth method. Under the plan $x_{11}, \ldots, x_{ij}, \ldots, x_{mn}$, the entire ith lot will yield $\sum_{j=1}^{n} a_{ijs}x_{ij}$ parts of the sth type, while the entire m lots will yield $\sum_{i=1}^{m}\sum_{j=1}^{n} a_{ijs}x_{ij}$ of them. Since each finished product requires k_s parts of the sth type, $\sum_{i=1}^{m}\sum_{j=1}^{n} a_{ijs}x_{ij}$ parts make it possible to construct

$$\frac{\sum_{i=1}^{m}\sum_{j=1}^{n} a_{ijs}x_{ij}}{k_s}$$

finished units, so the total number of finished units that can be completed under a given plan $\|x_{ij}\|$ is the smallest of the fractions

$$\frac{\sum_{i=1}^{m}\sum_{j=1}^{n} a_{ij1}x_{ij}}{k_1}, \ldots, \frac{\sum_{i=1}^{m}\sum_{j=1}^{n} a_{ijl}x_{ij}}{k_l}.$$

We have thus been led to the problem of Paragraph 2 of Section 1.

As we did in Paragraph 2 of Section 1, by introduction of an auxiliary variable ξ we can reduce the problem under discussion to the problem of maximizing the linear form $z = \xi$ under the constraints

$$\frac{\sum_{i=1}^{m}\sum_{j=1}^{n} a_{ijs}x_{ij}}{k_s} \geqslant \xi \qquad (s = 1, \ldots, l),$$

$$x_{i1} + \ldots + x_{in} = a_i \qquad (i = 1, \ldots, m),$$

$$\xi \geqslant 0, \quad x_{ij} \geqslant 0 \qquad (i = 1, \ldots, m; \quad j = 1, \ldots, n).$$

2. Example

Two lots of planks are received for production of a unit consisting of three parts, where the first lot contains 50 planks that are each 6.5 m long, while the second contains 200 planks that are each 4 m long. Each finished unit consists of two parts that are each 2 m long, and one part 1.25 m long.

How must the entire group of lots be cut so as to obtain the largest possible number of complete units?

A plank 6.5 m long can be cut into parts of the required dimensions in the following ways:

1) three parts 2 m long,
2) two parts 2 m long and two parts 1.25 m long,
3) one part 2 m long and three parts 1.25 m long,
4) five parts 1.25 m long.

A plank 4 m long can be cut into parts in the following ways:

1) two parts 2 m long.
2) one part 2 m long and one part 1.25 m long.
3) three parts 1.25 m long.

Let x_{11}, x_{12}, x_{13}, and x_{14} denote the numbers of planks 6.5 m long that are cut in accordance with the first, second, third, and fourth method, respectively, and let x_{21}, x_{22}, and x_{23} denote the numbers of planks 4 m long that are cut in accordance with the first, second, and third methods, respectively. Now the problem reduces to maximization of the linear form

$$z = \xi$$

under the constraints

$$\begin{gathered} x_{11} + x_{12} + x_{13} + x_{14} = 50, \\ x_{21} + x_{22} + x_{23} = 200, \\ \frac{3x_{11} + 2x_{12} + x_{13} + 2x_{21} + x_{22}}{2} \geqslant \xi, \\ 2x_{12} + 3x_{13} + 5x_{14} + x_{22} + 3x_{23} \geqslant \xi, \\ \xi \geqslant 0, \quad x_{ij} \geqslant 0 \qquad (i = 1, 2; \quad j = 1, 2, 3, 4). \end{gathered}$$

We rewrite the constraints in the form

$$\begin{aligned} y_1 &= 3x_{11} + 2x_{12} + x_{13} + 2x_{21} + x_{22} - 2\xi \geqslant 0, \\ y_2 &= 2x_{12} + 3x_{13} + 5x_{14} + x_{22} + 3x_{23} - \xi \geqslant 0, \\ 0 &= -x_{11} - x_{12} - x_{13} - x_{14} + 50, \\ 0 &= -x_{21} - x_{22} - x_{23} + 200, \end{aligned}$$

$$x_{11} \geqslant 0, \; x_{12} \geqslant 0, \; x_{13} \geqslant 0, \; x_{14} \geqslant 0, \; x_{21} \geqslant 0, \; x_{22} \geqslant 0, \; x_{23} \geqslant 0$$

and consider the table

	$-x_{11}$	$-x_{12}$	$-x_{13}$	$-x_{14}$	$-x_{21}$	$-x_{22}$	$-x_{23}$	$-\xi$	1
$y_1 =$	−3	−2	−1	0	−2	−1	0	2	0
$y_2 =$	0	−2	−3	−5	0	−1	−3	1	0
$0 =$	$\boxed{1}$	1	1	1	0	0	0	0	50
$0 =$	0	0	0	0	1	1	1	0	200
$z =$	0	0	0	0	0	0	0	−1	0

.

We eliminate the 0-rows by two modified Jordan eliminations, and then eliminate the columns under the zeros carried to the top of the table; we thus obtain the table

	$-x_{12}$	$-x_{13}$	$-x_{14}$	$-x_{22}$	$-x_{23}$	$-\xi$	1
$y_1 =$	1	2	3	1	2	2	550
$y_2 =$	−2	−3	−5	−1	−3	1	0
$x_{11} =$	1	1	1	0	0	0	50
$x_{21} =$	0	0	0	1	1	0	200
$z =$	0	0	0	0	0	−1	0

,

in which all the constant terms are nonnegative.

Turning to finding an optimal solution, we obtain a sequence of tables, of which the last is of the form

	$-x_{13}$	$-x_{11}$	$-y_1$	$-x_{22}$	$-x_{23}$	$-y_2$	1
$x_{14} =$							$\frac{75}{2}$
$\xi =$							$\frac{425}{2}$
$x_{12} =$							$\frac{25}{2}$
$x_{21} =$							200
$z =$	$\frac{1}{8}$	$\frac{1}{8}$	$\frac{3}{8}$	$\frac{1}{8}$	0	$\frac{1}{4}$	$\frac{425}{2}$

The coefficients of the z-row in this last table are nonnegative, so the process terminates and it is not necessary to compute the remaining coefficients. Since the solution must be integral, we can take, as an approximate solution, the integers closest to the solution obtained that satisfy the requirements of the problem. It is clear that they are

$$x_{14} = 38, \quad x_{12} = 12, \quad x_{21} = 200, \quad x_{13} = x_{11} = x_{22} = x_{23} = 0;$$
$$\max z = 212\ ^*.$$

*We may use one of the methods described in Section 8 of Chapter 2 to find an integral solution. When, as here, the values of the variables in an optimal solution are sufficiently large ($x_j \gg 1$), we can take, as an approximate solution, the integral feasible solution closest to the optimal solution obtained.

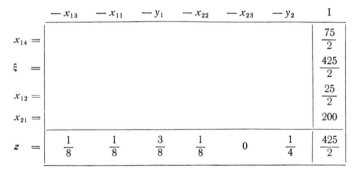

3. AGRICULTURAL PROBLEMS

1. The Diet (Mixture) Problem

Assume that the daily requirements of certain substances such as proteins, fat, carbohydrates, vitamins, etc., are given, the contents of these substances in available products are known, and the cost per unit of each product is also known. The problem is to compound a ration that will satisfy the daily requirements of the necessary substances and minimize cost.

More concretely, assume that a daily ration must contain no less than a_1 units of the first substance, no less than a_2 units of the second substance, ..., no less than a_m units of the mth substance. Moreover, assume that this ration requires n types of products costing p_j per unit of the jth product, where it is known that each unit of the jth product contains a_{ij} units of the ith substance. Then, if we let x_j denote the number of units of the jth product that are to be included in the daily ration, the policy $x_1, \ldots, x_n$ provides a daily ration of $a_{i1}x_1 + \ldots + a_{in}x_n$ units of the ith substance, and since it must satisfy the minimum daily requirements,

$$a_{i1}x_1 + \ldots + a_{in}x_n \geqslant a_i \qquad (i = 1, \ldots, m).$$

Under this policy, the cost of the entire daily ration is

$$z = p_1x_1 + \ldots + p_nx_n.$$

The problem consists in finding a nonnegative solution of the system of linear inequalities

$$\begin{array}{c} a_{11}x_1 + \ldots + a_{1n}x_n \geqslant a_1, \\ \cdots\cdots\cdots\cdots \\ a_{m1}x_1 + \ldots + a_{mn}x_n \geqslant a_m, \end{array}$$

for which the expression (cost)

$$z = p_1x_1 + \ldots + p_nx_n$$

is minimal. If we assume that the supplies of the ingredients of the ration are limited, then the variables $x_1, \ldots, x_n$ must be subjected to further constraints of the form $x_1 \leqslant b_1, \ldots, x_n \leqslant b_n$, where b_j is the available supply of the jth product.

The diet problem presented above has been successfully used, for example, to compound an optimally cheap ration for fattening cattle.

So-called mixture problems, i.e., problems on compounding mixtures that are optimal in some sense, reduce to the above problem. An example of such a problem is a problem of compounding a mixture of petroleum products that will meet given technical requirements with a minimum of cost and for the problem of minimizing the cost of the final product in mixing alloys.

2. The Problem on Best Use of Arable Land

Assume that n crops are to be grown on m plots with areas of $a_1, \ldots, a_m$, areas respectively, where the average yield of the jth crop from the ith lot is a_{ij} units per acre and the return from one unit of the jth crop is p_j dollars.

It is required to determine the area in each plot that should be sown in each crop so that a maximum return is obtained under a policy in which no less than b_j units of are planted in the jth crop ($j = 1, \ldots, n$).

Let x_{ij} denote the area sown in the jth crop on the ith plot, so that

$$x_{i1} + \ldots + x_{in} = a_i \qquad (i = 1, \ldots, m).$$

The average expected yield of the jth crop from all of the plots is

$$a_{1j}x_{1j} + \ldots + a_{mj}x_{mj}.$$

The policy requires no less than b_j units:

$$a_{1j}x_{1j} + \ldots + a_{mj}x_{mj} \geqslant b_j \qquad (j = 1, \ldots, n).$$

The expected return from the jth crop is

$$p_j(a_{1j}x_{1j} + \ldots + a_{mj}x_{mj}),$$

while the return from all of the crops is

$$p_1(a_{11}x_{11} + \ldots + a_{m1}x_{m1}) + \ldots$$
$$\ldots + p_n(a_{1n}x_{1n} + \ldots + a_{mn}x_{mn}).$$

Thus, the problem consists in maximizing the linear form

$$z = p_1(a_{11}x_{11} + \ldots + a_{m1}x_{m1}) + \ldots$$
$$\ldots + p_n(a_{1n}x_{1n} + \ldots + a_{mn}x_{mn})$$

in the $m \times n$ variables $x_{11}, \ldots, x_{ij}, \ldots, x_{mn}$ under the constraints

$$\begin{gathered} x_{11} + \ldots + x_{1n} = a_1, \\ \cdots\cdots\cdots\cdots \\ x_{m1} + \ldots + x_{mn} = a_m, \\ a_{11}x_{11} + \ldots + a_{m1}x_{m1} \geqslant b_1, \\ \cdots\cdots\cdots\cdots \\ a_{1n}x_{1n} + \ldots + a_{mn}x_{mn} \geqslant b_n, \\ x_{ij} \geqslant 0 \qquad (i = 1, \ldots, m; \quad j = 1, \ldots, n), \end{gathered}$$

and, as usual, can be solved by the simplex method.

Sometimes this problem is stated as follows: Given arable land, grow n crops so as to maximize the yield while preserving the ratios $k_1 : k_2 : \ldots : k_n$ in which these crops are produced.

Assuming that each group of agricultural products must contain k_1 units of the first crop, k_2 units of the second, ..., k_n units of the nth crop, we can see that this problem is analogous to the general problem of production planning (see Section 1, Paragraph 2). By introduction of an auxiliary variable ξ such that

$$\frac{a_{1j}x_{1j} + \ldots + a_{mj}x_{mj}}{k_j} \geqslant \xi \qquad (j = 1, \ldots, n),$$

we can reduce the problem under discussion to the linear programming problem of maximizing the form

$$z = \xi$$

under the constraints

$$\frac{a_{1j}x_{1j} + \ldots + a_{mj}x_{mj}}{k_j} \geqslant \xi \qquad (j = 1, \ldots, n),$$

$$x_{i1} + \ldots + x_{in} = a_i \qquad (i = 1, \ldots, m),$$

$$x_{ij} \geqslant 0 \qquad (i = 1, \ldots, m; \quad j = 1, \ldots, n).$$

4. THE FLIGHT-SCHEDULING PROBLEM

1. Statement of the Problem and Reduction to a Linear Programming Problem

This problem appears when it is necessary to make an optimal assignment of aircraft (or ships) to given routes so as to provide the necessary carrying capacity with minimal total operating cost. The problem is stated as follows:

Assume that there are n different types of aircraft that must be scheduled for m routes, and assume that the monthly load transported by an aircraft of the ith type on the jth route is a_{ij} units, with an associated monthly operating cost of b_{ij} dollars. It is necessary to determine the number x_{ij} of aircraft of the ith type that must be assigned to the jth route to provide this line with a_j units ($i = 1, \ldots, n; j = 1, \ldots, m$) of carrying capacity with a minimal total operating cost when it is known that N_i aircraft of the ith type ($i = 1, \ldots, n$) are available.

Since the load carried by the jth route is

$$a_{1j}x_{1j} + \ldots + a_{nj}x_{nj} \qquad (j = 1, \ldots, m)$$

and the total cost of carrying this load is

$$\sum_{j=1}^{m} \sum_{i=1}^{n} b_{ij}x_{ij},$$

the problem consists in minimizing the linear form

$$z=\sum_{j=1}^{m}\sum_{i=1}^{n} b_{ij}x_{ij}$$

under the constraints

$$a_{1j}x_{1j}+\dots+a_{nj}x_{nj}\geqslant a_j \qquad (j=1, \dots, m),$$
$$x_{i1}+\dots+x_{im}=N_i \qquad (i=1, \dots, n),$$
$$x_{ij}\geqslant 0 \qquad (i=1, \dots, n; \quad j=1, \dots, m)$$

the problem can be solved by the simplex method, with appropriate modifications that will provide integral x_{ij}.

2. Example

Assume that three types of aircraft must be assigned to four routes. The table below shows the number of aircraft of each type, the monthly capacity of each aircraft on each route, and the corresponding costs.

Aircraft	Number of Aircraft	Monthly capacity of one aircraft on a given route				Operating costs per aircraft on given routes			
		I	II	III	IV	I	II	III	IV
№ 1	50	15	10	20	50	15	20	25	40
№ 2	20	30	25	10	17	70	28	15	45
№ 3	30	25	50	30	45	40	70	40	65

The aircraft must be assigned to routes so as to minimize the total operating costs and provide the routes with no fewer than 300, 200, 1000, and 500 units of capacity, respectively.

Let x_{ij} denote the number of aircraft of the ith type (i = 1, 2, 3) that are to be assigned to the jth (j = 1, 2, 3, 4) route. Then the problem reduces to minimizing the linear form

$$z=15x_{11}+20x_{12}+25x_{13}+40x_{14}+70x_{21}+28x_{22}+$$
$$+15x_{23}+45x_{24}+40x_{31}+70x_{32}+40x_{33}+65x_{34}$$

under the constraints

$$15x_{11}+30x_{21}+25x_{31}\geqslant 300,$$
$$10x_{12}+25x_{22}+50x_{32}\geqslant 200,$$
$$20x_{13}+10x_{23}+30x_{33}\geqslant 1000,$$
$$50x_{14}+17x_{24}+45x_{34}\geqslant 500,$$
$$x_{11}+x_{12}+x_{13}+x_{14}=50,$$
$$x_{21}+x_{22}+x_{23}+x_{24}=20,$$
$$x_{31}+x_{32}+x_{33}+x_{34}=30,$$
$$x_{ij}\geqslant 0 \qquad (i=1, 2, 3; \quad j=1, 2, 3, 4).$$

We rewrite the constraints in the form

$$\begin{aligned}
y_1 &= 15x_{11} + 30x_{21} + 25x_{31} - 300 \geqslant 0,\\
y_2 &= 10x_{12} + 25x_{22} + 50x_{32} - 200 \geqslant 0,\\
y_3 &= 20x_{13} + 10x_{23} + 30x_{33} - 1000 \geqslant 0,\\
y_4 &= 50x_{14} + 17x_{24} + 45x_{34} - 500 \geqslant 0,\\
0 &= -x_{11} - x_{12} - x_{13} - x_{14} + 50,\\
0 &= -x_{21} - x_{22} - x_{23} - x_{24} + 20,\\
0 &= -x_{31} - x_{32} - x_{33} - x_{34} + 30,\\
x_{ij} &\geqslant 0 \quad (i = 1, 2, 3;\ j = 1, 2, 3, 4).
\end{aligned}$$

Now we construct the table

	$-x_{11}$	$-x_{12}$	$-x_{13}$	$-x_{14}$	$-x_{21}$	$-x_{22}$	$-x_{23}$	$-x_{24}$	$-x_{31}$	$-x_{32}$	$-x_{33}$	$-x_{34}$	1
$y_1 =$	−15	0	0	0	−30	0	0	0	−25	0	0	0	−300
$y_2 =$	0	−10	0	0	0	−25	0	0	0	−50	0	0	−200
$y_3 =$	0	0	−20	0	0	0	−10	0	0	0	−30	0	−1000
$y_4 =$	0	0	0	−50	0	0	0	−17	0	0	0	−45	−500
$0 =$	[1]	1	1	1	0	0	0	0	0	0	0	0	50
$0 =$	0	0	0	0	1	1	1	1	0	0	0	0	20
$0 =$	0	0	0	0	0	0	0	0	1	1	1	1	30
$z =$	−15	−20	−25	−40	−70	−28	−15	−45	−40	−70	−40	−65	0

and, eliminating the 0-equations, we obtain the transformed table

	$-x_{12}$	$-x_{13}$	$-x_{14}$	$-x_{21}$	$-x_{22}$	$-x_{24}$	$-x_{31}$	$-x_{32}$	x_{34}	1
$y_1 =$	15	15	15	−30	0	0	−25	0	0	450
$y_2 =$	[−10]	0	0	0	−25	0	0	50	0	−200
$y_3 =$	0	−20	0	10	10	10	30	30	30	100
$y_4 =$	0	0	−50	0	0	−17	0	0	−45	−500
$x_{11} =$	1	1	1	0	0	0	0	0	0	50
$x_{23} =$	0	0	0	1	1	1	0	0	0	20
$x_{33} =$	0	0	0	0	0	0	1	1	1	30
$z =$	−5	−10	−25	−55	−13	−30	0	−30	−25	2250

,

which still contains negative slack terms.

We seek next a basic solution. Two modified Jordan eliminations yield the table

	$-y_2$	$-x_{13}$	$-y_4$	$-x_{21}$	$-x_{22}$	$-x_{24}$	$-x_{31}$	$-x_{32}$	$-x_{34}$	1
$y_1 =$										0
$x_{12} =$										20
$y_3 =$										100
$x_{14} =$										10
$x_{11} =$										20
$x_{23} =$										20
$x_{33} =$										30
$z =$	$-\frac{1}{2}$	−10	$-\frac{1}{2}$	−55	$-\frac{1}{2}$	$-\frac{43}{2}$	0	−5	$-\frac{5}{2}$	2600

,

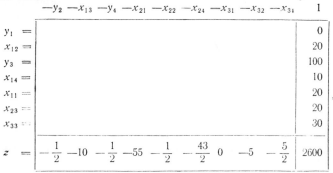

from which it is clear that the solution

$$x_{13}=x_{21}=x_{22}=x_{24}=x_{31}=x_{32}=x_{34}=0,$$
$$x_{11}=20,\ x_{12}=20,\ x_{14}=10,\ x_{23}=20,\ x_{33}=30,$$

for which

$$z=2600,$$

is not only a basic solution, but optimal (all the coefficients of the z-row are nonpositive!).

5. THE ALLOCATION PROBLEM

1. Statement of the Problem

We will consider the problem of assigning n mechanisms (workers) n tasks so that each mechanism (worker) is engaged in only one task. Here we assume the productivity of each mechanism is fixed for each task and we seek an arrangement for which the total effect is maximal.

Let c_{ij} $(i, j = 1, \ldots, n)$ denote the productivity of the ith mechanism at the jth task. The problem under discussion is well known as the ***allocation problem,*** consisting in choosing n entries of the matrix $\|c_{ij}\|$, one in each row and column, so that their sum $c_{1j_1}+c_{2j_2}+\ldots+c_{nj_n}$ $(j_k \neq j_l$ when $k \neq l)$ is maximal.

Let x_{ij} denote a variable that is equal to one if the ith mechanism is assigned the jth task, and is equal to zero if it is not assigned this task; this reduces the problem to the following linear programming problem:

Among the nonnegative integral solutions of the system of $2n$ equations

$$x_{i1}+x_{i2}+\ldots+x_{in}=1 \qquad (i=1, \ldots, n),$$
$$x_{1j}+x_{2j}+\ldots+x_{nj}=1 \qquad (j=1, \ldots, n),$$

which indicate that each mechanism executes only one task and that each task is done by one mechanism, find one that maximizes the linear form

$$z=\sum_{i=1}^{n}\sum_{j=1}^{n}c_{ij}x_{ij},$$

which denotes the total productivity of all the mechanisms.*

---

*This problem is usually solved by a special algorithm [30] that is less cumbersome than the simplex method.

2. Example

There are three mechanisms A_1, A_2, and A_3 that can each be used for each of three tasks B_1, B_2, and B_3; the productivities (in relative units) are given in the following table:

	B_1	B_2	B_3
A_1	1	2	3
A_2	2	4	1
A_3	3	1	5

It is required to assign each of the mechanisms one task so that the total productivity of all of the mechanisms is maximal.

As suggested above, let x_{ij} denote a variable equal to one if the mechanism A_i is assigned the task B_j, and equal to zero if the mechanism A_i is not assigned the task B_j. Then the total productivity of the mechanisms can be written in the form

$$z = x_{11} + 2x_{12} + 3x_{13} + 2x_{21} + 4x_{22} + x_{23} + 3x_{31} + x_{32} + 5x_{33},$$

while the constraints can be written in the form

$$\begin{aligned} x_{11} + x_{12} + x_{13} &= 1, \\ x_{21} + x_{22} + x_{23} &= 1, \\ x_{31} + x_{32} + x_{33} &= 1, \\ x_{11} + x_{21} + x_{31} &= 1, \\ x_{12} + x_{22} + x_{32} &= 1, \\ x_{13} + x_{23} + x_{33} &= 1; \end{aligned}$$

it is necessary to maximize the form z under these constraints.

Writing the constraints in the form of 0-equations, we obtain the table

	$-x_{11}$	$-x_{12}$	$-x_{13}$	$-x_{21}$	$-x_{22}$	$-x_{23}$	$-x_{31}$	$-x_{32}$	$-x_{33}$	1
0 =	1	1	1	0	0	0	0	0	0	1
0 =	0	0	0	1	1	1	0	0	0	1
0 =	0	0	0	0	0	0	1	1	1	1
0 =	1	0	0	1	0	0	1	0	0	1
0 =	0	1	0	0	1	0	0	1	0	1
0 =	0	0	1	0	0	1	0	0	1	1
z =	−1	−2	−3	−2	−4	−1	−3	−1	−5	0

After eliminating 0-rows and the columns located under the zeros carried to the top of the table, we obtain the table

	$-x_{22}$	$-x_{23}$	$-x_{32}$	$-x_{33}$	1
$x_{11} =$	$\boxed{-1}$	-1	-1	-1	-1
$x_{21} =$	1	1	0	0	1
$x_{31} =$	0	0	1	1	1
$x_{12} =$	1	0	1	0	1
$x_{13} =$	0	1	0	1	1
$z =$	1	3	3	0	9

,

which contains negative slack terms, so that a basic solution has not yet been found.

Modified Jordan elimination over the entry 1 shown in the square yields the table

	$-x_{11}$	$-x_{23}$	$-x_{32}$	$-x_{33}$	1
$x_{22} =$	-1	1	1	1	1
$x_{21} =$	$\boxed{1}$	0	-1	-1	0
$x_{31} =$	0	0	1	1	1
$x_{12} =$	1	-1	0	-1	0
$x_{13} =$	0	1	0	1	1
$z =$	-1	4	4	1	10

,

in which all of the slack terms are nonnegative, so that we may seek an optimal solution. By choosing a resolvent element as shown in the table and executing one modified Jordan elimination, we obtain the final table

	$-x_{21}$	$-x_{23}$	$-x_{32}$	$-x_{33}$	1
$x_{22} =$					1
$x_{11} =$					0
$x_{31} =$					1
$x_{12} =$					0
$x_{13} =$					1
$z =$	1	4	3	0	10

.

It follows from the last table that the maximal total productivity of all mechanisms is 10 (relative units) and is achieved when

$$x_{11} = 0, \quad x_{12} = 0, \quad x_{13} = 1, \quad x_{21} = 0, \quad x_{22} = 1,$$
$$x_{23} = 0, \quad x_{31} = 1, \quad x_{32} = 0, \quad x_{33} = 0,$$

i.e., with the following assignments:

mechanism	A_1	to job	B_3,
,,	A_2	,,	B_2,
,,	A_3	,,	B_1.

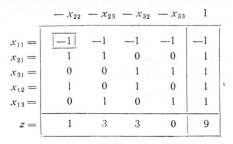

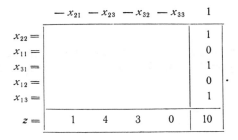

Since the z-row of the last table contains a zero element, the optimal solution obtained is not unique. Modified Jordan elimination over an entry in the column containing the zero of the z-row can be used to find another optimal solution.

6. MILITARY PROBLEMS [14]

Linear programming methods have been widely used for solution of certain military problems. Since complete information is frequently unavailable for solution of these problems, the constraints available for military problems are usually less complete than in the problems considered in the preceding sections.

1. The Bottle-Neck Problem

This is the problem of best distribution of limited resources among connected sections of some system.

We will consider the problem of distributing industrially produced aircraft among military theaters and firing ranges where crews are trained to provide the best possible anti-aircraft defense.

Assume that some military division flying combat missions and training crews on its firing range, is provided with a_j aircraft ($j = 1, \ldots, n$) at the beginning of each of n months. Of these aircraft, x_j, for which there are trained crews, are sent immediately to the front, while the remaining number $a_j - x_j$ is assigned to the firing range for training new crews. The military effectiveness of the different parts is determined by the number of aircraft with trained crews and their combat experience, the so-called number of active flight-months.

This raises the problem of determining how the monthly deliveries of aircraft must be distributed between the front and firing ranges so as to achieve maximal military effectiveness.

Assume that the firing range has z_0 aircraft prior to the beginning of the program under discussion. The number of aircraft z_j that can be used at the firing range for training during the jth month consists of z_{j-1} aircraft available from the preceding month, plus $a_j - x_j$ aircraft obtained at the beginning of the jth month:

$$z_j = z_{j-1} + (a_j - x_j) \qquad (j = 1, \ldots, n).$$

Assume that at the beginning of the program there are y_1 trained crews, which need not have aircraft, and during this month k crews can be trained with one aircraft. The number of crews y_j trained prior to the beginning of the jth month consists of the y_{j-1} trained crews available at the beginning of the preceding month, and the $k \cdot z_{j-1}$ crews that are trained during the $(j - 1)$th month:

$$y_j = y_{j-1} + k \cdot z_{j-1} \qquad (j = 2, \ldots, n).$$

The total number of aircraft sent to the front prior to the beginning of the jth month should not be larger than the number of trained crews, so

$$x_1 + \dots + x_j \leqslant y_j \qquad (j = 1, \dots, n).$$

Prior to the end of the period for which the program is designed, the aircraft received at the front in the first month will provide nx_1 active flight-months. The aircraft received in the second month will provide $(n-1)x_2$ active flight-months, etc. Aircraft received over the course of the entire n months will provide a capacity of

$$nx_1 + (n-1)x_2 + \dots + [n-(j-1)]x_j + \dots$$
$$\dots + 2x_{n-1} + x_n$$

active flight-months.

The problem consists in maximizing the linear form

$$u = nx_1 + (n-1)x_2 + \dots + 2x_{n-1} + x_n$$

under the constraints

$$\begin{aligned} x_j + z_j - z_{j-1} - a_j &= 0 \qquad (j = 1, \dots, n), \\ y_j - y_{j-1} - kz_{j-1} &= 0 \qquad (j = 2, \dots, n), \\ y_j - x_1 - x_2 - \dots - x_j &\geqslant 0 \qquad (j = 1, \dots, n), \\ x_j \geqslant 0,\ y_j \geqslant 0,\ z_j &\geqslant 0 \qquad (j = 1, \dots, n). \end{aligned}$$

Remark. This mathematical model holds for distribution of limited quantities of raw materials (such as metals) that must be distributed between production of some part and production of equipment used to produce this part when the ultimate goal is to maximize production of the part.

2. The Problem of Choosing Rational Ratios Between Different Types of Missiles

Assume it is known that an enemy has m types of tank armor, but the ratios in which they are used for production of his tanks are unknown. Moreover, assume that n types of defensive missiles are available and the destructive capability of each type of missile for each type of armor is known, i.e., the probability p_{ij} of neutralizing a tank with the ith type of armor by a missile of the jth type ($i = 1, \dots, m$; $j = 1, \dots, n$) is known.

It is required to determine the proportions of different types of missiles that must be produced so that, by mixing them and using them randomly, the mathematical expectation for neutralization of tanks is maximal, no matter what their armor. If we let y_j denote the number of missiles of the jth type ($j = 1, \dots, n$) in a given mixture, then the mathematical expectation for the number of tanks with the ith type of armor that can be neutralized is clearly

$$m_i = p_{i1}y_1 + \ldots + p_{in}y_n.$$

If this mathematical expectation is normalized to one missile, i.e., if we divide by $y_1 + \ldots + y_n$, we find that

$$M_i = p_{i1}x_1 + \ldots + p_{in}x_n,$$

where

$$x_j = \frac{y_j}{y_1 + \ldots + y_n},$$

i.e., x_j is the proportion of missiles of the jth type in the total number of missiles (the proportions are $x_1 : x_2 : \ldots : x_n$), so that

$$x_1 + x_2 + \ldots + x_n = 1,$$

while M_i is the mathematical expectation for the number of tanks with the ith type of armor that are neutralized by all the missiles, the mathematical expectation being normalized to one missile.

If we assume that the enemy knows the type of missiles available to be used against his tank armor, and that he will attempt to minimize his losses, then the guaranteed average number of neutralized tanks, normalized to one missile, is clearly the smallest of the numbers M_i ($i = 1, \ldots, m$). As a result, the problem consists in choosing x_j ($j = 1, \ldots, n$) so that

$$\max_x \min_{1 \leq i \leq m} M_i$$

is achieved.

Introduction of an auxiliary variable ξ such that

$$p_{i1}x_1 + \ldots + p_{in}x_n \geqslant \xi \qquad (i = 1, \ldots, m)$$

reduces the problem to a linear programming problem, i.e., to maximization of the form

$$z = \xi$$

under the constraints

$$\begin{gathered} x_1 + \ldots + x_n = 1, \\ p_{11}x_1 + \ldots + p_{1n}x_n \geqslant \xi, \\ \cdots\cdots\cdots\cdots \\ p_{m1}x_1 + \ldots + p_{mn}x_n \geqslant \xi, \\ x_j \geqslant 0 \quad (j = 1, \ldots, n). \end{gathered}$$

7. LINEAR PROGRAMMING AND MATRIX GAMES

Linear programming is closely related to the theory of so-called matrix games. As we will show below, any rectangular (or matrix) two-person zero-sum game with a finite number of strategies can be reduced to a linear programming problem and, conversely, any linear programming problem can be reduced to solution of some two-person zero-sum rectangular game.

Certain extremal problems are discussed in both theories: In linear programming it is necessary to solve the problem of best distribution of resources for achievement of desired results; in game theory it is necessary to solve the problem of choosing strategies so as to maximize the payoff. The relationship between game theory and linear programming was first established by von Neumann [3] and Dantzig [20].

1. Remarks on the Theory of Matrix (Rectangular) Games

By a ***two-person zero-sum matrix*** or ***rectangular game*** we mean a set of rules such that the sum of the payoffs v_1 and v_2 for the first and second players is equal to zero,

$$v_1 + v_2 = 0,$$

i.e., the payoff of one player is equal to the loss of the other.

A game is a single-move game if each play consists of one move by the first player and one move by the second, where neither knows the move of the other.

Assume that of m possible options (m pure strategies), the first player chooses his ith, while the second chooses, of n possible options (n pure strategies), his jth, and assume that in this play the payoff to the first player is a_{ij}, while to the second it is $-a_{ij}$. It is convenient to write these conditions in the form of the payoff matrix for the first player,

$$A = \begin{pmatrix} a_{11} & a_{12} & \dots & a_{1n} \\ \cdot & \cdot & \cdot & \cdot \\ a_{m1} & a_{m2} & \dots & a_{mn} \end{pmatrix} = \| a_{ij} \|,$$

where the a_{ij} ($i = 1, \dots, m$; $j = 1, \dots, n$) are real numbers; here the row indices correspond to the m possible pure strategies of the first player, while the column indices correspond to the n pure strategies of the second.

The game of "heads and tails" provides an example of a two-person zero-sum game: Each of two players, without knowing the move of the other, puts a coin down with either heads or tails up, and if the coins have both heads or both tails up, the second player pays the first, while if the coins have different faces up, the first player pays the second an equal amount. In this case, the matrix for the first player is of the form

$$A=\begin{pmatrix} 1 & -1 \\ -1 & 1 \end{pmatrix},$$

where the first (second) row shows all possible payoffs for the first player when he chooses heads (tails), while the columns show the payoffs of the first player when the second player chooses heads (tails).

If we let $x_1, \ldots, x_m$ denote the probabilities (frequencies) with which the first player chooses the first, second, etc., mth pure strategy, and let $y_1, \ldots, y_n$ denote the probabilities with which his opponent chooses his pure strategies, the sets of numbers

$$X=(x_1, \ldots, x_m) \text{ and } Y=(y_1, \ldots, y_n)$$

are called the ***mixed strategies*** of the first and second players, respectively. It is clear that here

$$\begin{aligned} &x_1+x_2+\ldots+x_m=1, \\ &x_i \geqslant 0 \quad (i=1, \ldots, m), \\ &y_1+y_2+\ldots+y_n=1, \\ &y_j \geqslant 0 \quad (j=1, \ldots, n). \end{aligned}$$

If

$$x_1=\ldots=x_{i-1}=0, \quad x_i=1, \quad x_{i+1}=\ldots=x_m=0,$$

this mixed strategy is the ith pure strategy of the first player; similarly, the second player's mixed strategies in which all components except the jth are equal to zero are his jth pure strategies.

When the players respectively, choose mixed strategies $X = (x_1, \ldots, x_m)$ and $Y = (y_1, \ldots, y_n)$, the mathematical expectation for the payoff of the first player is

$$E(X, Y)=\sum_{j=1}^{n}\sum_{i=1}^{m} a_{ij}x_iy_j.$$

If the second player chooses some mixed strategy Y', the first player will naturally choose his best mixed strategy X^*, on which $\max_X E(X, Y')$. is achieved:

$$E(X^*, Y')=\max_X E(X, Y').$$

Similarly, when the first player chooses some mixed strategy X', the second player will choose his best mixed strategy Y^*, on which $\min_Y E(X', Y)$ is achieved:

$$E(X', Y^*) = \min_Y E(X', Y).$$

It is clear that $X^*(Y^*)$ depends on the choice of $Y'(X')$. Each player is therefore faced with the problem of choosing an optimal mixed strategy, i.e., a mixed strategy $\overline{X}(\overline{Y})$ that will guarantee the maximal (minimal) mathematical expectation of his payoff (loss), i.e., he must choose his mixed strategy to maximize (minimize) the mathematical expectation for payoff (loss) in his opponent's best possible game.

In other words, an optimal strategy $\overline{X}(\overline{Y})$ must maximize (minimize) the quantity $\min_Y E(X, Y)$ $\left(\max_X E(X, Y)\right)$:

$$\max_X \min_Y E(X, Y) = \min_Y E(\overline{X}, Y)$$
$$\left(\min_Y \max_X E(X, Y) = \max_X E(X, \overline{Y})\right).$$

The fundamental theory of the theory of matrix games (see, for example, [10]) asserts that *every two-person zero-sum matrix game has a solution, i.e., there exists optimal mixed strategies* $\overline{X}$ *and* $\overline{Y}$ *for both players, and*

$$\max_X \min_Y E(X, Y) = \min_Y \max_X E(X, Y) = E(\overline{X}, \overline{Y}),$$

so that for arbitrary mixed strategies X *and* Y *and optimal strategies* $\overline{X}$ *and* $\overline{Y}$

$$E(X, \overline{Y}) \leqslant E(\overline{X}, \overline{Y}) \leqslant E(\overline{X}, Y).$$

The number $v = E(\overline{X}, \overline{Y})$ is called the *value* of the game.

In the above example of the game of heads and tails, for which the matrix is of the form

$$\begin{pmatrix} 1 & -1 \\ -1 & 1 \end{pmatrix},$$

if each partner chooses heads and tails with equal probabilities, i.e., if their strategies are of the form

$$X = \left(\frac{1}{2}, \frac{1}{2}\right) \quad \text{and} \quad Y = \left(\frac{1}{2}, \frac{1}{2}\right),$$

the mathematical expectation of the first player's payoff is

$$E(X, Y) = \sum_{j=1}^{2} \sum_{i=1}^{2} a_{ij} x_i y_j =$$
$$= 1 \cdot \frac{1}{2} \cdot \frac{1}{2} + (-1) \cdot \frac{1}{2} \cdot \frac{1}{2} + (-1) \cdot \frac{1}{2} \cdot \frac{1}{2} + 1 \cdot \frac{1}{2} \cdot \frac{1}{2} = 0.$$

Consequently, the mathematical expectation for the second player's loss is also zero.

It can be shown that the strategies chosen by the two players are optimal, i.e.,

$$\bar{X}=\left(\frac{1}{2}, \frac{1}{2}\right), \qquad \bar{Y}=\left(\frac{1}{2}, \frac{1}{2}\right),$$

and the value of the game is zero.

All ***symmetric*** games, i.e., games with skew-symmetric matrices ($a_{ij}=-a_{ji}$, $i=1, \ldots, m$; $j=1, \ldots, m$), have values equal to zero. In any such game the optimal strategies of the players coincide and the value of the game is zero.

For, let $\bar{X}$ and $\bar{Y}$ be optimal mixed strageties and let $E(\bar{X}, \bar{Y})=v$. For any mixed strategy Y of the second player we have the $v \leqslant E(\bar{X}, Y)$. Setting $Y=\bar{X}$ and keeping in mind that in a symmetric game $a_{ij}=-a_{ji}$, we find that

$$v \leqslant E(\bar{X}, \bar{X})=0.$$

Similarly,

$$v \geqslant E(\bar{Y}, \bar{Y})=0,$$

so that $v=0$ and v is achieved when the strategies of the opponents coincide.

Remark. By adding a fixed number w to each entry in the game matrix $\|a_{ij}\|$ we can, without changing the optimal strategy, change the value v of the game to $v+w$.

Indeed, for any pair of mixed strategies X and Y, the mathematical expectation

$$E(X, Y)=\sum_{j=1}^{n} \sum_{i=1}^{m} a_{ij} x_i y_j$$

of the payoff to the first player in a game with matrix $\|a_{ij}\|$ differs from the mathematical expectation $E'(X, Y)$ of the payoff to the first player in a game with matrix $\|a_{ij}+w\|$ by the same constant w,

$$E'(X, Y)=\sum_{j=1}^{n} \sum_{i=1}^{m}(a_{ij}+w) x_i y_j=\sum_{j=1}^{n} \sum_{i=1}^{m} a_{ij} x_i y_j+w= \\ =E(X, Y)+w.$$

so that

$$E'(\bar{X}, \bar{Y})=\max_X \min_Y E'(X, Y)=\max_X \min_Y E(X, Y)+w= \\ =E(\bar{X}, \bar{Y})+w=v+w.$$

2. Reduction of a Matrix Game to a Linear Programming Problem

Assume that a two-person zero-sum is given by the first player's payoff matrix

$$A = \begin{pmatrix} a_{11} & \dots & a_{1n} \\ \cdot & \cdot \; \cdot \; \cdot & \cdot \\ a_{m1} & \dots & a_{mn} \end{pmatrix}. \tag{3.4}$$

It follows from the fundamental theorem that the game has a solution $(\overline{X}, \overline{Y})$, and that the value of the game is $v = E(\overline{X}, \overline{Y})$.

For any of the second player's mixed strategies Y,

$$E(\overline{X}, Y) \geqslant v.$$

In particular, for his pure strategy

$$y_1 = \dots = y_{j-1} = 0, \quad y_j = 1, \quad y_{j+1} = \dots = y_n = 0$$

we have

$$E(\overline{X}, j) = \sum_{i=1}^{m} a_{ij}\overline{x}_i \geqslant v \qquad (j = 1, \dots, n).$$

Thus, the problem of the first player, which consists in finding an optimal mixed strategy $\overline{X}$ that will maximize his guaranteed mathematical payoff-expectation v, reduces to finding an $\overline{X} = (\overline{x}_1, \dots, \overline{x}_m)$ that will satisfy the constraints

$$\left.\begin{array}{c} a_{11}x_1 + a_{21}x_2 + \dots + a_{m1}x_m \geqslant v, \\ \cdot \; \cdot \; \cdot \; \cdot \; \cdot \; \cdot \; \cdot \; \cdot \; \cdot \; \cdot \; \cdot \; \cdot \\ a_{1n}x_1 + a_{2n}x_2 + \dots + a_{mn}x_m \geqslant v, \\ x_i \geqslant 0 \quad (i = 1, \dots, m), \\ x_1 + x_2 + \dots + x_m = 1 \end{array}\right\} \tag{3.5}$$

and maximize v..

Similarly, for any mixed strategy X of the first player we have

$$E(X, \overline{Y}) \leqslant v,$$

and, in particular, for any pure strategy

$$x_1 = \dots = x_{i-1} = 0, \quad x_i = 1, \quad x_{i+1} = \dots = x_m = 0$$

we have

$$E(i, \overline{Y}) = \sum_{j=1}^{n} a_{ij}\overline{y}_j \leqslant v \qquad (i = 1, \dots, m).$$

The problem of the second player therefore consists in finding an optimal mixed strategy $\bar{Y}$ that will minimize the guaranteed mathematical expectation for his loss v, i.e., consists in finding a $\bar{Y} = (\bar{y}_1, \ldots, \bar{y}_n)$ satisfying the constraints

$$\left.\begin{array}{l} a_{11}y_1 + a_{12}y_2 + \ldots + a_{1n}y_n \leqslant v, \\ \cdots\cdots\cdots\cdots\cdots\cdots \\ a_{m1}y_1 + a_{m2}y_2 + \ldots + a_{mn}y_n \leqslant v, \\ y_j \geqslant 0 \quad (j = 1, \ldots, n), \\ y_1 + y_2 + \ldots + y_n = 1 \end{array}\right\} \tag{3.6}$$

and minimizing v.

By virtue of the remark at the end of the preceding section, v can be assumed to be positive.

We divide relations (3.5)-(3.6) by v term by term and set

$$\frac{x_i}{v} = x'_i \quad (i = 1, \ldots, m), \quad \frac{y_j}{v} = y'_j \quad (j = 1, \ldots, n).$$

We thus obtain

$$\left.\begin{array}{l} a_{1j}x'_1 + a_{2j}x'_2 + \ldots + a_{mj}x'_m \geqslant 1 \ (j = 1, \ldots, n), \\ x'_i \geqslant 0 \quad (i = 1, \ldots, m), \\ x'_1 + x'_2 + \ldots + x'_m = \frac{1}{v} \end{array}\right\} \tag{3.7}$$

and

$$\left.\begin{array}{l} a_{i1}y'_1 + a_{i2}y'_2 + \ldots + a_{in}y'_n \leqslant 1 \quad (i = 1, \ldots, m), \\ y'_j \geqslant 0 \quad (j = 1, \ldots, n), \\ y'_1 + y'_2 + \ldots + y'_n = \frac{1}{v}. \end{array}\right\} \tag{3.8}$$

Since the first player is attempting to maximize v, his problem consists in minimizing the form

$$w = x'_1 + x'_2 + \ldots + x'_m = \frac{1}{v}$$

under constraints (3.7); the problem of the second player, who is attempting to minimize v, consists in maximizing the form

$$u = y'_1 + y'_2 + \ldots + y'_n = \frac{1}{v}$$

under constraints (3.8).

Thus, the problem of finding the solution of the zero-sum matrix game given by matrix (3.4) reduces to the pair of dual linear programming problems defined by the following table:

	$\xi_1 =$	...	$\xi_j =$	...	$\xi_n =$	$w =$
	$-y_1'$	...	$-y_j'$	...	$-y_n'$	1
x_1' $\eta_1 =$	a_{11}	...	a_{1j}	...	a_{1n}	1
....	...	...	...	...	...	...
x_i' $\eta_i =$	a_{i1}	...	a_{ij}	...	a_{in}	1
....	...	...	...	...	...	...
x_m' $\eta_m =$	a_{m1}	...	a_{mj}	...	a_{mn}	1
1 $u =$	-1	...	-1	...	-1	0

Example. Assume that a two-person game is given by the following matrix, which represents the first player's payoff:

$$A = \begin{pmatrix} -2 & -1 & 5 \\ 1 & -2 & 3 \\ 3 & 1 & -4 \end{pmatrix}.$$

The equivalent linear programming problems consist in finding a nonnegative solution of the system

$$\begin{aligned} -2x_1' + x_2' + 3x_3' &\geqslant 1, \\ -x_1' - 2x_2' + x_3' &\geqslant 1, \\ 5x_1' + 3x_2' - 4x_3' &\geqslant 1, \end{aligned}$$

that will minimize the linear form

$$w = x_1' + x_2' + x_3',$$

and in finding a nonnegative solution of the system

$$\begin{aligned} -2y_1' - y_2' + 5y_3' &\leqslant 1, \\ y_1' - 2y_2' + 3y_3' &\leqslant 1, \\ 3y_1' + y_2' - 4y_3' &\leqslant 1, \end{aligned}$$

that will minimize the linear form

$$u = y_1' + y_2' + y_3'.$$

Constructing the combined table

	$\xi_1 =$	$\xi_2 =$	$\xi_3 =$	$w =$
	$-y_1'$	$-y_2'$	$-y_3'$	1
x_1' $\eta_1 =$	-2	-1	5	1
x_2' $\eta_2 =$	1	-2	3	1
x_3' $\eta_3 =$	3	1	-4	1
1 $u =$	-1	-1	-1	0

and solving this pair of dual problems, we find that

$$\max u = \min w = 11;$$

it is achieved at

$$y_1' = 0, \quad y_2' = 9, \quad y_3' = 2; \quad x_1' = 5; \quad x_2' = 0, \quad x_3' = 6,$$

so that

$$v = \frac{1}{11}, \quad \bar{X} = \left(\bar{x}_1 = \frac{5}{11}, \quad \bar{x}_2 = 0, \quad \bar{x}_3 = \frac{6}{11}\right),$$
$$\bar{Y} = \left(\bar{y}_1 = 0, \quad \bar{y}_2 = \frac{9}{11}, \quad \bar{y}_3 = \frac{2}{11}\right).$$

3. Reduction of Linear Programming Problems to Matrix Games

Consider the following linear programming problem: Find a nonnegative solution of the system

$$\left.\begin{array}{l} a_{11}x_1 + a_{21}x_2 + \ldots + a_{m1}x_m \geqslant p_1, \\ \ldots\ldots\ldots\ldots\ldots\ldots\ldots\ldots \\ a_{1n}x_1 + a_{2n}x_2 + \ldots + a_{mn}x_m \geqslant p_n, \end{array}\right\} \tag{3.9}$$

that will minimize the linear form

$$w = a_1x_1 + \ldots + a_mx_m. \tag{3.10}$$

It is clear from the combined table

		$\xi_1 =$ $-y_1$	...	$\xi_j =$ $-y_j$	...	$\xi_n =$ $-y_n$	$w =$ 1
x_1	$\eta_1 =$	a_{11}	...	a_{1j}	...	a_{1n}	a_1
. . . .		. . . .	. . . .	. . . .	. . . .	. . . .	. . .
x_i	$\eta_i =$	a_{i1}	...	a_{ij}	...	a_{in}	a_i
. . . .		. . . .	. . . .	. . . .	. . . .	. . . .	. . .
x_m	$\eta_m =$	a_{m1}	...	a_{mj}	...	a_{mn}	a_m
1	$u =$	$-p_1$	...	$-p_j$	...	$-p_n$	0

that the problem dual to the one under discussion consists in finding a nonnegative solution of the system

$$\left.\begin{array}{l} a_{11}y_1 + a_{12}y_2 + \ldots + a_{1n}y_n \leqslant a_1, \\ \ldots\ldots\ldots\ldots\ldots\ldots\ldots\ldots \\ a_{m1}y_1 + a_{m2}y_2 + \ldots + a_{mn}y_n \leqslant a_m, \end{array}\right\} \tag{3.11}$$

that will maximize the linear form

$$u = p_1y_1 + \ldots + p_ny_n. \tag{3.12}$$

By the fundamental duality theorem (Chapter 2, Section 7, Paragraph 3), if one of the dual problems has an optimal solution, so does the second, and

$$\min w = \max u.$$

As we showed in Chapter 2, Section 7, Paragraph 4, finding optimal solutions for the pair of problems under consideration is equivalent to solving the following system of linear inequalities:

$$\left.\begin{array}{l}
a_{11}x_1 + a_{21}x_2 + \ldots + a_{m1}x_m - p_1 \geqslant 0, \\
\ldots\ldots\ldots\ldots\ldots\ldots\ldots\ldots \\
a_{1n}x_1 + a_{2n}x_2 + \ldots + a_{mn}x_m - p_n \geqslant 0, \\
-a_{11}y_1 - a_{12}y_2 - \ldots - a_{1n}y_n + a_1 \geqslant 0, \\
\ldots\ldots\ldots\ldots\ldots\ldots\ldots\ldots \\
-a_{m1}y_1 - a_{m2}y_2 - \ldots - a_{mn}y_n + a_m \geqslant 0, \\
p_1y_1 + \ldots + p_ny_n - a_1x_1 - \ldots - a_mx_m \geqslant 0, \\
x_i \geqslant 0 \quad (i = 1, \ldots, m), \\
y_j \geqslant 0 \quad (j = 1, \ldots, n).
\end{array}\right\} \qquad (3.13)$$

By multiplying the inequalities of this system by a positive variable z, we obtain the equivalent system

$$\left.\begin{array}{l}
a_{11}\bar{x}_1 + \ldots + a_{m1}\bar{x}_m - p_1z \geqslant 0, \\
\ldots\ldots\ldots\ldots\ldots\ldots \\
a_{1n}\bar{x}_1 + \ldots + a_{mn}\bar{x}_m - p_nz \geqslant 0, \\
-a_{11}\bar{y}_1 - \ldots - a_{1n}\bar{y}_n + a_1z \geqslant 0, \\
\ldots\ldots\ldots\ldots\ldots\ldots\ldots\ldots \\
-a_{m1}\bar{y}_1 - \ldots - a_{mn}\bar{y}_n + a_mz \geqslant 0, \\
p_1\bar{y}_1 + \ldots + p_n\bar{y}_n - a_1\bar{x}_1 - \ldots - a_m\bar{x}_m \geqslant 0, \\
\bar{x}_i \geqslant 0 \quad (i = 1, \ldots, m), \\
\bar{y}_j \geqslant 0 \quad (j = 1, \ldots, n),
\end{array}\right\} \qquad (3.14)$$

where $\bar{x}_i = x_iz$, $\bar{y}_j = y_jz$.

The solutions of this last system can, if $z > 0$, be used to find optimal solutions of the pair of dual problems by means of the formulas

$$x_i = \frac{\bar{x}_i}{z} \quad (i = 1, \ldots, m), \quad y_j = \frac{\bar{y}_j}{z} \quad (j = 1, \ldots, n).$$

We show now that the solution of the zero-sum symmetric matrix game given by the skew symmetric matrix

$$\begin{Vmatrix} 0 & \dots & 0 & -a_{11} & \dots & -a_{m1} & p_1 \\ \cdot & \cdot & \cdot & \cdot & \cdot & \cdot & \cdot \\ 0 & \dots & 0 & -a_{1n} & \dots & -a_{mn} & p_n \\ a_{11} & \dots & a_{1n} & 0 & \dots & 0 & -a_1 \\ \cdot & \cdot & \cdot & \cdot & \cdot & \cdot & \cdot \\ a_{m1} & \dots & a_{mn} & 0 & \dots & 0 & -a_m \\ -p_1 & \dots & -p_n & a_1 & \dots & a_m & 0 \end{Vmatrix} \tag{3.15}$$

is a solution of system (3.14) and, consequently, a solution of the pair of dual linear programming problems (3.9)-(3.12).

Indeed, let $(\bar{y}_1, \dots, \bar{y}_n, \bar{x}_1, \dots, \bar{x}_m, z)$ be an optimal strategy for the first player. Then, no matter what pure strategy the second player chooses, the mathematical expectation for the first player's payoff is nonnegative (since it is no less than the value of the game v, which is equal to zero). This indicates satisfaction of the following inequalities:

$$\begin{aligned} & a_{11}\bar{x}_1 + \dots + a_{m1}\bar{x}_m - p_1 z \geqslant 0, \\ & \dots\dots\dots\dots\dots \\ & a_{1n}\bar{x}_1 + \dots + a_{mn}\bar{x}_m - p_n z \geqslant 0, \\ -a_{11}\bar{y}_1 - \dots - a_{1n}\bar{y}_n & \qquad\qquad + a_1 z \geqslant 0, \\ & \dots\dots\dots\dots\dots \\ -a_{m1}\bar{y}_1 - \dots - a_{mn}\bar{y}_n & \qquad\qquad + a_m z \geqslant 0, \\ p_1\bar{y}_1 + \dots + p_n\bar{y}_n & - a_1\bar{x}_1 - \dots - a_m\bar{x}_m \geqslant 0, \\ \bar{y}_1 + \dots + \bar{y}_n & + \bar{x}_1 + \dots + \bar{x}_m + z = 1, \\ & \bar{x}_i \geqslant 0 \quad (i = 1, \dots, m), \\ & \bar{y}_j \geqslant 0 \quad (j = 1, \dots, n), \\ & z \geqslant 0. \end{aligned}$$

We have obtained system (3.14), to which we add the constraint

$$\bar{y}_1 + \dots + \bar{y}_n + \bar{x}_1 + \dots + \bar{x}_m + z = 1,$$

which is permissible if the homogeneous system (3.14) has a nontrivial solution.

Thus, the problem of solving the pair of dual linear programming problems (3.9)-(3.12) reduces to the problem of solving the matrix game with matrix (3.15), so that the solution

$$(\bar{y}_1, \dots, \bar{y}_n, \bar{x}_1, \dots, \bar{x}_m, z)$$

of the matrix game for $z \neq 0$ provides a solution of the pair of dual linear programming problems by way of the formulas

$$y_j = \frac{\bar{y}_j}{z}, \quad x_i = \frac{\bar{x}_i}{z}.$$

Remark 1. If $z = 0$ in all optimal strategies of a game, the corresponding pair of dual linear programming problems is unsolvable. For a solvable pair of dual linear programming problems, however, at least one optimal strategy of the equivalent game contains the component $z \neq 0$.

Remark 2. The following should be added to the result of Paragraph 2: The final solution $x_1, \ldots, x_m; y_1, \ldots, y_n$ of a pair of dual linear programming problems corresponding to a symmetric game problem with matrix (3.15) can be obtained with the formulas

$$\bar{y}_j = y_j z = \frac{y_j}{\sum_{j=1}^{n} y_j + \sum_{i=1}^{m} x_i + 1},$$

$$\bar{x}_i = x_i z = \frac{x_i}{\sum_{j=1}^{n} y_j + \sum_{i=1}^{m} x_i + 1}, \quad z = \frac{1}{\sum_{j=1}^{n} y_j + \sum_{i=1}^{m} x_i + 1}.$$

4

The Transportation Problem

In this chapter we consider one of the most important linear programming problems, the transportation problem i.e., the problem of linking supply depots with demand depots so that the shipping cost of the goods in question is minimal.

Since it is a linear programming problem, the transportation problem can, of course, be solved by the simplex method. However, direct application of the simplex method to the transportation problem is usually undesirable. Because it is a universal method of solving any linear programming problem, the simplex method is not sensitive to the specific properties of the transportation problem and application of the simplex method to this problem is too cumbersome.

In Section 2 we present one of the most widely used methods for solution of the transportation problem, the method of potentials which makes complete use of the special properties of this problem and leads to the desired end considerably faster and more simply than does the simplex method.

In Section 3 we solve the transportation problem with a "time" criterion, where it is not the total cost that must be minimized, but the time required for shipping to the demand depot.

Finally, in Sections 4, 5, and 6 we consider the problem of determining the shortest paths over a given network of roads, construction of a network of roads with minimal length that will connect a given set of depots, and of maximizing the flow in a network.

1. THE TRANSPORTATION PROBLEM AS A LINEAR PROGRAMMING PROBLEM

1. General Statement of the Problem

The transportation problem can be stated as follows:

At m production points, a given commodity is produced in quantities of a_1, a_2, ..., a_m units, respectively. This commodity must be delivered to n given demand depots that require $b_1, b_2, \ldots, b_n$ units, respectively. Let the cost of transporting a unit of this commodity from the ith supply depot to the jth demand depot (customer) be c_{ij}, and let the corresponding quantity of transported commodities be x_{ij} ($i = 1, \ldots, m; j = 1, \ldots, n$) units. The conditions of this problem can be written compactly in a tableau like the following:

b_j / a_i	b_1	b_2	$\ldots$	$\ldots$	b_n
a_1	c_{11} x_{11}	c_{12} x_{12}	$\ldots$	$\ldots$	c_{1n} x_{1n}
a_2	c_{21} x_{21}	c_{22} x_{22}	$\ldots$	$\ldots$	c_{2n} x_{2n}
$\ldots$	$\ldots$	$\ldots$	$\ldots$	$\ldots$	$\ldots$
$\ldots$	$\ldots$	$\ldots$	$\ldots$	$\ldots$	$\ldots$
a_m	c_{m1} x_{m1}	c_{m2} x_{m2}	$\ldots$	$\ldots$	c_{mn} x_{mn}

(4.1)

We call the set of $m \times n$ numbers x_{ij}, i.e., the matrix $\|x_{ij}\|$, the ***shipping plan,*** while we call the matrix $\|c_{ij}\|$ ***the matrix of shipping costs.***

We will say that a plan is feasible if the x_{ij} satisfy the natural constraints

$$\left.\begin{aligned} x_{ij} \geqslant 0 \quad (i=1, \ldots, m;\ j=1, \ldots, n), \\ x_{i1}+x_{i2}+\ldots+x_{in}=a_i \quad (i=1, \ldots, m), \\ x_{1j}+x_{2j}+\ldots+x_{mj}=b_j \quad (j=1, \ldots, n), \end{aligned}\right\} \tag{4.2}$$

in which the first m equations indicate that all the produced commodity is removed from the supply depots, while the last n indicate that each demand depot is completely satisfied.

The transportation problem consists in finding an optimal feasible plan, i.e., a plan that minimizes the transportation cost

$$z=\sum_{i=1}^{m} \sum_{j=1}^{n} c_{ij} x_{ij} . \tag{4.3}$$

If system (4.2) is consistent, then

$$\sum_{i=1}^{m} a_i=\sum_{i=1}^{m} \sum_{j=1}^{n} x_{ij}=\sum_{j=1}^{n} \sum_{i=1}^{m} x_{ij}=\sum_{j=1}^{n} b_j;$$

and hence the condition

$$\sum_{i=1}^{m} a_i = \sum_{j=1}^{n} b_j \tag{4.4}$$

is necessary for consistency of (4.2). Condition (4.4) is also sufficient for consistency of (4.2), for, as we can easily verify, the values

$$x_{ij} = \frac{a_i b_j}{\sum_{i=1}^{m} a_i} \qquad (i = 1, \ldots, m;\ j = 1, \ldots, n)$$

satisfy system (4.2) when condition (4.4) is satisfied.*

Thus, the transportation problem is a linear programming problem and can be solved by the simplex method. However, in view of the exceptional practical importance of this problem and the special properties of constraints (4.2), i.e., the facts that

a) the constraints are all equations,

b) every unknown is contained in only two equations, and

c) the coefficients of all the unknowns are equal to one,

special algorithms that are considerably less cumbersome than the simplex method have been developed for solution of the transportation problem. One of them—the method of potentials, which is discussed below—is an application of L. V. Kantorovich's [6] general method for solution of the transportation problem and was proposed by L. V. Kantorovich and M. K. Gavurin [8], and somewhat later, was independently discovered by Dantzig [19].*

Another method, the so-called Hungarian method (see, for example, [14]), was discussed by Egervary [25] and improved by Kuhn [30] for solution of a special case of the transportation problem, the assignment problem, which we considered in Section 5 of Chapter 3; it was then applied by Munkres [32] to solve the general transportation problem.

2. An Open Model of the Transportation Problem (a Model with an Imbalance of Supply and Demand)

As we showed in Paragraph 1, a necessary and sufficient condition for solvability of the transportation problem is the equality of all supplies at the supply depots and the requirements at the demand depots:

$$\sum_{i=1}^{m} a_i = \sum_{j=1}^{n} b_j.$$

*It is not difficult to see that the last $m+n$ equations in (4.2) are dependent, and that any $m+n-1$ of them are linearly independent.

**Our exposition of this method is drawn primarily from [14], while Section 3 and Paragraph 7 of Section 2 have been drawn from [1].

Sometimes this condition is not satisfied, i.e., either the supply exceeds the demand,

$$\left(\sum_{i=1}^{m} a_i > \sum_{j=1}^{n} b_j\right),$$

or the demand exceeds the supply,

$$\left(\sum_{i=1}^{m} a_i < \sum_{j=1}^{n} b_j\right).$$

We can, however, state the problem of constructing a shipping plan that will minimize the transportation costs even for these cases.

To find an optimal shipping plan for the case in which supply exceeds demand,

$$\left(\sum_{i=1}^{m} a_i > \sum_{j=1}^{n} b_j\right),$$

we introduce a fictitious $(n + 1)$-th demand point that requires $b_{n+1} = \sum_{i=1}^{m} a_i - \sum_{j=1}^{n} b_j$ units of the product in question and set the cost of transporting the product to this point equal to zero, $c_{i,\,n+1} = 0$ $(i = 1, \ldots, m)$. The new problem obtained in this manner is the ordinary transportation problem, since here the equation $\sum_{i=1}^{m} a_i = \sum_{j=1}^{n+1} b_j$ is satisfied.

It is not difficult to show that the plan $\|x_{ij}\|_{m,\,n}$ obtained from an optimal plan $\|x_{ij}\|_{m,\,n+1}$ for the new problem is also optimal for the initial problem, since a better plan for the old problem would mean that there would have to be a better (than optimal) plan for the new problem, which is impossible.

Similarly, when

$$\sum_{i=1}^{m} a_i < \sum_{j=1}^{n} b_j ,$$

we introduce a fictitious $(m + 1)$-th supply depot with a supply $a_{m+1} = \sum_{j=1}^{n} b_j - \sum_{i=1}^{m} a_i$ and a shipping cost of $c_{m+1,\,j} = 0\ (j = 1, \ldots, n)$.

This problem reduces to the ordinary transportation problem, and, as above, we can obtain an optimal solution for the initial problem from the optimal solution of the modified problem.

2. THE METHOD OF POTENTIALS

1. Preliminary Remarks

In contrast to the preceding section here we use a table of the form

	c_{11}	...	c_{1j}	...	c_{1n}	a_1
	...	...	...	...	...	...
	c_{i1}	...	c_{ij}	...	c_{in}	a_i
	...	...	...	...	...	...
	c_{m1}	...	c_{mj}	...	c_{mn}	a_m
	b_1	...	b_j	...	b_n	b_j \ a_i

(4.5)

The loads x_{ij} will be placed in the lower left-hand corners of the squares (i, j) as the plan is constructed.

By a *choice* we mean an arbitrary set of squares, while by a *chain* we mean a choice of the form

$$(i_1, j_1), (i_1, j_2), (i_2, j_2), (i_2, j_3), \ldots$$

or

$$(i_1, j_1), (i_2, j_1), (i_2, j_2), (i_3, j_2), \ldots,$$

so that each pair of adjacent squares in a chain is located either in the same row or column of Table (4.5), and no three squares in a chain lie in the same row (column). If the last square is in the same column (row) as the first, i.e., if the chain is of the form

$$(i_1, j_1), (i_1, j_2), (i_2, j_2), (i_2, j_3), \ldots, (i_k, j_1)$$

or

$$(i_1, j_1), (i_2, j_1), (i_2, j_2), (i_3, j_2), \ldots, (i_1, j_k),$$

we call the chain a cycle. The table

c_{11}	c_{12}	c_{13}	c_{14}	c_{15}
c_{21}	c_{22}	c_{23}	c_{24}	c_{25}
c_{31}	c_{32}	c_{33}	c_{34}	c_{35}
c_{41}	c_{42}	c_{43}	c_{44}	c_{45}

illustrates the cycle (1, 2), (1, 3), (3, 3), (3, 5), (4, 5), (4, 2).

We say that any feasible transportation plan $X = \|x_{ij}\|_{m,n}$ is acyclic if a choice of squares with nonzero entries x_{ij} from this plan contains no cycles. As we show below, an optimal transportation plan may be found among the acyclic plans and the number N of entries $x_{ij} > 0$ in any acyclic plan satisfies the inequalities $\max\{m, n\} \leqslant N \leqslant m+n-1$.

If an acyclic plan $X = \|x_{ij}\|_{m,n}$ is such that $N = m+n-1$, the entries c_{ij} in the choice of $m+n-1$ squares (i, j) with $x_{ij} > 0$ are said to be X-determined.

Now let $N < m+n-1$. Then we supplement the choice of squares (i, j) with $x_{ij} > 0$ by $m+n-1-N$ more squares with $x_{ij} = 0$ such that the new choice of $m+n-1$ squares contains no cycles and we assume that the entries c_{ij} in this new choice are X-determined.

2. Potentiality, a Test for Optimality of Shipping Plans

A plan $X = \|x_{ij}\|_{m,n}$ *for the transportation problem is optimal if and only if there is a system of* $m+n$ *numbers* $u_1, u_2, \ldots, u_m$; $v_1, v_2, \ldots, v_n$, *for which*

$$v_j - u_i \leqslant c_{ij} \qquad (i = 1, \ldots, m;\ j = 1, \ldots, n) \tag{4.6}$$

and

$$v_j - u_i = c_{ij} \quad \text{for all} \quad x_{ij} > 0\,(x_{ij} \in X). \tag{4.7}$$

The numbers u_i and v_j are called the *potentials* of the corresponding supply and demand depots, and the system of such numbers is called the *potential system;* conditions (4.6)-(4.7) are called the *potentiality conditions* of the u_i and v_j, while each separate inequality (equation) is called the *potentiality condition* for the corresponding square (i, j).

If a plan X for which there exists a potential system u_i, v_j is also called potential, the theorem can be more briefly stated as follows: *A plan for the transportation policy is optimal if and only if it is potential.*

Sufficiency. Assume that a plan X is potential, so that for it there is a system u_i, v_j satisfying conditions (4.6)-(4.7). For any feasible plan $X' = \|x'_{ij}\|_{m,\,n}$

$$\sum_{i=1}^{m}\sum_{j=1}^{n} c_{ij}x'_{ij} \geqslant \sum_{i=1}^{m}\sum_{j=1}^{n} (v_j - u_i)\,x'_{ij} = \sum_{j=1}^{n} v_j \sum_{i=1}^{m} x'_{ij} -$$
$$- \sum_{i=1}^{m} u_i \sum_{j=1}^{n} x'_{ij} = \sum_{j=1}^{n} v_j b_j - \sum_{i=1}^{m} u_i a_i = \sum_{j=1}^{n} v_j \sum_{i=1}^{m} x_{ij} -$$
$$- \sum_{i=1}^{m} u_i \sum_{j=1}^{n} x_{ij} = \sum_{i=1}^{m}\sum_{j=1}^{n} v_j x_{ij} - \sum_{i=1}^{m}\sum_{j=1}^{n} u_i x_{ij} =$$
$$= \sum_{i=1}^{m}\sum_{j=1}^{n} (v_j - u_i)\,x_{ij} = \sum_{i=1}^{m}\sum_{j=1}^{n} c_{ij}x_{ij},$$

i.e., the shipping costs for the given plan X' are no less than the shipping costs in the potential plan X, as a result of which X' is optimal.

Necessity. Treating transportation problem (4.5), in which the form

$$w = \sum_{i=1}^{m}\sum_{j=1}^{n} c_{ij}x_{ij}$$

is minimized under appropriate constraints, as a linear programming problem, we consider the dual problem, for which the constraints can be obtained easily from the following table:

	$0=$	...	$0=$	...	$0=$	$0=$	...	$0=$	...	$0=$	$w=$
	$-u_1$	...	$-u_i$	...	$-u_m$	$-v_1$	...	$-v_j$	...	$-v_n$	1
x_{11} y_{11} =	-1	...	0	...	0	1	...	0	...	0	c_{11}
...	...	...	...	...	...	...	...	...	...	...	...
x_{1n} y_{1n} =	-1	...	0	...	0	0	...	0	...	1	c_{1n}
...	...	...	...	...	...	...	...	...	...	...	...
x_{i1} y_{i1} =	0	...	-1	...	0	1	...	0	...	0	c_{i1}
...	...	...	...	...	...	...	...	...	...	...	...
x_{ij} y_{ij} =	0	...	-1	...	0	0	...	1	...	0	c_{ij}
...	...	...	...	...	...	...	...	...	...	...	...
x_{in} y_{in} =	0	...	-1	...	0	0	...	0	...	1	c_{in}
...	...	...	...	...	...	...	...	...	...	...	...
x_{m1} y_{m1} =	0	...	0	...	-1	1	...	0	...	0	c_{m1}
...	...	...	...	...	...	...	...	...	...	...	...
x_{mn} y_{mn} =	0	...	0	...	-1	0	...	0	...	1	c_{mn}
1 z =	a_1	...	a_i	...	a_m	$-b_1$	...	$-b_j$	...	$-b_n$	0

The dual problem thus consists in maximizing the form

$$z = \sum_{j=1}^{n} b_j v_j - \sum_{i=1}^{m} a_i u_i$$

under the constraints

$$y_{ij} = u_i - v_j + c_{ij} \geqslant 0 \quad (i = 1, \ldots, m;\ j = 1, \ldots, n),$$

i.e.,

$$v_j - u_i \leqslant c_{ij} \qquad (i = 1, \ldots, m;\ j = 1, \ldots, n). \tag{4.6}$$

Let $X = \|x_{ij}\|_{m,n}$ be an optimal solution for transportation problem (4.5). Then, by the fundamental duality theorem (Chapter 2, Section 7), the dual problem also has an optimal solution $u_1^*, \ldots, u_m^*$; $v_1^*, \ldots, v_n^*$. It can be seen that these numbers are the potentials of the corresponding depots in the transportation problem.

Indeed, all the u_i^* and v_j^*, constituting a basic solution of the dual problem, satisfy inequality (4.6). If, however, $x_{ij} > 0$, then, by the second duality theorem, the corresponding constraint $y_{ij}^* = u_i^* - v_j^* + c_{ij} \geqslant 0$ of the dual problem becomes a strict equality, so that $v_j^* - u_i^* = c_{ij}$.

3. An Algorithm for Solution of the Transportation Problem by the Method of Potentials

The algorithm consists of a preliminary step and an iterated general step.

The ***preliminary step*** consists in the following:

1) an initial acyclic plan X is constructed;

2) for the plan thus obtained, we construct a system of $m + n$ numbers $u_1, \ldots, u_m$; $v_1, \ldots, v_n$ such that

$$v_j - u_i = c_{ij} \tag{4.8}$$

for all X-determined c_{ij};

3) the system $u_1, \ldots, u_m$; $v_1, \ldots, v_n$ is investigated for potentiality (i.e., the plan X is investigated for optimality).

The ***general step*** (which is applied if the plan X constructed in the preceding step is not optimal, i.e., the system $u_1, \ldots, u_m$; $v_1, \ldots, v_n$ is not potential) consists in the following three operations:

1) the plan is improved, i.e., the plan X is replaced by a new plan X' with shipping costs no greater than the shipping cost for the plan X;

2) for the plan X', a new system $u_1', \ldots, u_m'$; $v_1', \ldots, v_n'$ is constructed (by changing the system $u_1, \ldots, u_m$; $v_1, \ldots, v_n$) so that

$$v_j' - u_i' = c_{ij} \tag{4.8'}$$

for all X-determined c_{ij}.

3) the system $u_1', \ldots, u_m'$; $v_1', \ldots, v_n'$ is investigated for potentiality.

We now consider this algorithm in detail.*

Preliminary step. 1) *Construction of the initial plan* $X = \|x_{ij}\|$. We begin with determination of the entry x_{11} (for which reason this method of constructing an initial plan is called the "rule of the northwest corner"), and $x_{11} = \min\{a_1, b_1\}$. If $a_1 < b_1$, then $x_{11} = a_1$

* The algorithm is rigorously proved in Paragraph 7.

and $x_{1j} = 0$ for $j = 2, 3, \ldots, n$. If $a_1 > b_1$, then $x_{11} = b_1$ and $x_{i1} = 0$ for $i = 2, 3, \ldots, m$. If, however $a_1 = b_1$, then $x_{11} = a_1 = b_1$ and all the remaining entries in both the first row and the first column are equal to zero. For definiteness, assume that $a_1 < b_1$. Then the supply of the commodity at the first supply depot reduces to zero, while the demand at the first demand depot is $b_1 - a_1$. We place these data under and at the right of the table:

c_{11} a_1	c_{12} 0	$\ldots$	c_{1n} 0	a_1	0
c_{21}	c_{22}	$\ldots$	c_{2n}	a_2	a_2
$\ldots$	$\ldots$	$\ldots$	$\ldots$	$\ldots$	$\ldots$
c_{m1}	c_{m2}	$\ldots$	c_{mn}	a_m	a_m
b_1	b_2	$\ldots$	b_n	$b_j \diagdown a_i$	
$b_1 - a_1$	b_2	$\ldots$	b_n		

We now set $x_{21} = \min\{a_2, b_1 - a_1\}$. If $a_2 < b_1 - a_1$, then $x_{21} = a_2$ and all the $x_{2j} = 0$ for $j = 2, \ldots, n$; if $a_2 > b_1 - a_1$, then $x_{21} = b_1 - a_1$ and all the $x_{i1} = 0$ for $i = 3, \ldots, m$; if, however, $a_2 = b_1 - a_1$, then $x_{21} = a_2 = b_1 - a_1$, and all the remaining entries in the first column and second row are equal to zero.

Assume that the second case occurs. Then the demand at the first demand depot is completely satisfied, and the remaining supply at the second supply depot is $a_2 - (b_1 - a_1)$. We also write these values to the right of the table and underneath it:

c_{11} a_1	c_{12} 0	$\ldots$	c_{1n} 0	a_1	0	0
c_{21} $b_1 - a_1$	c_{22}	$\ldots$	c_{2n}	a_2	a_2	$a_2 - b_1 + a_1$
$\ldots$	$\ldots$	$\ldots$	$\ldots$	$\ldots$	$\ldots$	$\ldots$
c_{m1} 0	c_{m2}	$\ldots$	c_{mn}	a_m	a_m	a_m
b_1	b_2	$\ldots$	b_n	$b_j \diagdown a_i$		
$b_1 - a_1$	b_2	$\ldots$	b_n			
0	b_2	$\ldots$	b_n			

We now set $x_{22} = \min\{a_2 - b_1 + a_1; b_2\}$, etc., until all of the x_{ij} ($i = 1, \ldots, m$; $j = 1, \ldots, n$) are determined.

We should note that each element x_{ij} is obtained from linear combinations of the a_i and b_j with coefficients 0, 1, and -1, and is either the remainder of the commodity at a supply depot or the requirement of the corresponding demand depot. As a result, if the a_i and b_j are initially nonnegative integers, the initial shipping plan $X = \|x_{ij}\|_{m,n}$ obtained according to the above procedure will consist of nonnegative integers x_{ij}. The number N of positive loads (i.e., elements $x_{ij} > 0$) in this plan is not greater than $m + n - 1$.

Indeed, the table contains (below and on the right) a total of $m + n$ numbers $a_1, \ldots, a_m$; $b_1, \ldots, b_n$. In each step one square of the table is filled with a positive x_{ij}, a zero is substituted for one or both of the numbers a_i and b_j, and zeros are simultaneously substituted for a_m and b_n in the last step. As a result, no more than $m + n - 1$ steps are required to construct a plan (at which point all the $m + n$ given numbers will have been replaced by zeros), and the plan will contain no more than $m + n - 1$ positive x_{ij}.

As we can see with no difficulty, the set of squares thus obtained contains no cycles. If $N = m + n - 1$, we proceed to construction of the system $u_1, \ldots, u_m$; $v_1, \ldots, v_n$. If, however, $N < m + n - 1$ (at which time the problem is said to be *degenerate*), we introduce $m + n - 1 - N$ new squares with zero loads $x_{ij} = 0$ into the choice, but we make certain that the choice still contains no cycles. After this, we proceed to construction of the system $u_1, \ldots, u_m$; $v_1, \ldots, v_n$.

Example. Consider the problem defined by the table

3	5	7	11	100
1	4	6	3	130
5	8	12	7	170
150	120	80	50	b_j \ a_i

By the rule of the northwest corner,

$$x_{11} = \min\{a_1, b_1\} = \min\{100; 150\} = 100; \ x_{12} = x_{13} = x_{14} = 0.$$

We now appropriately change the supply columns and demand rows:

3 100	5 0	7 0	11 0	0
1	4	6	3	130
5	8	12	7	170
50	120	80	50	a_i \ b_j

Now,

$$x_{21} = \min\{130;\ 50\} = 50, \quad x_{31} = 0.$$

Thus the requirements of the first demand depot are completely satisfied and vanish, while the supply at the second supply depot is 130 - 50 = 80, which is indicated in the last column and row of the following table:

3 100	5 0	7 0	11 0	0
1 50	4	6	3	80
5 0	8	12	7	170
0	120	80	50	a_i \ b_j

.

We also have

$$x_{22} = \min\{80;\ 120\} = 80; \ x_{23} = x_{24} = 0,$$

so that

3 100	5 0	7 0	11 0	0
1 50	4 80	6 0	3 0	0
5 0	8	12	7	170
0	40	80	50	a_i \ b_j

.

Similarly,

$$x_{32} = \min\{170;\ 40\} = 40,$$

and we obtain the table

3 100	5 0	7 0	11 0	0
1 50	4 80	6 0	3 0	0
5 0	8 40	12	7	130
0	0	80	50	b_j \ a_i

Finally,

$$x_{33} = \min\{130;\ 80\} = 80.$$

The requirements of the third demand depot have been reduced to zero, and the supply at the third supply depot is 50. This supply is exactly the requirement $b_4 = 50$ of the fourth demand depot, so $x_{34} = 50$.

We thus obtain the following acyclic plan, which contains $m + n - 1 = 3 + 4 - 1 = 6$ positive elements:

3 100	5 0	7 0	11 0
1 50	4 80	6 0	3 0
5 0	8 40	12 80	7 50

2) *Construction of the system u_i, v_j for an initial plan X.* We determine the numbers $u_1, \ldots, u_m$; $v_1, \ldots, v_n$ from the system of $m + n - 1$ linear equations

$$v_j - u_i = c_{ij}, \tag{4.9}$$

where the c_{ij} are X-determined elements. Since the number of unknowns is one more than the the number of equations, we set one of the unknowns equal to an arbitrary number, say, $u_1 = 0$, and we can easily obtain the values of the remaining unknowns from Eq. (4.9). We place the values $u_1, \ldots, u_m$ obtained in this way in the last column of the table, and we place the values $v_1, \ldots, v_n$ in the top row:

$u_i \backslash v_j$	v_1	v_2	...	v_n
u_1	c_{11} x_{11}	c_{12} x_{12}	...	c_{1n} x_{1n}
u_2	c_{21} x_{21}	c_{22} x_{22}	...	c_{2n} x_{2n}
...	...	...	...	...
u_m	c_{m1} x_{m1}	c_{m2} x_{m2}	...	c_{mn} x_{mn}

We now continue the solution of the example discussed in Paragraph 1. To construct an initial plan, we must determine $u_1, u_2, u_3, v_1, v_2, v_3$, and v_4 satisfying the equations

$$
\begin{aligned}
v_1 - u_1 &= 3,\\
v_1 - u_2 &= 1,\\
v_2 - u_2 &= 4,\\
v_2 - u_3 &= 8,\\
v_3 - u_3 &= 12,\\
v_4 - u_3 &= 7.
\end{aligned}
$$

Setting $u_1 = 0$, we find that

$$v_1 = 3,\ u_2 = 2,\ v_2 = 6,\ u_3 = -2,\ v_3 = 10,\ v_4 = 5.$$

We place these values in the table:

$u_i \backslash v_j$	3	6	10	5
0	3 100	5	7	11
2	1 50	4 80	6	3
−2	5	8 40	12 80	7 50

3) ***Investigation of the system*** u_i, v_j ***for potentiality.*** We compare each element c_{ij} that is not X-determined with the corresponding difference $v_j - u_i$. If the inequalities

$$v_j - u_i \leqslant c_{ij}$$

are satisfied for all such elements, the system u_i, v_j is potential and the plan that has been constructed is optimal. If the inequality $v_j - u_i > c_{ij}$ holds for some c_{ij}, the system u_i, v_j is not potential, the plan X is not optimal, and we must proceed to the following step.

For the example considered in Paragraph 1,

$$v_2 - u_1 = 6 - 0 > 5 = c_{12},$$
$$v_3 - u_1 = 10 - 0 > 7 = c_{13},$$
$$v_4 - u_1 = 5 - 0 < 11 = c_{14},$$
$$v_3 - u_2 = 10 - 2 > 6 = c_{23},$$
$$v_4 - u_2 = 5 - 2 = 3 = c_{24},$$
$$v_1 - u_3 = 3 + 2 = 5 = c_{31}.$$

Thus, the system $u_1 = 0$, $u_2 = 2, \ldots, v_4 = 5$ is not potential, and our plan is not optimal.

General step. 1) *Improvement of the plan.* Let $\alpha_{i_0 j_0}$ be the largest number

$$\alpha_{ij} = v_j - u_i - c_{ij} > 0.$$

The square (i_0, j_0) forms, with the X-determined squares in the choice, a single cycle. We trace this cycle counterclockwise, beginning with the square (i_0, j_0), and alternately mark each of the squares with + and - signs, where the first square, (i_0, j_0), is assigned a + sign. The squares marked with a + form the "positive" half-chain, while the — sign indicates the "negative" half-chain.

We consider the elements x_{ij} of our plan X that are located in the squares of the negative half-chain, and among them we find the smallest, θ, which is contained, say, in the square (i', j'). We now improve the shipping plan as follows: We decrease the elements (loads) x_{ij} in the negative half-chain by θ, while we increase the elements x_{ij} in the positive half-chain by θ; the elements x_{ij} that are not contained in the chain do not change. Thus, the new plan X' consists of the numbers

$$x'_{ij} = \begin{cases} x_{ij} - \theta, & \text{if } (i, j) \text{ is in the negative half-chain.} \\ x_{ij} + \theta, & \text{if } (i, j) \text{ is in the positive half-chain.} \\ x_{ij}, & \text{if } (i, j) \text{ is not in the chain.} \end{cases}$$

The plan X' is feasible and contains an acyclic choice of $m + n - 1$ squares obtained by replacing the square (i', j'), for which $x'_{i'j'}$ is now equal to zero, by the square (i_0, j_0), for which $x'_{i_0 j_0} = \theta$.

We will illustrate this method of improving a plan by applying it to the example discussed in Paragraph 1. The largest difference $\alpha_{ij} = v_j - u_i - c_{ij} > 0$ is $\alpha_{13} = v_3 - u_1 - c_{13} = 3$, so that the square (1, 3) must be introduced into the choice. We construct the cycle of the squares

$$(1, 3), (1, 1), (2, 1), (2, 2), (3, 2), (3, 3)$$

and alternately mark them with + and — signs, as in the following table:

u_i \ v_j	3	6	10	5
0	— 3 / 100	5	+ 7	11
2	+ 1 / 50	— 4 / 80	6	3
—2	5	+ 8 / 40	— 12 / 80	7 / 50

We now find the smallest of the loads x_{ij} in the squares in the negative half-chain: $\theta = x_{33} = 80$ (or $\theta = x_{22} = 80$). We subtract $\theta = 80$ from the loads in the negative half-chain, and we add it to the loads in the positive half-chain. Eliminating the square (3, 3), in which x'_{33} is now equal to zero, from the chain, we obtain a new choice, and hence a new plan X':

u_i \ v_j	3	6	10	5
0	3 / 20	5	7 / 80	11
2	1 / 130	4 / 0	6	3
—2	5	8 / 120	12	7 / 50
			—3	

2) *Correction of the system* u_i, v_j. For the square (i_0, j_0) in the new choice we have

$$\alpha_{i_0 j_0} = v_{j_0} - u_{i_0} - c_{i_0 j_0} > 0,$$

i.e., potentiality condition (4.9) is not satisfied and the system u_i, v_j must be corrected. This can be done, as we noted above, in the preliminary step, by constructing a new system u_i, v_j, but it is usually simpler to construct the new system u_i, v_j by means of the following corrections. To ensure that the potentiality condition is satisfied for the square (i_0, j_0), we decrease v_{j_0} by $\alpha_{i_0 j_0}$. Then for all squares (i_{λ_1}, j_0), ..., (i_{λ_l}, j_0) of the j_0th column that are contained in the new choice, except for (i_0, j_0), the potentiality condition is satisfied and becomes

$$(v_{j_0} - \alpha_{i_0 j_0}) - u_i < c_{i j_0} \quad (i = i_{\lambda_1}, \ldots, i_{\lambda_l};\ i \neq i_0).$$

To restore these squares to potentiality, we also decrease the numbers $u_{i_{\lambda_1}}, \ldots, u_{i_{\lambda_l}}$ by α_{i_0, j_0}. However, in this case we disturb the potentiality of the squares in the rows $i_{\lambda_1}, \ldots, i_{\lambda_l}$ (except for the square in the j_0th column), so that the corresponding v_j must be decreased by α_{i_0, j_0}, etc., until potentiality conditions (4.9) are satisfied for all the squares in the new choice.

We illustrate this on the example considered above. The potentiality condition (see the preceding table) is not satisfied for the square (1, 3), which has been introduced into the choice. To restore potentiality, we subtract $\alpha_{13} = 3$ from v_3, which yields $v_3' = 10 - 3 = 7$. Since, except for (1, 3), there are no other squares of the choice in the third column, the potentiality of the remaining squares in the choice is not disturbed. We obtain the table

u_i \ v_j	3	6	7	5
0	3 20	5	7 80	11
2	1 130	4 0	6	3
−2	5	8 120	12	7 50

3) *The investigation of the potentiality of the new system* u_i', v_j' is conducted as in Paragraph 3 of the preliminary step by comparing the differences $v_j' - u_i'$ with the corresponding c_{ij}.

In our example this investigation proceeds as follows:

$$v_2 - u_1 = 6 > 5 = c_{12},$$
$$v_4 - u_1 = 5 < 11 = c_{14},$$
$$v_3 - u_2 = 5 < 6 = c_{23},$$
$$v_4 - u_2 = 3 = c_{24},$$
$$v_1 - u_3 = 5 = c_{31},$$
$$v_3 - u_3 = 9 < 12 = c_{33}.$$

The new system u_i', v_j' is not potential, so the plan X' must be improved.

We repeat the general step until, after a finite number of repetitions, we obtain an optimal plan for the transportation problem.

In our example, except for the first step, which we have already considered for the purposes of illustration, obtaining an optimal plan requires two more steps.

Second step. 1) *Improvement of the plan.* We introduce the square (1, 2), for which $\alpha_{12} = v_2 - u_1 - c_{12} = 1 > 0$ into the choice, construct the closed chain

(1, 2), (1, 1), (2, 1), (2, 2),

and alternately mark these squares with + and — signs:

u_i \ v_j	3	6	7	5
0	— 3 / 20	+ 5	7 / 80	11
2	+ 1 / 130	— 4 / 0	6	3
—2	5	8 / 120	12	7 / 50

.

We now transfer the minimal load of $\theta = 0$ from the negative half-chain to the positive half-chain, which yields the plan

u_i \ v_j	3	6	7	5	
0	3 / 20	5 / 0	7 / 80	11	
2	1 / 130	4	6	3	
—2	5	8 / 120	12	7 / 50	—1
		—1		—1	

,

in which there is no change in the quantity of units shipped, but the new choice contains the square (1, 2) instead of (2, 2).

2) ***Correction of the system*** u_i, v_j. Potentiality does not hold for the square (1, 2) that has just been introduced into the choice. We therefore correct v_2 by subtracting $\alpha_{12} = 1$ from it:

$$v_2' = v_2 - \alpha_{12} = 6 - 1 = 5.$$

This disturbs the potentiality of the square (3, 2), and to restore potentiality we subtract $\alpha_{12} = 1$ from u_3:

$$u_3' = -2 - 1 = -3.$$

This last operation disturbs the potentiality of (3, 4), so we subtract $\alpha_{12} = 1$ from v_4:

$$v_4' = 5 - 1 = 4.$$

The fourth column contains no squares of the choice and correction of u_i, v_j now terminates, so that the final table takes the form

u_i \ v_j	3	5	7	4
0	3 20	5 0	7 80	11
2	1 130	4	6	3
—3	5	8 120	12	7 50

.

3) *Investigation of the potentiality* of u'_i, v'_j. The new plan is still not optimal, because $\alpha_{31} = v_1 - u_3 - c_{31} = 1 > 0$.

Third step. 1) *Improvement of the plan.* We introduce the square (3, 1) into the choice, construct the closed chain

(3, 1), (3, 2), (1, 2), (1, 1),

alternately mark the squares with + and — signs, and transfer the smallest element $\theta = 20$ from the negative half-chain to the positive half-chain.

Eliminating (1, 1) from the chain, we obtain a new choice, and hence a new plan:

u_i \ v_j	3	5	7	4	
0	3	5 20	7 80	11	
2	1 130	4	6	3	—1.
—3	5 20	8 100	12	7 50	
	—1				

2) *Correction of the system* u_i, v_j. For this we subtract $\alpha_{31} = 1$ from v_1 and u_2, which yields

u_i \ v_j	2	5	7	4
0	3	5 20	7 80	11
1	1 130	4	6	3
—3	5 20	8 100	12	7 50

.

3) *Investigation of the potentiality of the new system* u_i, v_j. It is easy to verify that the system u_i, v_j is potential, so that the last plan is optimal. The shipping costs for this plan are

$$w = 5 \cdot 20 + 7 \cdot 80 + 1 \cdot 130 + 5 \cdot 20 + \\ + 8 \cdot 100 + 7 \cdot 50 = 2040.$$

4. Simplification of the Computational Scheme for the Method of Potentials

In the above algorithm, each step is computed by way of the following three operations: 1) improvement of a plan that is already constructed, 2) correction of the entire system u_i, v_j, and 3) investigation of the potentiality of the new system u_i', v_j'. When the matrix $\|c_{ij}\|$ is very large, not only is operation 1) cumbersome, but so is operation 2). To reduce the amount of work somewhat, we can use a slightly modified algorithm that is particularly convenient when (as usually occurs), the number of supply depots is considerably smaller than the number of demand depots.

The initial plan is constructed in the same way as in the basic algorithm.

To determine the u_i and v_j, we first connect one of the squares in the choice with all the remaining squares of the choice in this column by means of line segments. Each such line segment connects two rows. If a column contains k squares in the choice, there will be $k - 1$ segments in this column.

The total number of segments in the table is $m - 1$ (where m is the number of supply depots). Indeed, the choice consists of $m + n - 1$ squares, and each column contains no fewer than one square of the choice, so $m - 1$ segments can be drawn to the remaining $(m + n - 1) - n = m - 1$ squares.

In the preliminary step we construct all the u_i and only the v_j that are necessary for construction of all of the u_i: We choose an arbitrary u_1, compute v_j for all the columns that contain segments connecting different rows with the first, and then compute u_i for all these rows, etc., until we have found all the u_i. It is clear that this requires computation of no more than $m - 1$ of the v_j.

The potentiality of the squares not contained in the choice is begun with the first column, then the second, etc., until there are no squares (i_0, j_0) that are not potential. If, prior to this point, we encounter a column for which v_j is still unknown, it must be computed. We introduce the square (i_0, j_0) into the choice by executing operation 1). We improve the plan by correcting, as in operation 2), only the numbers $u_1, \ldots, u_m$ and all the v_j that have been constructed. Then the only squares of the first j_0 rows that need be investigated for potentiality are those that simultaneously belong to the rows with the corrected u_i and columns with uncorrected v_j. We introduce the nonpotential squares for which $v_j - u_i - c_{ij} = \alpha_{ij}$

has a maximal value into the choice, and we then improve the plan by introducing a nonpotential square into the choice.

If there are no nonpotential squares in the first j_0 columns, we use (4.8) to determine v_{j_0+1} (if it has not yet been determined), check the potentiality of the squares of the $(j_0 + 1)$-th column that do not belong to the choice, and repeat the above procedure. The modified algorithm is therefore of the following form:

Preliminary step. As in the basic algorithm, we construct an initial plan and the system of u_i and those v_j necessary for determination of the u_i.

We investigate the potentiality of these squares not contained in the choice. We treat the first column, then the second, etc., until, at some column, say, the j_0th, we observe a nonpotential square.

General step. 1) *Improvement of the plan.* As in the basic algorithm, the plan is improved by introducing the nonpotential square that has been observed into the choice.

2) *Correction of the system* $u_1, \ldots, u_m$ and all the computed v_j proceeds as in the basic algorithm.

3) *Investigation for potentiality of those squares of the first* j_0 *columns that are not contained in the choice of the new plan.* This investigation is conducted only for those squares of the first j_0 columns that are not in the choice and are such that the difference $v_j - u_i$ increases when the system u_i, v_j is corrected, i.e., the investigation is conducted only for the squares (i, j) with corrected u_i and uncorrected v_j.

If all the squares in the first j_0 columns are potential, we proceed to investigate the squares in the $(j_0 + 1)$-th column, etc., until a nonpotential square is observed, and we then compute the unknown v_j.

Example.

3	5	7	11	100
1	4	6	3	130
5	8	12	7	170
150	120	80	50	b_j \ a_i

1) The construction of the initial plan coincides with the corresponding operations of the preliminary step in the basic algorithm.

2) We connect the squares of the choice in each column by line segments:

u_i \ v_j				
	3 100	5	7	11
	1 50	4 80	6	3
	5	8 40	12 80	7 50

.

It is clear from this table that determination of all of the u_i requires computation of only v_1 and v_2. Set $u_1 = 0$. Then $v_1 = 3$, $u_2 = 2$, $v_2 = 6$, $u_3 = -2$, and we enter these numbers into the table:

u_i \ v_j	3	6		
0	— 3 100	+ 5	7	11
2	+ 1 50	— 4 80	6	3
—2	5	8 40	12 80	7 50

.

3) For the first column we have $v_1 - u_3 = c_{31}$, while for the second column we have $v_2 - u_1 = 6 > 5 = c_{12}$ so that the square (1, 2) is not potential.

First step. 1) We improve the plan by introducing the square (1, 2) into the choice, construct the closed chain (1, 2), (1, 1), (2, 1), (2, 2), and transfer the smallest load $\theta = 80$ from the negative half-chain to the positive half-chain. This yields

u_i \ v_j	3	6			
0	— 3 20	+ 5 80	7	11	
2	1 130	4	6	3	
—2	+ 5	— 8 40	12 80	7 50	—1
		—1			

.

2) We now correct the system, u_1, u_2, u_3, v_1, v_2 by subtracting $\alpha_{12} = v_2 - u_1 - c_{12} = 1$ from v_2 and u_3.

3) We now investigate the potentiality of the square (3, 1), which is not contained in the choice, but is located in the row with the corrected u_3 but uncorrected v_1.

We have $v_1 - u_3 = 6 > 5 = c_{31}$, so that (3, 1) is not a potential square.

Second step. 1) We introduce the square (3, 1) into the choice, transfer the load $\theta = 20$, and eliminate the square (1, 1) from the choice (see the preceding table). We have

u_i \ v_j	3	5		
0	3	— 5 100	+ 7	11
2	1 130	4	6	3
—3	5 20	+ 8 20	— 12 80	7 50

1.

—1

2) We now correct the system u_1, u_2, u_3, v_1, v_2 by subtracting $\alpha_{31} = 1$ from v_1 and u_2.

3) A check shows that the square (2, 2) is potential.

We now proceed to investigation of the squares in the third row. Toward this end, we compute $v_3 = c_{33} + u_3 = 12 - 3 = 9$. Moreover, $\alpha_{13} = 2 > 0$, $\alpha_{23} = 2 > 0$.

Third step. 1) We introduce the square (1, 3) into the choice. Toward this end, we transfer $\theta = 80$ along the chain (1, 3), (1, 2), (3, 2), (3, 3) from the negative half-chain to the positive half-chain, which yields

u_i \ v_j	2	5	9	
	3	5 20	7 80	11
1	1 130	4	6	3
—3	5 20	8 100	12	7 50

—2

2) We now correct the numbers $u_1, u_2, u_3, v_1, v_2, v_3$ by subtracting $\alpha_{13} = 2$ from v_3. Since, except for the square (1, 3), the third column contains no other members of the choice, correction of the number $u_1, u_2, u_3, v_1, v_2, v_3$ terminates here.

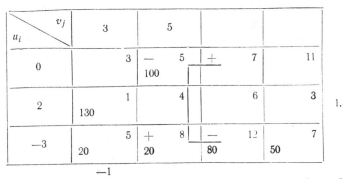

3) Because the first three columns have no squares for which the u_i have been corrected and v_j have not, and because $\alpha_{13} = \max_i \alpha_{i3}$, there are no nonpotential squares among those squares of the first three columns that are not contained in the choice. We have

$$v_4 = c_{34} + u_3 = 7 - 3 = 4.$$

Moreover, we have the table

u_i \ v_j	2	5	7	4
0	3	5 20	7 80	11
1	1 130	4	6	3
—3	5 20	8 100	12	7 50

.

We now investigate the fourth column for potentiality:

$$v_4 - u_1 = 4 < 11 = c_{14},$$
$$v_4 - u_2 = 3 = c_{24},$$

i.e., these squares are potential and the last plan is optimal.

5. Construction of an Initial Plan by the Method of Minimal Elements

We write the conditions of the problem in the form of Table (4.5):

c_{11}	c_{12}	...	c_{1n}	a_1
c_{21}	c_{22}	...	c_{2n}	a_2
. . .	. . .	. . .	. . .	. . .
c_{m1}	c_{m2}	...	c_{mn}	a_m
b_1	b_2	...	b_n	b_j \ a_i

.

In the method of the northwest corner, the initial plan depends only on the a_i and b_j and completely ignores the shipping costs, so that it is usually nonoptimal. We now present the so-called ***method of the minimal element,*** which allows for the matrix $\|c_{ij}\|$ of transportation costs. This method successively fills squares with minimal shipping costs c_{ij}, and the quantities x_{ij} corresponding to the shipments are determined in exactly the same way as in the method of the northwest corner, i.e., x_{ij} is set equal to the minimum of the differences of amount of commodity at the ith supply depot and the requirement at the jth demand depot. We obtain an acyclic plan consisting of no more than $m+n-1$ positive shipments.

We illustrate this method in the example of constructing the initial plan of the problem (see p. 132) whose conditions are given by the table

3	5	7	11	100
1	4	6	3	130
5	8	12	7	170
150	120	80	50	b_j \\ a_i

In each step we fill the square with the minimal cost. In our example, squares are filled in the following order

$$x_{21}=\min\{a_2;\ b_1\}=\min\{130;\ 150\}=130,$$
$$x_{22}=x_{23}=x_{24}=0;$$

Moreover,

$$x_{11}=\min\{100;\ 20\}=20,\quad x_{31}=0,$$

so that

$$x_{12}=\min\{80;\ 120\}=80,\quad x_{13}=x_{14}=0$$

and, finally,

$$x_{34}=\min\{170;\ 50\}=50;$$
$$x_{32}=\min\{120;\ 40\}=40;\quad x_{33}=80.$$

We thus obtain the initial plan

3 20	5 80	7	11	100
1 130	4	6	3	130
5	8 40	12 80	7 50	170
150	120	80	50	b_j \ a_i

.

6. Construction of the Initial Plan by the Method of Approximation [13]

First step. We write the conditions in the form of Table (4.5) with empty zeroth row and zeroth column:

α_i \ β_j					
	c_{11}	c_{12}	...	c_{1n}	a_1
	c_{21}	c_{22}	...	c_{2n}	a_2
	...	...	...	...	...
	c_{m1}	c_{m2}	...	c_{mn}	a_m
	b_1	b_2	...	b_n	b_j \ a_i

. (4.5)

and we fill the empty rows with the quantities (differences)

$$\alpha_i^{(1)} \text{ and } \beta_j^{(1)} \quad (i = 1, \ldots, m; \quad j = 1, \ldots, n)$$

computed in the following manner. The quantity

$$\alpha_i^{(1)} \geqslant 0 \ (i = 1, \ldots, m)$$

is the difference of the minimal element in the ith row of the matrix $\|c_{ij}\|$ and the next largest entry in this row; similarly,

$$\beta_j^{(1)} \geqslant 0 \quad (j = 1, \ldots, n)$$

is the difference of the minimal element in the jth column and the next largest entry. If the ith row (column) contains more than one minimal entry, then $\alpha_i^{(1)} = 0$ $(\beta_j^{(1)} = 0)$.

After the rows and columns are filled with these differences, we choose the largest of the $m+n$ numbers in the table. Two cases are possible:

a) ***There is only one largest difference.*** In this case we consider the row (column) containing this largest difference, and in this row (column) we choose the largest entry c_{ij}, say, $c_{i_0j_0}$, and the square (i_0, j_0) containing this entry. In this square we enter the number (of shipment)

$$x_{i_0j_0} = \min\{a_{i_0}; b_{j_0}\}.$$

If $a_{i_0} < b_{j_0}$, we mark all of the other squares in the i_0th row with crosses, which will indicate that they have not been filled in the process of constructing the initial plan, and we erase $\alpha_{i_0}^{(1)}$. If $a_{i_0} > b_{j_0}$, we proceed similarly with the remaining squares in the j_0 th column and erase $\beta_{j_0}^{(1)}$. If, however, $a_{i_0} = b_{j_0}$, so that $x_{i_0j_0} = a_{i_0} = b_{j_0}$, we use crosses to eliminate all remaining squares in the i_0th row and j_0th column, erasing $\alpha_{i_0}^{(1)}$ and $\beta_{j_0}^{(1)}$. Entering $x_{i_0j_0}$ in the square (i_0, j_0) ends the first step.

Example. Consider the problem whose conditions are given by the following table:

α_i \ β_j					
	3	5	7	11	100
	1	4	6	3	130
	5	8	12	7	170
	150	120	80	50	b_j \ a_i

.

We fill the zeroth column with the differences $\alpha_i^{(1)}$, and the zeroth row with the differences $\beta_j^{(1)}$:

$\alpha_i^{(1)}$ \ $\beta_j^{(1)}$	2	1	1	4	
2	3	5	7	11	100
2	1	4	6	3	130
2	5	8	12	7	170
	150	120	80	50	b_j \ a_i

.

Among these differences, $\beta_4^{(1)} - 4$ is the largest. We enter the corresponding largest element $c_{24} = 3$ from the fourth column in the square (2, 4): $x_{24} = \min\{130;\ 50\} = 50$. Since the demand $b_4 = 50$ is completely satisfied, we place crosses in the remaining squares of the fourth column and erase $\beta_4^{(1)} = 4$:

$\alpha_i^{(1)}$ \ $\beta_j^{(1)}$	2	1	1		
2	3	5	7	11 ×	100
2	1	4	6	3 50	80
2	5	8	12	7 ×	170
	150	120	80	0	b_j \ a_i

b) *There are several equal largest differences.* In this case we use the following procedure to choose the squares to be filled. Let $\alpha_{i_0}^{(1)}$ be one of the largest differences, and let the smallest entry $c_{i_0 j_0}$ in the i_0th row also be the smallest in the j_0th column, where it is assumed that this situation does not occur for any of the remaining differences. Then we fill the square (i_0, j_0) and proceed as in case a).

If, however, the smallest entries c_{ij} of certain rows (columns) are also the smallest in their columns (rows) for several largest differences $^{(1)}_i$ and $^{(1)}_j$, we fill the square with the entry in the column (row) with the largest difference $\beta_j^{(1)}$ $(\alpha_i^{(1)})$.

For example, in the table

α_i \ β_j	2	1	1
2	3	5	7
3	1	4	6
3	5	8	12

there are two maximal differences $\alpha_2 = \alpha_3 = 3$ and the square (2, 1) must be filled, since the smallest entry $c_{21} = 1$ in the second row is the smallest in its column (first), which is not true of the entry $c_{31} = 5$ in the third row.

In the table

α_i \ β_j	4	2	1	4	4
1	5	1	6	2	6
2	8	7	4	6	2
2	10	3	5	9	7
3	1	4	10	9	8

,

which has three maximal differences $\beta_1 = \beta_4 = \beta_5 = 4$, it is necessary to fill the square (4, 1), since, of the two smallest entries $c_{41} = 1 = c_{25} = 2$, which correspond to the differences β_1 and β_5 and are the smallest in their rows, the entry c_{41} is in the row with the larger difference $\alpha_4 = 3 > 2 = \alpha_2$.

Now assume that no smallest entry c_{ij} that is also smallest in its row (column) exists for a maximal difference. In this case the square that must be filled is chosen as follows: We find the smallest entry in the first row with a maximal difference and subtract the smallest entry in its column from it. We proceed thus with all rows containing maximal differences, and we proceed similarly with all columns containing maximal differences. We thus obtain a collection of positive numbers, and the square corresponding to the smallest of these numbers must be filled. It is clear that when the smallest entry in a row with a largest difference is the smallest in its column, this rule implies the rule given above.

For example, in the table

α_i \ β_j	1	3	1	2	3
1	2	4	3	5	8
3	3	7	6	8	9
2	4	10	2	10	5
3	9	8	4	7	10

.

with four largest differences $\alpha_2 = \alpha_4 = \beta_2 = \beta_5 = 3$, the smallest entries $c_{21} = 3$ and $c_{43} = 4$ in the second and fourth rows are not the smallest in their columns, while the smallest entries $c_{12} = 4$ and $c_{35} = 5$ in the second and fifth columns are not the smallest in their rows.

We compute the following differences: the difference between the entry $c_{21} = 3$ and the smallest entry in the first row $c_{11} = 2$:

$$c_{21} - c_{11} = 3 - 2 = 1;$$

the difference between $c_{43} = 4$ and the smallest entry in the third column $c_{33} = 2$:

$$c_{43} - c_{33} = 4 - 2 = 2;$$

the difference between $c_{12} = 4$ and the smallest entry in the first row $c_{11} = 2$:

$$c_{12} - c_{11} = 4 - 2 = 2;$$

finally, the difference between $c_{35} = 5$ and the smallest entry in the third row $c_{33} = 2$:

$$c_{35} - c_{33} = 5 - 2 = 3.$$

The smallest of these differences is $c_{21} - c_{11} = 1$, so the square (2, 1) must be filled.

In all the above cases the squares are filled and the remaining operations proceed as in case a).

After the squares are filled, we appropriately change the supply columns and demand rows, and then proceed to the next step.

The second and all subsequent steps are begun by filling (previously, correcting) the zeroth row and column with new values for the differences $\alpha_i^{(k)}$ and $\beta_j^{(k)}$ and are repetitions of the first step, except that filled rows and columns are not considered and for each square to be filled we consider the minimum of the difference between the quantity not available from a given supply depot and the remaining requirements of the demand depot in question.

If only one unfilled square remains in a given row, it is filled with the remainder of the supply at the supply depot. The same holds true for columns.

As a result, the table will be filled after $N \leqslant m + n - 1$ steps, and an initial plan will have been constructed.

It can be shown that the choice obtained in this manner is acyclic. The initial plan obtained with this method is, as a rule, considerably closer to an optimal plan than the plan provided by the rule of the northwest corner or the method of the minimal element.

We continue the discussion of the above example by constructing an initial plan with the method just described. The first step yields the table

$\alpha_i^{(1)} \backslash \beta_j^{(1)}$	2	1	1		
2	3	5	7	11 ×	100
2	1	4	6	3 50	80
2	5	8	12	7 ×	170
	150	120	80	0	$b_j \backslash a_i$

.

Second step. We construct new differences $\alpha_i^{(2)}$ (see the following table). In this case we do not consider the fourth column. The differences $\beta_j^{(2)}$ $(j = 1, 2, 3)$ coincide with the corresponding $\beta_j^{(1)}$, because the first three columns have not been filled. Among the differences thus constructed there are two largest,

$$\alpha_2^{(2)} = \alpha_3^{(2)} = 3,$$

so that we have case b). The smallest entry, $c_{21} = 1$, which corresponds to the difference $\alpha_2^{(2)}$, is the smallest in its column, so we fill its square:

$$x_{21} = \min\{80;\ 150\} = 80.$$

In this case the entire supply $a_2 = 130$ is shipped from the supply depot, so we place crosses in the second row and eliminate $\alpha_2^{(2)}$:

$\alpha_i^{(2)} \backslash \beta_j^{(2)}$	2	1	1		
2	3	5	7	11 ×	100
3	1 80	4 ×	6 ×	3 50	0
3	5	8	12	7 ×	170
	70	120	80	0	$b_j \backslash a_i$

.

Third step. We first compute the differences $\alpha_i^{(3)}$ and $\beta_j^{(3)}$.

Since the first and third rows were not filled in the preceding step, $\alpha_1^{(3)} = \alpha_1^{(2)} = 2$ and $\alpha_3^{(3)} = \alpha_3^{(2)} = 3$:

$\alpha_i^{(3)}$ \ $\beta_j^{(3)}$	2	3	5		
2	3	5	7	11 / ×	100
	1 / 80	4 / ×	6 / ×	3 / 50	0
3	5	8	12	7 / ×	170
	70	120	80	0	b_j \ a_i

.

The largest difference, which is unique, is $\beta_3^{(3)} = 5$ [case a)]. We have $x_{13} = \min\{100; 80\} = 80$ and we eliminate the third column from further discussion.

Fourth step. We compute the differences $\alpha_i^{(4)}$ and $\beta_j^{(4)}$:

$\alpha_i^{(4)}$ \ $\beta_j^{(4)}$	2	3			
2	3	5	7 / 80	11 / ×	20
	1 / 80	4 / ×	6 / ×	3 / 50	0
3	5	8	12 / ×	7 / ×	170
	70	120	0	0	b_j \ a_i

.

There are two smallest: $\alpha_3^{(4)} = \beta_2^{(4)} = 3$.

The smallest entry $c_{31} = 5$, which corresponds to the difference $\alpha_3^{(4)}$, is not the smallest in its column. Similarly, the smallest entry $c_{12} = 5$, which corresponds to the difference $\beta_2^{(4)}$, is not the smallest in its row.

We consider the difference between the entry $c_{31} = 5$ and the smallest entry in its column, $c_{11} = 3$,

$$c_{31} - c_{11} = 5 - 3 = 2,$$

as well as the difference between the entry $c_{12} = 5$ and the smallest entry in its row, $c_{11} = 3$:

$$c_{12} - c_{11} = 5 - 3 = 2.$$

These differences are the same, so we can fill either (3, 1) or (1, 2), and we choose to fill (1, 2):

$$x_{12} = \min\{20;\ 120\} = 20.$$

We now eliminate the first row from further discussion. We have obtained the table

$\alpha_i^{(4)}$ \ $\beta_j^{(4)}$	2	3			
	3 ×	5 20	7 80	11 ×	0
	1 80	4 ×	6 ×	3 50	0
3	5	8	12 ×	7 ×	170
	70	100	0	0	b_j \ a_i

.

Fifth step. There is one unfilled square in each of the first two columns, so we need not consider differences for them—we can fill them by inspection:

$$x_{31} = 70,$$
$$x_{32} = 100.$$

We have thus obtained the initial plan

3	5 20	7 80	11	0
1 80	4	6	3 50	0
5 70	8 100	12	7	0
0	0	0	0	b_j \ a_i

.

The shipping cost for this plan is

$$w = 5 \cdot 20 + 7 \cdot 80 + 1 \cdot 80 + 3 \cdot 50 + 5 \cdot 70 + 8 \cdot 100 = 2040$$

and coincides with the shipping cost of the optimal plan that has already been found for this problem in Paragraph 3. Thus, the initial plan constructed here is already optimal.

7. Justification of the Method of Potentials

The above exposition of the method of potentials is based on a series of still unproved facts, which we prove below.

1) ***Existence of feasible and optimal solutions.*** The existence of some feasible solution to the transportation problem was proved in Paragraph 1, Section 1. The existence of an optimal solution, however, will follow from our proof (see below) of the monotonicity and finiteness of the algorithm of the method of potentials.

2) ***An optimal plan is acyclic.*** Here we prove the assertion of Paragraph 1 that optimal plans can be found by searching among the acyclic plans. To prove this statement, we show that any plan $X = \|x_{ij}\|_{m,n}$, containing a cycle can be replaced by an acyclic plan without increasing the total shipping costs.

Indeed, assume that among the positive entries of the matrix $\|x_{ij}\|_{m,n}$ there are some that form a closed chain. We successively examine all the squares in the chain, say, counterclockwise, and we alternately mark them with + and − signs, thus obtaining "positive" and "negative" half-chains, and we use the notation $\sum^{+}(\sum^{-})$ to indicate summation over the positive (negative) half-chain.

Assume, for example, that $\sum^{+} c_{ij} \leqslant \sum^{-} c_{ij}$ and that θ is the smallest of the members x_{ij} of the negative half-chain. We correct our plan $X = \|x_{ij}\|_{m,n}$, by subtracting θ from all the x_{ij} in the negative half-chain and adding it to all the x_{ij} in the positive half-chain. Since the chain consists only of links connecting, by way of a column or row, two squares, of which one must belong to the positive half-chain and the other must belong to the negative, in the corrected plan the loads entering and leaving at each point do not change, i.e., the new plan X' is feasible. However, a comparison of the shipping costs under the two plans yields

$$\sum_{i=1}^{m}\sum_{j=1}^{n} c_{ij}x'_{ij} = \sum_{i=1}^{m}\sum_{j=1}^{n} c_{ij}x_{ij} + \left(\sum^{+} c_{ij} - \sum^{-} c_{ij}\right)\theta \leqslant$$
$$\leqslant \sum_{i=1}^{m}\sum_{j=1}^{n} c_{ij}x_{ij},$$

from which it is clear that the total shipping cost under the plan X' is no greater than under X, although in the corrected plan X' the closed chain under consideration is open, since the square containing θ has been eliminated.

Thus, the number of cycles in the plan X is reduced in the new plan; by continuing similarly, we eventually obtain an acyclic plan with shipping costs no greater than the those under the initial plan X.

3) *The initial plan is acyclic.* We can see that the initial plan constructed with the rule of the northwest corner is acyclic, and that it contains no more than $m + n - 1$ positive elements. The proof is by induction on $p = m + n$. For $p = 2$, when $m = n = 1$, there is only one feasible plan, $X = \|x_{11}\|$, which is clearly acyclic and consists of $1 = m + n - 1$ elements. Assume that the assertion is proved for $p = m + n - 1$, and that, for example, $x_{11} = \min\{a_1, b_1\} = a_1$, so that $x_{12} = x_{13} = \ldots = x_{1n} = 0$, and the rule of the northwest corner must be used to construct an initial plan for a transportation problem with matrix $\|c_{ij}\|_{m-1, n}$, which, by hypotheses, is acyclic and consists of no more than $(m - 1) + n - 1$ $(=(m + n - 1) - 1)$ positive elements. But this plan, together with $x_{11} = a_1$, is clearly an initial plan for the initial problem that consists of no more than $m + n - 1$ positive elements, and is, in fact, acyclic, since the first row contains only one positive element x_{11} and it cannot be connected to our acyclic plan by a cycle.

4) *Two-sided estimation of the number of positive elements in an acyclic plan.* The number N of positive elements for any feasible plan is clearly no less than max $\{m, n\}$. We show now that for any acyclic plan the number N is bounded above by $m + n - 1$, so that, for example, if $m \leqslant n$, we have

$$n \leqslant N \leqslant m + n - 1.$$

Indeed, by treating each square (i, j) as a vector $P_{ij}(\alpha_1, \ldots, \alpha_i, \ldots, \alpha_m, \alpha_{m+1}, \ldots, \alpha_{m+j}, \ldots, \alpha_{m+n})$ in $(m + n)$-dimensional space with coordinates $\alpha_i = \alpha_{m+j} = 1$ and the remaining coordinates equal to zero, we can see easily that if a choice $\{(i, j)\}$ of squares is cyclic, the system $\{P_{ij}\}$ is linearly dependent and conversely. This follows from the fact that a linear combination of vectors $\{P_{ij}\}$ vanishes if and only if it contains, in addition to a vector of the form $P_{i_1 j_1}$, the vectors $P_{i_1 j_k}$ and $P_{i_l j_1}$, which indicates that the squares $\{(i, j)\}$ form a closed chain.

However, any choice of $m + n$ squares is acyclic, since the vector

$$Q(\overbrace{-1, \ldots, -1}^{m}, \overbrace{1, \ldots, 1}^{n}),$$

is clearly orthogonal to any of our vectors P_{ij}, so that these $m + n$ vectors belong to an $(m + n - 1)$-dimensional subspace and, consequently, are linearly dependent, i.e., the choice is cyclic.

Thus, the number N of squares in an acyclic choice is less than $m + n$, i.e., $N \leqslant m + n - 1$.

5) *Making a plan cyclic by adjoining an additional square.* We show now that adjoining an additional square (i_0, j_0) to an acyclic

choice of $m + n - 1$ squares generates a single cycle in the new choice of $m + n$ squares.

Indeed, if some choice $\{(i, j)\}$ of $m + n - 1$ squares is acyclic, the corresponding set $\{P_{ij}\}$ of $m + n - 1$ vectors is linearly independent, and is therefore a basis for the $(m + n - 1)$-dimensional space of all vectors P_{ij}. Because each vector $P_{i_0 j_0}$ that does not belong to the basis is uniquely representable in terms of a linear combination of $m + n - 1$ basis vectors, adjoining the new square (i_0, j_0) to an acyclic choice of $m + n - 1$ squares results in a choice containing a single cycle.

6) ***Proof that the new choice is acyclic.*** The fact that elimination of a square $(i', j') \neq (i_0, j_0)$ from a cycle again leads to an acyclic choice can be proved as follows: The vector $P_{i_0 j_0}$, as we have already noted, can be uniquely represented as a linear combination of $m + n - 1$ basis vectors. A cycle is clearly formed by the vector $P_{i_0 j_0}$ and those basis vectors contained in the linear combination with nonzero coefficients. As a result, elimination of the vector $P_{i'j'}$ leads to a linearly independent system of $m + n - 1$ vectors, since otherwise the vector $P_{i_0 j_0}$ would have two different representations in terms of the same basis vectors.

7) ***Monotonicity of the algorithm,*** i.e., the fact that the shipping cost under the plan X' obtained with the algorithm from a preceding plan X is not larger can be proved by direct computation.

Indeed, assume that a cycle is formed from the squares of an acyclic choice by

$$(i_1, j_1), (i_2, j_1), (i_2, j_2), (i_3, j_2), \ldots, (i_s, j_{s-1}), (i_s, j_s)$$

adjoining a square $(i_0, j_0) = (i_1, j_s)$ for which

$$\alpha_{i_0 j_0} = v_{j_0} - u_{i_0} - c_{i_0 j_0} > 0.$$

Then, if we denote the sum over all squares not in the cycle by $\sum'$, we obtain the expression

$$\begin{aligned}
w' &= \sum_{i=1}^{m} \sum_{j=1}^{n} c_{ij} x'_{ij} = \sum{}' c_{ij} x_{ij} + \sum_{\lambda=1}^{s}{}^{-} c_{i_\lambda j_\lambda} (x_{i_\lambda j_\lambda} - \theta) + \\
&+ \sum_{\lambda=1}^{s-1}{}^{+} c_{i_{\lambda+1} j_\lambda} (x_{i_{\lambda+1} j_\lambda} + \theta) + c_{i_1 j_s} \theta = \\
&= \sum_{i=1}^{m} \sum_{j=1}^{n} c_{ij} x_{ij} - \sum_{\lambda=1}^{s} c_{i_\lambda j_\lambda} \theta + \sum_{\lambda=1}^{s-1} c_{i_{\lambda+1} j_\lambda} \theta + c_{i_1 j_s} \theta = \\
&= w + \theta (c_{i_1 j_s} - c_{i_1 j_1} + c_{i_2 j_1} - c_{i_2 j_2} + c_{i_3 j_2} - \ldots \\
&\ldots - c_{i_{s-1} j_{s-1}} + c_{i_s j_{s-1}} - c_{i_s j_s}) = w + \theta [c_{i_1 j_s} - (v_{j_1} - u_{i_1}) + \\
&+ (v_{j_1} - u_{i_2}) - (v_{j_2} - u_{i_2}) + \ldots + (v_{j_{s-1}} - u_{i_s}) - (v_{j_s} - u_{i_s})] = \\
&= w + \theta [c_{i_1 j_s} - (v_{j_s} - u_{i_1})] \leqslant w
\end{aligned}$$

for the cost w' under the new plan X', because

$$\theta \geqslant 0, \quad c_{i_1 j_s} - (v_{j_s} - u_{i_1}) = c_{i_0 j_0} - v_{j_0} + u_{i_0} = -\alpha_{i_0 j_0} < 0.$$

8) *Degeneration in the transportation problem.* The transportation problem, as a linear programming problem, may also be degenerate. When the method of potentials is used, degeneration may cause the minimal element θ of the negative half-chain to be equal to zero, since degeneration in the case of the transportation problem, as we can see with little difficulty, indicates that among the acyclic plans there is one containing fewer than $m + n - 1$ positive elements.

It can be shown that the transportation problem is degenerate if and only if there exists a group of $p < m$ supply depots at which the total supply is equal to the total requirement of some group of $q < n$ demand depots:

$$\sum_{k=1}^{p<m} a_{i_k} = \sum_{k=1}^{q<n} b_{j_k}.$$

To prevent cycling in a degenerate problem, i.e., to avoid returning to a plan that has already been encountered, we consider, together with the initial degenerate problem, the so-called ε-problem, which has the same matrix $C = \|c_{ij}\|_{m,n}$, as the initial problem, but has new supplies

$$a_i(\varepsilon) = a_i + \varepsilon \quad (i = 1, \ldots, m)$$

at the supply depots, and new demands

$$b_j(\varepsilon) = \begin{cases} b_j & \text{for } j \neq n, \\ b_j + m\varepsilon & \text{for } j = n, \end{cases}$$

at the demand depots, where ε is a sufficiently small positive number.

It is clear that the equation

$$\sum_{i=1}^{m} a_i(\varepsilon) = \sum_{j=1}^{n} b_j(\varepsilon)$$

is satisfied for the ε-problem; but ε can be chosen so that no partial sums of the form

$$\sum_{k=1}^{p} a_{i_k}(\varepsilon) \text{ and } \sum_{k=1}^{q} b_{j_k}(\varepsilon) \qquad (p < m, \quad q < n)$$

are equal.

Indeed, the equation

$$\sum_{k=1}^{p} a_{i_k}(\varepsilon) = \sum_{k=1}^{q} b_{j_k}(\varepsilon)$$

can occur only when

$$\sum_{k=1}^{p} a_{i_k} + p\varepsilon = \sum_{k=1}^{q} b_{j_k}$$

or

$$\sum_{k=1}^{p} a_{i_k} + p\varepsilon = \sum_{k=1}^{q} b_{j_k} + m\varepsilon.$$

By choosing ε different from the roots of these equations, we eliminate the possibility of degeneration.

In practice, one may merely choose $\varepsilon > 0$ sufficiently small, usually less than $1/2m$.

9) ***Finiteness of the algorithm.*** For a nondegenerate problem, the finiteness of the algorithm follows from its monotonicity, which does not permit a return to a previously encountered feasible plan, and from the finiteness of the number of acyclic plans.

However, for a degenerate problem, when $\theta = 0$, the algorithm is not strictly monotonic and, as we have already noted, it becomes possible to return to a previously encountered plan, i.e., cycling may occur, and this process may be infinite.

To avoid cycling, we can consider, together with the initial problem, the corresponding nondegenerate ε-problem (as shown above). Because the matrices $C = \|c_{ij}\|_{m,n}$ of the initial and ε-problems coincide, and because ε is small, the choices of squares for the initial plans of both problems coincide, the squares (i_0, j_0) introduced into the choices of both problems coincide, the closed chains (cycles) are the same, and the positions of minimal elements in the positive and negative half-chains are also the same.

The transition from a plan $X(\varepsilon)$ to a plan $X'(\varepsilon)$ in the ε-problem corresponds to the transition from the plan X to the plan X' in the initial problem, and the optimal plan obtained for the ε-problem after a finite number of steps coincides with an optimal plan for the initial problem, where this optimal plan can be obtained in the same number of steps.

As S. Gass [2] has noted, no example of a transportation problem leading to cycling has been reported.

10) ***Proof that solutions are integral.*** In Paragraph 3 of Section 10 we showed that in the case of nonnegative integers a_i and b_j ($i = 1, \ldots, m$; $j = 1, \ldots, n$) the initial plan consists of integral nonnegative loads x_{ij}. As the method of constructing plan X' from X implies (θ is integral and minimal in the negative half-chain), all plans constructed in this way consist of integral nonnegative loads. Thus, an optimal plan obtained with this algorithm also consists of integral nonnegative loads.

3. THE LEAST-TIME TRANSPORTATION TIME [1]

1. Statement of the Problem

In contrast to the transportation problem discussed in Sections 1 and 2, (the least-cost transportation problem) the so-called least-time transportation problem is concerned with the time required for filling the entire need of the demand depots. Hence an optimal shipping plan is one in which the requirements of the demand depots are met most rapidly. Such problems appear, for example, when perishable products are shipped and excessive transportation costs are justified by the reduction in spoilage; another example is shipment of military supplies to a military theater, when rapid shipment is required and the shipping cost is a secondary consideration.

The problem can be rigorously formulated as follows.

Assume that m supply depots with supplies of $a_1, a_2, \ldots, a_m$ units of a single product are given, along with n demand depots that require, respectively, $b_1, b_2, \ldots, b_n$ units of this product, where

$$\sum_{i=1}^{m} a_i = \sum_{j=1}^{n} b_j.$$

Assume, moreover, that we are given the matrix $T = \|t_{ij}\|_{m,n}$, where t_{ij} is the time required for shipping a load from the point i to the point j.

It is required to find, among the feasible shipping plans $X = \|x_{ij}\|_{m,n}$, where, as usual, x_{ij} is the quantity of goods shipped from the point i to the point j and

$$\sum_{j=1}^{n} x_{ij} = a_i \quad (i = 1, \ldots, m), \quad \sum_{i=1}^{m} x_{ij} = b_j \quad (j = 1, \ldots, n),$$

a shipping plan $X^* = \|x^*_{ij}\|_{m,n}$, that is optimal with respect to time, by which we mean that the requisite shipments are made in the least possible time.

For each feasible plan $X = \|x_{ij}\|_{m,n}$ there is an associated choice $\{t_{ij}\}_X$ consisting of entries of the matrix $\|t_{ij}\|_{m,n}$ that correspond to the positive x_{ij} of the plan X, i.e.,

$$t_{ij} \in \{t_{ij}\}_X,$$

if goods are shipped from the point i to the point j under the plan X.

The time t_X necessary to realize the plan X is given by the formula

$$t_X = \max \{t_{ij}\}_X,$$

so that the optimal shipping time, i.e., the time required for realization of an optimal X^*, is given by the formula

$$t_{X^*} = \min_X t_X = \min_X \max \{t_{ij}\}_X.$$

The problem we have just stated is a special case of a more general extremal problem, which we shall state in the following paragraph and solve by means of Jordan elimination.

2. A Method for Solving General Extremal Problems (of the Same Form as That of the Least-Time Transportation Problem)

Assume that we are given a system of m linear equations in n unknowns

$$\left.\begin{matrix} a_{11}x_1 + a_{12}x_2 + \dots + a_{1n}x_n = a_1, \\ \dots\dots\dots\dots\dots\dots\dots \\ a_{m1}x_1 + a_{m2}x_2 + \dots + a_{mn}x_n = a_m \end{matrix}\right\} \quad (4.10)$$

and a set $T = \{t_1, t_2, \dots, t_n\}$ of real numbers.

With each nonnegative solution $X = \{x_j\}$ of system (4.10), we associate the set $\{t_j\}_X$ consisting of those t_j in T for which the corresponding x_j are positive. We write $t_X = \max \{t_j\}_X$ and consider the problem of finding an optimal solution of system (4.10), i.e., of finding a nonnegative solution X^* for which the corresponding t_{X^*} is minimal among all the $\{t_X\}$:

$$t_{X^*} = \min_X t_X = \min_X \max \{t_j\}_X.$$

For solution of this problem, we present the following finite algorithm, which is based primarily on Jordan elimination.

Preliminary step. We write system (4.10), in which we can clearly assume that $a_i \geqslant 0$ ($i = 1, \dots, m$), in the form of a table

	$-x_1$	$-x_2$	$\dots$	$-x_n$	1
$0 =$	a_{11}	a_{12}	$\dots$	a_{1n}	a_1
$\dots$	$\dots$	$\dots$	$\dots$	$\dots$	$\dots$
$0 =$	a_{i1}	a_{i2}	$\dots$	a_{in}	a_i
$\dots$	$\dots$	$\dots$	$\dots$	$\dots$	$\dots$
$0 =$	a_{m1}	a_{m2}	$\dots$	a_{mn}	a_m

and, by means of the simplex method (Chapter 2, Section 4, Paragraph 1), we find some nonnegative solution (if one exists). Assume that it is obtained from the table

$$\begin{array}{r|cccc|c|}
 & -x_{m+1} & -x_{m+2} & \dots & -x_n & 1 \\
\hline
x_1 = & b_{1,\,m+1} & b_{1,\,m+2} & \dots & b_{1n} & b_1 \geqslant 0 \\
\dots & \dots & \dots & \dots & \dots & \dots \\
x_i = & b_{i,\,m+1} & b_{i,\,m+2} & \dots & b_{in} & b_i \geqslant 0 \\
\dots & \dots & \dots & \dots & \dots & \dots \\
x_m = & b_{m,\,m+1} & b_{m,\,m+2} & \dots & b_{mn} & b_m \geqslant 0 \\
\hline
\end{array},$$

so that $X_0 \equiv (x_1 = b_1,\ \dots,\ x_m = b_m,\ x_{m+1} = \dots = x_n = 0)$.

General step. Let

$$t_i = \max\{t_j\}_{X_0} = \max\{t_1,\ t_2,\ \dots,\ t_m\},$$

and consider the $t_{m+1},\ t_{m+2},\ \dots,\ t_n$ with the same indices as the variables at the top of the table. The columns underneath the x_j for which the corresponding t_j are no less than the t_i obtained must, of course, be eliminated, i.e., below we will consider only the nonnegative solutions in which the indicated x_j are equal to zero.

Consider the ith row: If it has positive entries, we execute one or more modified Jordan eliminations over the columns containing these positive entries. We then follow the usual rule to choose the resolvent elements, until either x_i is carried to the top of the table, say, to replace x_{j_1}, or all the entries in the ith row are nonpositive.

In the first case we set $x_i = 0$ and eliminate the column under it. Now

$$t_l = \max\{t_1,\ \dots,\ t_{i-1},\ t_{j_1},\ t_{i+1},\ \dots,\ t_k\} \leqslant t_i$$

and the new plan X_1 is generally closer to an optimal plan than X_0. We now repeat the general step, by substituting t_l for t_i.

In the second case, when all the b_{ij} are nonpositive, there are two possibilities:

1) $b_i > 0$ and 2) $b_i = 0$.

If $b_i > 0$, system (4.10) has no nonnegative solution with $x_i = 0$, since, for $b_i > 0$ and $x_{k+1} \geqslant 0,\ \dots,\ x_n \geqslant 0,\ b_{ij} \leqslant 0$, we have

$$x_i = -(b_{i,\,k+1}x_{k+1} + \dots + b_{in}x_n) + b_i > 0.$$

As the result, it is impossible to reduce t_i and the plan that has been obtained is optimal.

If, however, $b_i = 0$, we set $x_j = 0$ for all j for which $b_{ij} < 0$, eliminate the corresponding columns and the ith row (since now $x_i = 0$), and repeat the general step.

Example. We are given the system of equations

$$\begin{aligned}
x_1 - x_2 + x_3 + 2x_4 \qquad - 4x_6 &= -1, \\
2x_2 - x_3 + x_4 - 2x_5 \qquad &= 4, \\
2x_1 + x_2 \qquad - 3x_4 - x_5 + 4x_6 &= 4,
\end{aligned}$$

and the set

$$T = \{t_1 = 3,\ t_2 = 8,\ t_3 = 5,\ t_4 = 15,\ t_5 = 12,\ t_6 = 6\}.$$

Find a nonnegative solution X^* for which the corresponding t_{X^*} satisfies the condition

$$t_{X^*} = \min_X \max \{t_j\}_X.$$

Preliminary step. We write the equations in the form of a table,

	$-x_1$	$-x_2$	$-x_3$	$-x_4$	$-x_5$	$-x_6$	1
$0 =$	−1	[1]	−1	−2	0	4	1
$0 =$	0	2	−1	1	−2	0	4
$0 =$	2	1	0	−3	−1	4	4

,

and, by way of three modified Jordan eliminations and elimination of the corresponding columns, we obtain a nonnegative solution of the system:

	$-x_1$	$-x_3$	$-x_4$	$-x_5$	$-x_6$	1
$x_2 =$	−1	−1	−2	0	4	1
$0 =$	2	[1]	5	−2	−8	2
$0 =$	3	1	−1	−1	0	3

→

	$-x_1$	$-x_4$	$-x_5$	$-x_6$	1
$x_2 =$	1	3	−2	−4	3
$x_3 =$	2	5	−2	−8	2
$0 =$	1	−6	[1]	8	1

→

	$-x_1$	$-x_4$	$-x_6$	1
$x_2 =$	3	−9	12	5
$x_3 =$	4	−7	8	4
$x_5 =$	1	−6	8	1

.

Thus,

$$X_0 \equiv (x_1 = 0,\ x_2 = 5,\ x_3 = 4,\ x_4 = 0,\ x_5 = 1,\ x_6 = 0).$$

First step. For convenience, we write the values of the corresponding t_j at the left and on top of the last table:

t_j		3	15	6	
		$-x_1$	$-x_4$	$-x_6$	1
8	$x_2 =$	3	−9	12	5
5	$x_3 =$	4	−7	8	4
12	$x_5 =$	[1]	−6	8	1

.

We have

$$\max\{t_2 = 8,\ t_3 = 5,\ t_5 = 12\} = 12.$$

Since $t_4 = 15 > 12$, we set $x_4 = 0$ and eliminate the column under it. Modified Jordan elimination now carries x_5 to the top of the table,

t_j		12	6	
		$-x_5$	$-x_6$	1
8	$x_2 =$	-3	-12	2
5	$x_3 =$	-4	-24	0
3	$x_1 =$	1	8	1

,

and, after we set $x_5 = 0$, we eliminate the column under it.

Second step. Now

$$\max\{t_2 = 8,\ t_3 = 5,\ t_1 = 3\} = 8.$$

The corresponding row for x_2 contains no positive entries, and the slack term 2 is positive, so the problem is solved. The solution

$$X^* \equiv (x_1 = 1,\ x_2 = 2,\ x_3 = 0,\ x_4 = 0,\ x_5 = 0,\ x_6 = 0)$$

is optimal, and, correspondingly, $t_{X^*} = t_2 = 8$.

3. Solution of the Least-Time Transportation Problem

The transportation problem stated in Paragraph 1 is a special case of the problem of Paragraph 2 [in which case the coefficients of Eqs. (4.10) are zeros and ones] and, consequently, can be completely solved with the algorithm of Paragraph 2.

Example. Assume that the conditions of the problem are given by the table

1 x_{11}	3 x_{12}	7 x_{13}	12 x_{14}	18
2 x_{21}	8 x_{22}	10 x_{23}	8 x_{24}	10
6 x_{31}	1 x_{32}	4 x_{33}	5 x_{34}	12
11	9	13	7	a_i \ b_j

,

where the t_{ij} are in the upper right-hand corners.

Preliminary step. The corresponding system of constraints is

$$x_{11}+x_{12}+x_{13}+x_{14}=18,$$
$$x_{21}+x_{22}+x_{23}+x_{24}=10,$$
$$x_{31}+x_{32}+x_{33}+x_{34}=12,$$
$$x_{11}+x_{21}+x_{31}=11,$$
$$x_{12}+x_{22}+x_{32}=9,$$
$$x_{13}+x_{23}+x_{33}=13,$$
$$x_{14}+x_{24}+x_{34}=7,$$
$$x_{ij}\geqslant 0\ (i=1,\ 2,\ 3;\ j=1,\ 2,\ 3,\ 4).$$

Writing the conditions of the problem in the form of a table and eliminating 0-equations, we obtain the table

	$-x_{22}$	$-x_{23}$	$-x_{24}$	$-x_{31}$	$-x_{32}$	$-x_{34}$	1
$x_{12}=$	1	0	0	0	1	0	9
$x_{13}=$	0	1	0	−1	−1	−1	1
$x_{33}=$	0	0	0	1	1	1	12
$x_{11}=$	−1	−1	−1	1	0	0	1
$x_{21}=$	1	1	1	0	0	0	10
$x_{14}=$	0	0	1	0	0	1	7

,

which yields the feasible solution

$$x_{12}=9,\ x_{13}=1,\ x_{33}=12,\ x_{11}=1,\ x_{21}=10,\ x_{14}=7,$$
$$x_{22}=x_{23}=x_{24}=x_{31}=x_{32}=x_{34}=0.$$

First step. We write the corresponding values of t_{ij} at the left and at the top of the table:

t_{ij}		8	10	8	6	1	5	
		$-x_{22}$	$-x_{23}$	$-x_{24}$	$-x_{31}$	$-x_{32}$	$-x_{34}$	1
3	$x_{12}=$	1	0	0	0	1	0	9
7	$x_{13}=$	0	1	0	−1	−1	−1	1
4	$x_{33}=$	0	0	0	1	1	1	12
1	$x_{11}=$	−1	−1	−1	1	0	0	1
2	$x_{21}=$	1	1	1	0	0	0	10
12	$x_{14}=$	0	0	1	0	0	[1]	7

.

We have

$$\max\{t_{12}=3,\ t_{13}=7,\ t_{33}=4,\ t_{11}=1,\ t_{21}=2,\ t_{14}=12\}=12.$$

There is no $t_{ij}\geqslant 12$ in the upper row, so we immediately proceed to changing the plan, which we begin with a modified Jordan elimination over the entry shown in the square.

This yields the table

t_{ij}		8	10	8	6	1	12	
		$-x_{22}$	$-x_{23}$	$-x_{24}$	$-x_{31}$	$-x_{32}$	$-x_{14}$	1
3	$x_{12}=$	1	0	0	0	1	0	9
7	$x_{13}=$	0	1	1	−1	−1	1	8
4	$x_{33}=$	0	0	−1	1	1	−1	5
1	$x_{11}=$	−1	−1	−1	1	0	0	1
2	$x_{21}=$	1	1	1	0	0	0	10
5	$x_{34}=$	0	0	1	0	0	1	7

We eliminate the column under x_{14}, set $x_{14} = 0$, and proceed to the second step.

Second step. We have

$$\max\{t_{12}=3,\ t_{13}=7,\ t_{33}=4,\ t_{11}=1,\ t_{21}=2,\ t_{34}=5\}=7.$$

Then we eliminate all the columns under the $t_{ij} \geqslant 7$, i.e., under $t_{22} = 8$, $t_{23} = 10$, and $t_{24} = 8$, so that $x_{22} = x_{23} = x_{24} = 0$. In the table

		6	1	
		$-x_{31}$	$-x_{32}$	1
3	$x_{12}=$	0	1	9
7	$x_{13}=$	−1	−1	8
4	$x_{33}=$	1	1	5
1	$x_{11}=$	1	0	1
2	$x_{21}=$	0	0	10
5	$x_{34}=$	0	0	7

that remains, all the coefficients in the row of x_{13}, which correspond to the largest t, $t_{13} = 7$, are negative, while the slack term is positive, so the process ends.

The optimal plan consists of the shipments

$$x_{12}=9,\ x_{13}=8,\ x_{33}=5,\ x_{11}=1,\ x_{21}=10,\ x_{34}=7$$

and requires a time of $t = 7$.

This optimal plan is clearly not unique, since, by executing a modified Jordan elimination over, say, an entry in the third or fourth row, we can obtain another plan whose realization requires a time of $t = 7$.

4. Another Computational Scheme (for the Case of the Transportation Problem)

In the computation scheme given in Paragraph 3 for solution of the least-time transportation problem, the preliminary step—finding a feasible solution—is very cumbersome. This disadvantage is not characteristic of another computational scheme for the same algorithm for solving the transportation problem under discussion.

We write the conditions of the problem in the form of a table in which the times t_{ij} are placed in the upper right-hand corner of each square and the shipment sizes are placed in the lower left-hand corners of the squares:

t_{11} x_{11}	t_{12} x_{12}	...	t_{1n} x_{1n}	a_1
t_{21} x_{21}	t_{22} x_{22}	...	t_{2n} x_{2n}	a_2
...	...	...	...	...
t_{m1} x_{m1}	t_{m2} x_{m2}	...	t_{mn} x_{mn}	a_m
b_1	b_2	...	b_n	a_i \ b_j

Preliminary step. We use either the method of the northwest corner or the method of minimal elements (see pp. 130 and 145) to construct an initial feasible plan.

General step. We consider all t_{ij} corresponding to positive x_{ij}, choose the largest, $t'_{ij} = \max_{x_{ij}>0} \{t_{ij}\}$, and eliminate all squares for which $t_{ij} \geqslant t'_{ij}$.

We now correct the plan X_0 by attempting to force the shipment x'_{ij} in a square with t'_{ij} to vanish, and thus to decrease the time required for realization of the new plan X_1. To construct the plan X_1, we construct a closed chain as in the method of potentials.

We choose the first square in the negative half-chain to be the square with t'_{ij}, while for the remaining squares of the negative half-chain we choose squares with $x_{ij} > 0$, and for the positive half-chain we choose squares with $t_{ij} < t'_{ij}$. We now shift the minimal element θ from the negative half-chain to the positive half-chain. If this makes x'_{ij} vanish, the new plan generally requires less time.

We now repeat the general step until it is impossible to make an entire shipment x'_{ij} in a square with maximal time t'_{ij} vanish.

Example. The conditions of the problem are given by the table

1	3	7	12	18
2	8	10	8	10
6	1	4	5	12
11	9	13	7	b_j \ a_i

It is required to find a shipping plan $X = \|x_{ij}\|_{3,4}$ requiring minimal time for its realization.

Preliminary step. We use the method of the northwest corner to construct the initial plan, which yields

— 1 11	3 7	+ 7	12	18
+ 2	8 2	— 10 8	8	10
6	1	4 5	5 7	12
11	9	13	7	b_j \ a_i

First step. We find the maximal t_{ij} in a square with positive x_{ij},

$$t'_{ij} = t_{23} = 10,$$

and eliminate the square (1, 4), since $t_{14} = 12 > 10$.

We construct a closed chain of the squares (2, 3), (1, 3), (1, 1), and (2, 1), and then transfer the minimal load $\theta = x_{23} = 8$ of the negative half-chain to the positive half-chain, which yields the new plan

— 1 3	+ 3 7	7 8	12 ×	18
+ 2 8	— 8 2	10 ×	8	10
6	1	4 5	5 7	12
11	9	13	7	b_j \ a_i

Second step. We find $t'_{ij} = t_{22} - 8$ and eliminate the square (2, 3) ($t_{33} = 10 > 8$), construct a closed chain of the squares (2, 2), (1, 2), (1, 1), and (2, 1), and transfer the minimal element $\theta = x_{22} = 2$ from the negative half-chain to the positive half-chain. This yields the plan

1 1	3 9	7 8	12 ×	18
2 10	8 ×	10 ×	8 ×	10
6	1	4 5	5 7	12
11	9	13	7	a_i / b_j

.

Third step. We find $t'_{ij} = t_{13} = 7$ and eliminate the squares (2, 2) and (2, 4) with $t_{22} = t_{24} = 8 > 7$.

It is impossible to construct a closed chain beginning with the square (1, 3), since every square in the negative half-chain contains a zero shipment. Thus, it is impossible to improve the last plan, so it is optimal. It consists of the shipments

$$x_{11} = 1,\ x_{12} = 9,\ x_{13} = 8,\ x_{21} = 10,\ x_{33} = 5,\ x_{34} = 7$$

and, incidentally, coincides with the optimal plan computed in the preceding paragraph. The minimal time required is 7 hours.

The optimal plan constructed with this method is clearly not unique, since the closed chains constructed with this method are not.

4. SHORTEST ROUTE PROBLEMS

1. Statement of the Problem. Relationship to Linear Programming

Assume that on a plane we are given n points $P_1, P_2, \ldots, P_n$, where certain ordered pairs (P_i, P_j) of these points are connected by paths of a given length

$$\rho(P_i, P_j) = l_{ij},$$

so that we obtain a connected chain of paths, i.e., a network along which it is possible to move from any one point to any other.

The problem is to determine the shortest distances and the corresponding paths over the given network between any two of the points $P_1, \ldots, P_n$.

It is easy to see that each problem of finding the shortest route in a network between any two fixed points is a linear programming problem.

Indeed, for example, assume that it is required to determine the shortest path from P_1 to P_n. We set $l_{ij} = \rho(P_i, P_j)$ if the points P_i and P_j are connected by an arc, and $l_{ij} = +\infty$ otherwise. With each path $\mu(P_1, P_{i_1}, \ldots, P_{i_k}, P_n)$ consisting of arcs connecting P_1 to P_n and not containing any loops, we associate the set of n^2 numbers ξ_{ij} $(i, j = 1, \ldots, n)$ equal to one if (P_i, P_j) belongs to μ, and zero otherwise. Then the problem of finding the shortest path between P_1 and P_n is equivalent to finding an integral solution $\| \xi^*_{ij} \|_{nn}$ minimizing the linear form (length of the path from P_1 to P_n)

$$z = \sum_{i=1}^{n} \sum_{j=1}^{n} l_{ij} \xi_{ij}$$

under the constraints

$$1)\ 0 \leqslant \xi_{ij} \leqslant 1 \quad (i, j = 1, \ldots, n),$$

$$2)\ \sum_{j=1}^{n} (\xi_{ij} - \xi_{ji}) = 0, \quad (i \neq 1, i \neq n),$$

$$3)\ \sum_{j=1}^{n} (\xi_{1j} - \xi_{j1}) = 1,$$

$$4)\ \sum_{j=1}^{n} (\xi_{nj} - \xi_{jn}) = -1.$$

We assume initially that for any path μ between P_1 and P_n (and thus for the shortest path) the set of corresponding ξ_{ij} satisfies constraints 1)-4).

This is obvious for constraint 1). Constraint 2) consists of $n - 2$ equations, each of which is written for a fixed point P_i in the set $P_1, P_2, \ldots, P_{n-1}, P_n$, except for the initial and terminal points of μ, and contains only those ξ_{ij} and ξ_{ji} that correspond to arcs with one end at P_i.

If P_i does not belong to μ, then none of the arcs (P_i, P_j) and (P_j, P_i) $(j = 1, \ldots, n)$ belongs to μ, so that $\xi_{ij} = \xi_{ji} = 0$ $(j = 1, \ldots, n)$ and $\sum_{j=1}^{n} (\xi_{ij} - \xi_{ji}) = 0$. If P_i belongs to μ, then the path μ contains two arcs with one end at the point P_i, where, in one of them, say, (P_k, P_i), the point P_i is the end, while in the other, say, (P_i, P_l), it is the origin (Fig. 10). Thus, of all the ξ_{ij} $(i, j = 1, \ldots, n)$ in the sum $\sum_{j=1}^{n} (\xi_{ij} - \xi_{ji})$, only $\xi_{ki} = 1$ and $\xi_{il} = 1$, and the others are equal to zero. Since all the terms with fixed index i in the first position in the ordered pair enter the sum with a + sign, and those with the index i in the second position enter the sum with a — sign when P_i belongs to μ, we have

$$\sum_{j=1}^{n} (\xi_{ij} - \xi_{ji}) = 0.$$

Satisfaction of constraints 3) and 4) is a consequence of analogous considerations and the fact that of all the arcs with one of their ends at P_1, the path μ contains only one—the first arc in the path—and, of all the arcs with one of their ends at the point P_n, the path μ contains only one—the last arc in the path (see Fig. 10).

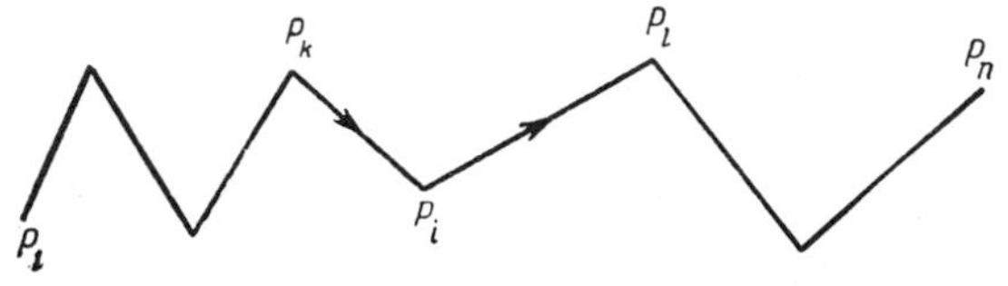

Fig. 10

It now remains to show that, conversely, every integral solution of our linear programming problem determines a set of numbers

$$\xi_{1j_1} = \xi_{j_1 j_2} = \dots = \xi_{j_{n-1} n} = 1$$

corresponding to some path μ.

Indeed, it follows from the equation

$$\sum_{j=1}^{n} \xi_{1j} = 1 + \sum_{j=1}^{n} \xi_{j1}$$

that there is at least one $\xi_{1j_1} = 1$. In turn, it follows from the equation

$$\sum_{j=1}^{n} \xi_{j_1 j} = \sum_{j=1}^{n} \xi_{jj_1} \geqslant 1$$

that there is at least one $\xi_{j_1 j_2} = 1$. Proceeding analogously, we continue to construct this chain, which can end only at P_n, since we have

$$\sum_{j=1}^{n} (\xi_{lj} - \xi_{jl}) = 0$$

at any other point P_l.

As a linear programming problem, our problem can, in principle, be solved by means of the simplex method, although this approach is cumbersome. Because the conditions of the problem are so specialized, however, more effective methods for solving it have been developed. Of these methods, below we consider Ford's algorithm [26] for finding the shortest distance and the shortest path from any fixed point to the remaining points.

2. Description of the Algorithm

Preliminary step.

Assume, for example, that it is required to determine the shortest distances along a network from a point P_1 to all remaining points. In the table

$P_i \backslash P_j$		P_1	...	P_j	...	P_n
	$\lambda_i \backslash \lambda_j$	λ_1	...	λ_j	...	λ_n
P_1	λ_1		...		...	
...	...	...	...	...	...	...
P_i	λ_i		...	l_{ij}	...	
...	...	...	...	...	...	...
P_n	λ_n		...		...	

we place all the distances l_{ij} from each point P_i ($i = 1, \ldots, n$) to only those points P_j connected with it, i.e., to those points that form arcs with P_i. We use the following rule to associate a number λ_j with each point P_j. We associate $\lambda_1 = 0$ with the initial point P_1, and then, beginning with $i = 1$, consider the squares in the ith row that contain l_{ij}; if λ_i is already defined for some square (i, j) and λ_j is not, we set

$$\lambda_j = \lambda_i + l_{ij}$$

and introduce it into the square with index j in the top row and left column of the table. Here, if the jth column contains more than one square with l_{ij} and λ_i is known when λ_j is computed, we set

$$\lambda_j = \min_i \{\lambda_i + l_{ij}\}.$$

We illustrate the preliminary step by determining the shortest distances from the point P_1 to the points $P_2, P_3, \ldots, P_8$ in the network shown in Fig. 11, where the arrows indicate that movement can occur along the arcs (P_3, P_1) (P_4, P_3), and (P_7, P_4) in only one direction, so that, for example $l_{74} = 3$ and l_{47} is not defined.

We have the table

$P_i \backslash P_j$		P_1	P_2	P_3	P_4	P_5	P_6	P_7	P_8
	$\lambda_i \backslash \lambda_j$								
P_1			7		5	9			
P_2		7		1			7		
P_3		3	1					4	15
P_4		5		1		2	6		
P_5		9			2				11
P_6			7		6				10
P_7				4	3				5
P_8				15		11	10	5	

We assume that $\lambda_1 = 0$ and write it in the corresponding square of the table, and then we consider the squares with l_{1j}, i.e., the squares (1, 2), (1, 4), (1, 5), and since $\lambda_1 = 0$, we obtain the following expressions for λ_2, λ_4, and λ_5:

$$\lambda_2 = \lambda_1 + l_{12} = 7, \quad \lambda_4 = \lambda_1 + l_{14} = 5, \quad \lambda_5 = \lambda_1 + l_{15} = 9.$$

We now introduce these values into the table.

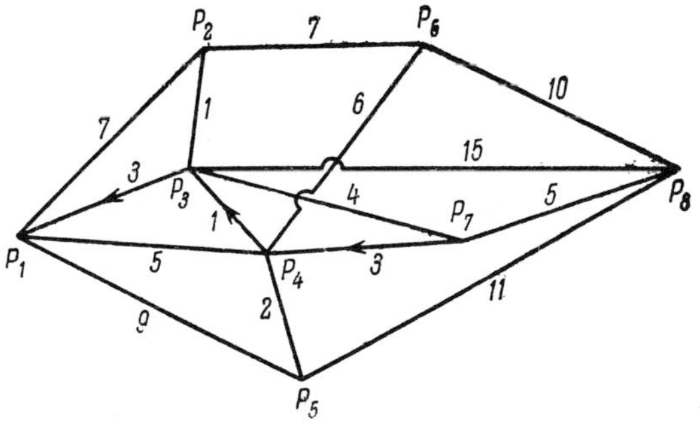

Fig. 11

Then we compute the remaining λ_j and enter them in the table:

$$\lambda_3 = \min\{\lambda_2 + l_{23} = 8;\ \lambda_4 + l_{43} = 6\} = 6,$$

$$\lambda_6 = \min\{\lambda_2 + l_{26} = 14;\ \lambda_4 + l_{46} = 11\} = 11,$$

$$\lambda_7 = \lambda_3 + l_{37} = 10,$$

$$\lambda_8 = \min\{\lambda_3 + l_{38} = 21;\ \lambda_5 + l_{58} = 20;$$

$$\lambda_6 + l_{68} = 21;\quad \lambda_7 + l_{78} = 15\} = 15.$$

We have

P_j \ P_i		P_1	P_2	P_3	P_4	P_5	P_6	P_7	P_8
	λ_j \ λ_i	0	7	6	5	9	11	10	15
P_1	0		7		5	9			
P_2	7	7		1			7		
P_3	6	3	1					4	15
P_4	5	5		1		2	6		
P_5	9	9			2				11
P_6	11		7		6				10
P_7	10			4	3				5
P_8	15			15		11	10	5	

.

General step. We consider the entries in the filled squares (i, j), beginning, for definiteness, with the first row. For them, we compare the differences $\lambda_j - \lambda_i$ with the corresponding l_{ij}. Two cases are possible:

1) For all filled squares

$$\lambda_j - \lambda_i \leqslant l_{ij}; \tag{*}$$

2) For some squares (i, j)

$$\lambda_j - \lambda_i > l_{ij}.$$

In the first case we say that the numbers $\lambda_1, \ldots, \lambda_n$ and all the filled squares satisfy the optimality condition and, as we show below, each number λ_j yields the shortest distance between P_1 and the corresponding point P_j ($j = 1, \ldots, n$).

Assume, in the second case, that optimality does not hold for the square (i_0, j_0), i.e.,

$$\lambda_{j_0} - \lambda_{i_0} > l_{i_0 j_0}.$$

To refine λ_{j_0}, we replace it by

$$\lambda'_{j_0} = \lambda_{i_0} + l_{i_0 j_0} < \lambda_{j_0}.$$

We continue this for all squares for which optimality does not hold, and we successively consider all the rows in the table.

We repeat the general step until the optimality condition (*) is satisfied for all filled squares.

We illustrate the general step by means of the preceding example.

First step. For the squares in the first row we have

$$\lambda_2 - \lambda_1 = 7 = l_{12}, \; \lambda_4 - \lambda_1 = 5 = l_{14}, \; \lambda_5 - \lambda_1 = 9 = l_{15}.$$

For the second row,

$$\lambda_1 - \lambda_2 = -7 < 7 = l_{21}, \; \lambda_3 - \lambda_2 = -1 < 1 = l_{23},$$
$$\lambda_6 - \lambda_2 = 4 < 7 = l_{26}.$$

For the third row,

$$\lambda_1 - \lambda_3 = -6 < 3 = l_{31}, \; \lambda_2 \quad \lambda_3 = 1 = l_{32},$$
$$\lambda_7 - \lambda_3 = 4 = l_{37}, \; \lambda_8 - \lambda_3 = 9 < 15 = l_{38}.$$

For the fourth row,

$$\lambda_1 - \lambda_4 = -5 < 5 = l_{41}, \; \lambda_3 - \lambda_4 = 1 = l_{43},$$
$$\lambda_5 - \lambda_4 = 4 > 2 = l_{45}, \; \lambda_6 - \lambda_4 = 6 = l_{46}.$$

We compute $\lambda'_5 = \lambda_4 + l_{45} = 7$ and enter the following correction into the table: $\lambda'_5 = 7$ must be substituted for $\lambda_5 = 9$.

We now examine all the filled squares in the remaining rows (from the fifth to the eighth), which shows that for them $\lambda_j - \lambda_i \leqslant l_{ij}$.

The improved table is

$P_i \backslash P_j$		P_1	P_2	P_3	P_4	P_5	P_6	P_7	P_8
	$\lambda_i \backslash \lambda_j$	0	7	6	5	7	11	10	15
P_1	0		7		5	9			
P_2	7	7		1			7		
P_3	6	3	1					4	5
P_4	5	5		1		2	6		
P_5	7	9			2				11
P_6	11		7		6				10
P_7	10			4	3				5
P_8	15			15		11	10	5	

Second step. Here we show that the numbers $\lambda_1, \ldots, \lambda_n$ that have been obtained satisfy the optimality condition, so that the shortest distances $l(P_1, P_j)$ from the point P_1 to any point P_j are given by the numbers λ_j ($j = 1, \ldots, 8$):

$$l(P_1, P_2) = \lambda_2 = 7, \quad l(P_1, P_3) = \lambda_3 = 6, \quad l(P_1, P_4) = \lambda_4 = 5,$$
$$l(P_1, P_5) = \lambda_5 = 7, \quad l(P_1, P_6) = \lambda_6 = 11, \quad l(P_1, P_7) = \lambda_7 = 10,$$
$$l(P_1, P_8) = \lambda_8 = 15.$$

3. Construction of Shortest Routes

The final table, which contains the lengths of the shortest paths connecting a point P_1 with all remaining points, makes it easy to find the shortest route μ_0 for each point P_j, i.e., the sequence of points between P_1 and P_j.

To construct such a route, we note the quantity $l_{t_1j} = \lambda_j - \lambda_{t_1}$ in the column under the end-point P_j; by virtue of the method of computing λ_j, l_{t_1j} must exist. If there is more than one such l_{t_1j} in the column under P_j, we choose one arbitrarily.

We write down the length of (P_{t_1}, P_j), which will be the last link in the route. Repeating this procedure with the column under P_{t_1}, we find the next-to-last link (P_{t_2}, P_{t_1}) in the route, where the length of this link is $l_{t_2t_1} = \lambda_{t_1} - \lambda_{t_2}$. By continuing this process, we eventually reach (after $k + 1$ steps) the first link (P_1, P_{t_k}) (which has length $l_{1, t_k} = \lambda_{t_k} - \lambda_1 = \lambda_{t_k}$) since

$$\lambda_j > \lambda_{t_1} > \lambda_{t_2} > \ldots > \lambda_{t_k} > \lambda_1 = 0.$$

This procedure provides a route μ_0 $(P_1, P_{t_k}, P_{t_{k-1}}, \ldots, P_{t_1}, P_j)$ with length

$$l(\mu_0) = l_{1t_k} + l_{t_k t_{k-1}} + \ldots + l_{t_1 j} =$$

$$= \lambda_{t_k} - \lambda_1 + \lambda_{t_{k-1}} - \lambda_{t_k} + \ldots + \lambda_j - \lambda_{t_1} = \lambda_j - \lambda_1 = \lambda_j.$$

In our example, the shortest route from the point P_1 to, say, the point P_7 is μ_0 (P_1, P_4, P_3, P_7).

We show that μ_0 is the shortest route.

Indeed, let $\mu(P_1, P_{s_1}, P_{s_2}, \ldots, P_{s_r}, P_j)$ be an arbitrary path of length $l(\mu)$ between P_1 and P_j. Because the optimality conditions are satisfied, we have

$$\lambda_{s_1} - \lambda_1 \leqslant l_{1s_1}, \quad \lambda_{s_2} - \lambda_{s_1} \leqslant l_{s_1 s_2}, \quad \ldots, \quad \lambda_j - \lambda_{s_r} \leqslant l_{s_r j}$$

for $(P_1, P_{s_1}), (P_{s_1}, P_{s_2}), \ldots, (P_{s_r}, P_j)$. When we recall that $\lambda_1 = 0$, addition of these last inequalities yields

$$l(\mu) = l_{1s_1} + l_{s_1 s_2} + \ldots + l_{s_r j} \geqslant \lambda_j = l(\mu_0),$$

i.e., the path $\mu_0(P_1, P_{t_k}, P_{t_{k-1}}, \ldots, P_{t_1}, P_j)$ is the shortest route from P_1 to P_j and λ_j is the length of this route.

Remark. If we solve the problem of this section for each of the points $P_1, \ldots, P_n$, we obtain a matrix $\|c_{ij}\|_{nn}$ of shortest routes between any two points P_i and P_j in a network; this matrix is customarily used in the transportation problem.

5. THE NETWORK MINIMIZATION PROBLEM

1. Statement of the Problem and Fundamental Concepts

We now consider an extremal problem that does not reduce to the ordinary transportation problem, but is of very great practical value to the transportation industry. The problem may be stated as follows.

Assume that we are given in a plane points $P_1, P_2, \ldots, P_n$ and the distances c_{ij} between each of the pairs of points P_i and P_j $(i, j = 1, \ldots, n)$. These can be conveniently written in the form of a table with a symmetric matrix $\|c_{ij}\|_{n,n}$:

	P_1	P_2	$\ldots$	P_{n-1}	P_n
P_1	$\times$	c_{12}	$\ldots$	$c_{1,n-1}$	c_{1n}
.					
.					
.					
P_n	c_{n1}	c_{n2}	$\ldots$	$c_{n,n-1}$	$\times$

.

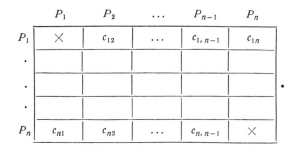

It is required to connect all the points in the network by linear arcs so that the length of the entire network is minimal.*

There is no known convenient algorithm for constructing a minimal network, but we present one network-constructing method that is convenient in practice, although it need not provide a minimal network.

We need the following definitions. We say that a point is ***isolated*** if it is not connected by an arc to any other point. We call a subset of points connected by arcs a ***fragment***. By the ***distance*** of a point from a fragment we mean the smallest of the distances from this point to all the points in the fragment. By the ***closest neighbor of a given point*** we mean a point to which the distance from the given point is no greater than to all the remaining points. By the ***closest neighbor to a fragment*** we mean any point having positive minimum distance to it.

2. Construction of a Connecting Network

The technique is based on assuring satisfaction of two conditions:

1) Every isolated point is connected by an arc to its closest neighbor;

2) Every fragment is connected by an arc to its closest neighbor.

We demonstrate our construction on the following example.

Example. Assume that the conditions of the problem are given by the table

	P_1	P_2	P_3	P_4	P_5	P_6
P_1	×	5.7	9.3	4	8	9
P_2	5.7	×	6.7	8.4	5	7
P_3	9.3	6.7	×	11.3	4.2	5
P_4	4	8.4	11.3	×	6.1	7
P_5	8	5	4.2	6.1	×	5.5
P_6	9	7	5	7	5.5	×

. (4.11)

Zeroth step. We begin the construction with the first point P_1. According to the first condition, it must be connected by an arc to its closest neighbor. To find it, we write the first row of the table without the first square:

P_2	P_3	P_4	P_5	P_6
5.7_1	9.3_1	4_1	8_1	9_1

. (4.12)

*Here the basic requirement is that it be possible to pass from any point to any other over the arcs of the network.

The index on each number indicates the index of the point whose distance from P_1 is shown in the square.

Of the numbers in this table, the smallest is 4_1 (in the column under P_4), so the closest neighbor to P_1 is P_4. We connect these two points by an arc (P_1, P_4), which we introduce, together with its length 4, into a separate table (4.16) (see below).

First step. We eliminate the column of P_4 from Table (4.12). We now consider the row of P_4 in Table (4.11). We compare each number in this row with the corresponding number in Table (4.12) that belongs to this column (among the remaining columns P_2, P_3, P_5, P_6), i.e., we compare the numbers in the following pairs:

$$(5.7_1;\ 8.4_4),\quad (9.3_1;\ 11.3_4),\quad (8_1;\ 6.1_4),\quad (9_1;\ 7_4).$$

In each pair we choose the smaller number and consider the table

P_2	P_3	P_5	P_6
5.7_1	9.3_1	6.1_4	7_4

, (4.13)

which shows the distances from each of the points P_2, P_3, P_5 and P_6 to the fragment $\{P_1, P_4\}$.

The point P_2, which has the number 5.7_1 under it in Table (4.13), is the closest neighbor to the fragment $\{P_1, P_4\}$, and it must be connected by an arc to the point P_1 (since the index 1 on 5.7_1 shows that P_2 is closer to P_1 than to P_4). We introduce the arc (P_1, P_2) and its length 5.7 into Table (4.16) (see below) and proceed to the second step.

Second step. We eliminate the column of P_2 from Table (4.13), consider the row P_2 in Table (4.11), and compare the numbers of this row (in the remaining columns P_3, P_5, and P_6) with the corresponding numbers in Table (4.13):

$$6.7_2 \text{ with } 9.3_1;\ 5_2 \text{ with } 6.1_4;\ 7_2 \text{ with } 7_4.$$

We introduce the smaller of each pair of numbers into the table

P_3	P_5	P_6
6.7_2	5_2	7_4

, (4.14)

and find that the point P_5, under which we find the smallest of these numbers, 5_2, is the closest neighbor to the fragment $\{P_1, P_4, P_2\}$. It is closest of all to the point P_2, so we write the arc (P_2, P_5) and its length 5 in Table (4.16).

Third step. We eliminate the column of P_5 from Table (4.14), consider the row of P_5 in Table (4.11), and compare the numbers in this row with the numbers of the remaining columns (P_3 and P_6) with the corresponding numbers of Table (4.14):

4.2_5 with 6.7_2; 5.5_5 with 7_4.

We introduce the smallest of each pair of numbers into the table

P_3	P_6
4.2_5	5.5_5

. (4.15)

The smallest of the entries in this table is 4.2_5, so the closest neighbor to the fragment $\{P_1, P_4, P_2, P_5\}$ is the point P_3, and it is closest to the point P_5.

We enter the arc (P_3, P_5) and its length 4.2 into Table (4.16).

Fourth step. We eliminate the column of P_3 from Table (4.15), consider the row of P_3 in Table (4.11), and compare the number in the remaining column (of P_6) of this row with the corresponding number in Table (4.15):

5_3 with 5.5_5.

The smaller of these two numbers is 5_3, so the construction ends with the arc (P_3, P_6), which we enter in the table. We therefore obtain the table

Arc	Length of arc
(P_1, P_4)	4
(P_1, P_2)	5.7
(P_2, P_5)	5
(P_5, P_3)	4.2
(P_3, P_6)	5

. (4.16)

A diagram of the network is shown in Fig. 12.

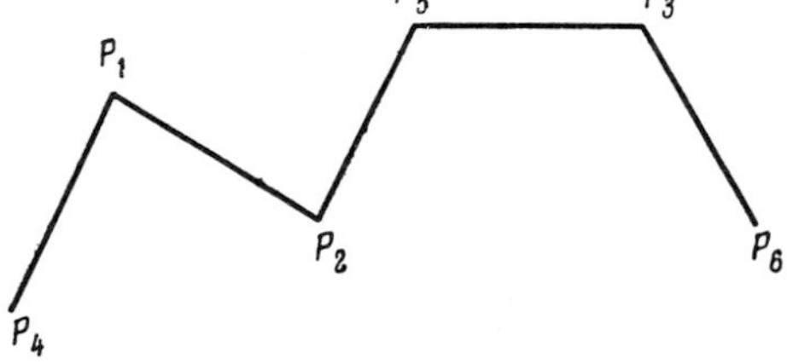

Fig. 12

6. MAXIMAL FLOW IN A NETWORK

1. Statement of the Problem

Assume that we are given a network consisting of $n + 2$ points $P_0, P_1, \ldots, P_n, P_{n+1}$ and a set of arcs (P_i, P_j) connecting certain ordered pairs (P_i, P_j) of these points (Fig. 13). The arcs (P_i, P_j) and (P_j, P_i) are said to be ***symmetric***.

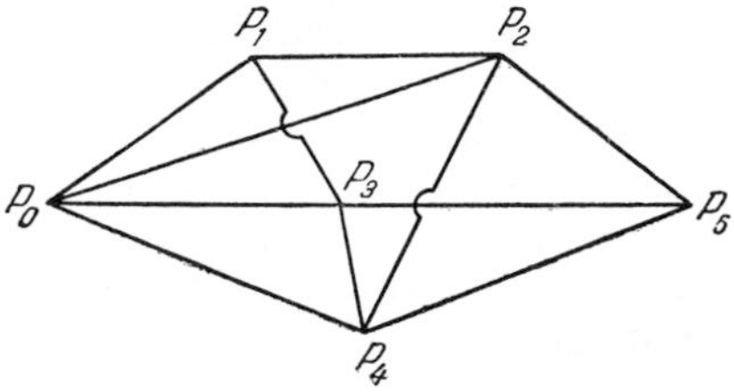

Fig. 13

Along the paths $\mu(P_0, P_{i_1}, P_{i_2}, \ldots, P_{i_k}, P_{n+1})$ which are composed of the arcs $(P_0, P_{i_1}), (P_{i_1}, P_{i_2}), \ldots, (P_{i_k}, P_{n+1})$ of the network and contain no loops, a liquid, gas, or commodity is directed from the point P_0—the input of the network—to the point P_{n+1}—the output of the network. For each ordered pair of points (P_i, P_j) $(i, j = 0, 1, \ldots, n+1)$ we are given a nonnegative number a_{ij}, called the ***capacity*** of the arc (P_i, P_j). This number determines the maximal quantity of substance that can be carried per unit time along the arc (P_i, P_j), where, for each pair of points P_l and P_m that are not connected by an arc, $a_{lm} = 0$.

By the ***flow*** x_{ij} along the arc (P_i, P_j) $(i, j = 0, 1, \ldots, n+1)$ we mean the quantity of substance passed over this arc per unit time. We assume that the flow satisfies the constraints

$$0 \leqslant x_{ij} \leqslant a_{ij} \qquad (i, j = 0, 1, \ldots, n+1), \tag{4.17}$$

$$\sum_{k=0}^{n} x_{ki} - \sum_{j=1}^{n+1} x_{ij} = 0 \qquad (i = 1, \ldots, n). \tag{4.18}$$

Constraints (4.17) indicate that the flow along each arc (P_i, P_j) is nonnegative and does not exceed its capacity.

Constraints (4.18) indicate that the quantity of substance leaving each point P_i (except P_0 and P_{n+1}) is exactly equal to the quantity of substance entering.

It follows from constraints (4.18) that the total quantity of substance $\sum_{j=1}^{n+1} x_{0j}$ flowing from P_0 coincides with the total quantity of substance $\sum_{i=0}^{n} x_{i,n+1}$ entering P_{n+1}, i.e.,

$$\sum_{j=1}^{n+1} x_{0j} = \sum_{i=0}^{n} x_{i,n+1} = z. \tag{4.19}$$

the linear form z is called the ***flow*** in the network.

Consider the problem of ***finding the maximal flow in a network***, i.e., of finding a solution x^*_{ij} $(i, j = 0, 1, \ldots, n+1)$ of system (4.17)-(4.18) that ***maximizes*** the linear form (4.19).

This problem, as we can see, is a linear programming problem and can be solved by the simplex method, although this approach is cumbersome. A special case of the problem under consideration is the problem of finding the maximal transport capacity over a given transportation network. In this problem the capacities a_{ij} of the arcs are integers and the solution is integral.

Because the constraints of the problem on maximal flow are so specialized, special algorithms that are more effective than the simplex algorithm have been developed to solve it. One of these, which coincides essentially with the algorithm of [26a]* is given below.

2. Algorithm

Before describing the algorithm, we need some preliminary concepts. We partition the set of all points of a network into two disjoint subsets U and V with $P_0 \in U$ and $P_{n+1} \in V$. We now consider the set of all arcs leaving U and entering V, which we call a cut and denote by (U, V). By the capacity (U, V) of a cut we mean the number

$$A(U, V) = \sum_{P_i \in U, P_j \in V} a_{ij}. \tag{4.20}$$

A cut with minimal capacity is said to be ***the minimal cut.*** For any flow z and any cut (U, V), every particle of substance moving from P_0 to P_{n+1} must move along at least one arc in the cut (U, V), so goods cannot move faster from P_0 to P_{n+1} than they can across a cut, i.e.,

$$z \leqslant A(U, V). \tag{4.21}$$

We can now describe the algorithm in detail.

Preliminary step. We write the conditions of the problem in the form of a table

	P_0	...	P_i	...	P_j	...	P_{n+1}
P_0			a_{0i}	...	a_{0j}	...	$a_{0\ n+1}$
...	...	...	...	...	...	...	....
P_i	a_{i0}				a_{ij}		$a_{i,\ n+1}$
...	...	...	...	...	...	...	....
P_j	a_{j0}		a_{ji}				$a_{j,\ n+1}$
...	...	...	...	...	...	...	....
P_{n+1}	$a_{n+1,0}$	...	$a_{n+1,i}$	...	$a_{n+1,j}$		

, (4.22)

*See also D. Hale, The Theory of Linear Economic Models [Russian translation], IL, Moscow, 1963.

where the points of the network are shown in the row at the top and the column at the left and the remaining squares show the corresponding capacities a_{ij} of the network arcs. Here, if P_i and P_j are connected by an arc, the square (j, i) must contain an entry unless $a_{ij} = a_{ji} = 0$, in which case we do not fill the squares (i, j) and (j, i).

To maximize the flow in the network, we must obviously find all the different paths over which goods can move from P_0 to P_{n+1}, and we must use the total available transport capacity. Here it must be recalled that if an arc is contained in some path, it may also play a part in other paths, if its capacity is not exceeded.

Each feasible path and its capacity are noted by means of the following transformations of Table (4.22).

General step. A general step in the algorithm consists of the following three operations: 1) using a table of the form (4.22) to find a new path from P_0 to P_{n+1} and labeling the associated squares and columns; 2) determining the capacity of the path that has been found; 3) computing new capacities of all the arcs in the path found and the symmetric path, with subsequent elimination of all labels.

1) A new path is found and marked in the following manner. In the P_0-row we find a filled square with $a_{0j} \neq 0$, say, the square $(0, j_0)$ [i.e., we consider the arc (P_0, P_{j_0})], mark a_{0j_0} with a − sign, and mark a_{j_00} with a + sign. We mark the columns (the zeroth and j_0th) that contain marked a_{j_00} and a_{0j_0} with an *.

We now consider the P_{j_0}-row, find a square in it with an unmarked column that does not contain a zero [say, (j_0, i_0)], mark its entry $a_{j_0i_0} \neq 0$ with a − sign, mark $a_{i_0j_0}$ with a + sign, and label the i_0th column [we obtain a second arc (P_{j_0}, P_{i_0})].

We then continue this construction, i.e., in the i_0th row we find a nonzero relative cost in an unmarked column, etc., until

a) either we reach the P_{n+1}-column and a path has been constructed from P_0 to P_{n+1},

b) or the row under discussion contains no nonzero relative cost not belonging to an unmarked column.

In case a) we proceed to operation 2), but in case b) we proceed with a new form of operation 1) in order to find a path from P_0 to P_{n+1}, if such a path exists. If no such path exists, the process terminates.

2) The capacity θ_1 of the path that has been found, i.e., the maximal quantity of material that can be moved per unit time from P_0 to P_{n+1} over the network under discussion, is easy to compute, since it is clearly equal to the smallest of the capacities of the arcs in the path:

$$\theta_1 = \min \{a_{ij}^-\}.$$

3) The capacities of all of the arcs in the new path must be computed, because, as we have already noted, a new path may contain arcs from a preceding path, but these arcs will clearly have

capacities decreased by θ_1. Moreover, we must also allow for the possibility of a path being replaced by another path containing some arc symmetric to one of the arcs in the preceding path.

It turns out that the capacity of an arc (P_j, P_i) symmetric to an arc (P_i, P_j) used in a preceding path must be set equal to $a_{ji} + \theta_1$. This occurs because the arc (P_j, P_i) removes barriers to a contribution (to P_i) of a_{ji} along the new path (when this arc is used), plus the quantity θ_1 over part of the old path from P_0 to P_i. This is true because the capacity of all of the arcs in the old path is no less than θ_1 (i.e., we assume that P_i is now connected to P_0 by two paths). We find that the arc (P_j, P_i) behaves as if it has been replaced by a new path with a capacity of $a_{ji} + \theta_1$.

In Fig. 14 the old path

$$\mu(P_0, A, P_i, P_j, B, P_{n+1})$$

uses the arc (P_i, P_j), while the new path

$$\mu(P_0, a, P_j, P_i, b, P_{n+1})$$

uses the symmetric arc (P_j, P_i), so P_i is connected to P_0 by two paths: 1) $\mu(P_0, a, P_j, P_i)$ and 2) $\mu(P_0, A, P_i)$.

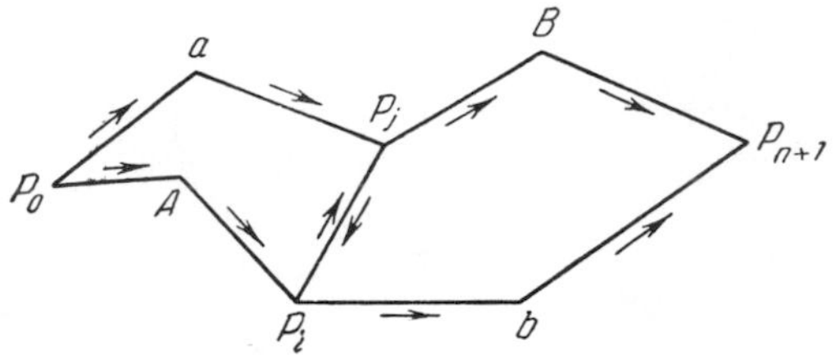

Fig. 14

Thus, the new capacities of the arcs must be computed in accordance with the following rule: θ_1 must be subtracted from those marked with − signs, while θ_1 must be added to those marked with + signs.

The method of noting paths and their capacities in the general step of the algorithm deserves further comment.

It is clear that all arcs of the old path $\mu(P_0, A, P_i, P_j, B, P_{n+1})$ are tagged by the fact that θ_1 must be subtracted from the capacities of all of the arcs in this path, and the new capacities are used in the next step of the new problem. It is impossible to return to an old path, since at least one of its arcs now has zero capacity.

If the new path $\mu(P_0, a, P_j, P_i, b, P_{n+1})$ (see Fig. 14) with capacity θ_2, where, for example, $\theta_2 > \theta_1$, uses a symmetric arc (P_j, P_i), it means that the old path $\mu(P_0, A, P_i, P_j, B, P_{n+1})$ is not used and material moves along the following three paths:

1) along $\mu(P_0, a, P_j, P_i, b, P_{n+1})$ which has a capacity of $\theta_2 - \theta_1$,

2) along $\mu(P_0, a, P_j, B, P_{n+1})$ which has a capacity of θ_1, and

3) along $\mu(P_0, A, P_i, b, P_{n+1})$ which has a capacity of θ_1.

Along these three paths, $\theta_1 + \theta_2$ units of material will be moved to P_{n+1} per unit time. This is equivalent to the statement that the old path $\mu(P_0, A, P_i, P_j, B, P_{n+1})$ delivers θ_1 units of material, and the new path $\mu(P_0, a, P_j, P_i, b, P_{n+1})$ delivers θ_2.

After the capacities of the arcs are computed, we eliminate all labels in the table and apply the general step to the transformed table. The process is repeated until we obtain a table in which there is no path from P_0 to P_{n+1}.

To determine the flow

$$x_{ij} \quad (i, \ j=0, 1, \ldots, n+1),$$

we subtract, from all entries in the initial table, the capacities of the arcs of the corresponding entries of the table obtained in the next step. The positive values of the differences found also clearly determine the flows x_{ij} along the various arcs and the flow in the network can then be computed with formula (4.19).

It can be seen that the following assertion holds for the final flow obtained after application of the above algorithm:

If $x_{ij} > 0$, then there is no flow along the symmetric arc (P_j, P_i) $(i, j = 0, 1, \ldots, n + 1)$. Indeed, assume that a total of θ' units of material moves along all paths passing through (P_i, P_j). This means that the capacity of this arc is $a_{ij} - \theta'$ and the capacity of (P_j, P_i) is $a_{ji} + \theta'$. In addition, assume that a total of θ'' $(\theta'' < \theta')$ units of material pass over all paths through (P_j, P_i), so the capacity of this arc is $a_{ji} + \theta' - \theta''$ and the capacity of (P_i, P_j) is $a_{ij} - \theta' + \theta''$. It is thus clear that when

$$x_{ij} = a_{ij} - (a_{ij} - \theta' + \theta'') = \theta' - \theta'' > 0$$

we must have

$$x_{ji} = a_{ji} - (a_{ji} + \theta' - \theta'') = \theta'' - \theta' < 0,$$

i.e., there is no flow along the arc (P_j, P_i).

3. Justification of the Algorithm

In constructing the algorithm we stop when we obtain a table in which it is impossible to construct a path from P_0 to P_{n+1}. We will now show that the flow obtained in this manner is maximal, for which purpose we construct a cut (U^*, V^*) in the following manner: $P_0 \in U^*$, and, when $k \neq 0$ $P_k \in U^*$ if and only if P_k can be reached from P_0, i.e., there exists a path $\mu(P_0, P_{i_1}, P_{i_2}, \ldots, P_k)$ from P_0 to P_k; we place the remaining points of the network in V^*. Since there is no path from P_0 to P_{n+1}, we have $P_{n+1} \in V^*$.

Assume that a point $P_i \in U^*$ is connected by a link to $P_j \in V^*$. Since there exists a path from P_0 to P_i, and there is no path from P_0 to P_j, the capacity of the link (P_i, P_j) is, in the final table, equal to zero. As a result, we have either $x_{ij} = a_{ij}$ and $x_{ij} = 0$, or $x_{ji} = 0$, because $a_{ij} = 0$, $a_{ji} \neq 0$, and (P_j, P_i) is not used. As a result, the flow z from U^* to V^* (or, equivalently, from P_0 to P_{n+1}) is given by the equation

$$z = \sum_{P_i \in U^*,\ P_j \in V^*} a_{ij}.$$

On the other hand, for the capacity $A(U^*, V^*)$ of the cut (U^*, V^*) we have

$$A(U^*, V^*) = \sum_{P_i \in U^*,\ P_j \in V^*} a_{ij}.$$

Thus, the flow z is equal to the capacity of the cut (U^*, V^*), and since, by (4.21), we have

$$z \leqslant A(U, V)$$

for an arbitrary flow z and an arbitrary cut (U, V), equality of the flow and the capacity of the cut indicates that the flow z thus obtained is maximal, i.e.,

$$z = z^*, \quad x_{ij} = x_{ij}^* \qquad (i, j = 0, 1, \ldots, n+1),$$

and the cut (U^*, V^*), is minimal, i.e.,

$$A(U^*, V^*) = \min_{(U, V)} A(U, V).$$

We call the problem of finding a minimal cut the dual of the problem of finding maximal flow. We have thus proved the following

Duality theorem. *The maximal flow in a network is equal to the capacity of a minimal cut.*

4. Example

Given a network with input P_0 and output P_7 with the capacities of all links shown by Fig. 15, determine the maximal flow from P_0 to P_7.

Preliminary step. We construct the table

	*		*			*		*
	P_0	P_1	P_2	P_3	P_4	P_5	P_6	P_7
P_0		2	5^-	2	3			
P_1	1		3			2	2	
P_2	3^+	1				4^-	3	
P_3	2				2	5		4
P_4	3			2			2	
P_5		4	2^+	0			1	4^-
P_6		2	4		3	0		3
P_7				4		3^+	2	

.

***First step*.** 1) We find some path from P_0 to P_7, say, $\mu_1(P_0\ P_2, P_5, P_7)$, and we label a_{02}, a_{25}, and a_{57} with – signs, while we label a_{20}, a_{52}, and a_{75} with + signs.

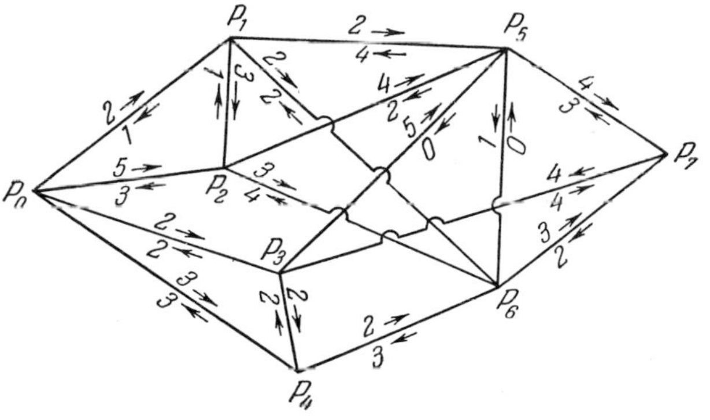

Fig. 15

2) We compute the capacity of the path we have found:

$$\theta_1 = \min\{a_{02}^-,\ a_{25}^-,\ a_{57}^-\} = \min\{5;\ 4;\ 4\} = 4.$$

3) We subtract $\theta_1 = 4$ from a_{02}^-, a_{25}^-, and a_{57}^-, while we add it to a_{20}^+, a_{52}^+, and a_{75}^+. This yields the table at the top of p. 188.

***Second step*.** 1) We find a path from P_0 to P_7, say, $\mu_2(P_0, P_4, P_6, P_7)$, label a_{04}, a_{46}, a_{67} with – signs, and label a_{40}, a_{64}, and a_{76} with + signs.

2) The capacity of the path is

$$\theta_2 = \min\{a_{04}^-,\ a_{46}^-,\ a_{67}^-\} = \min\{3;\ 2;\ 3\} = 2.$$

3) We subtract $\theta_2 = 2$ from a_{04}^-, a_{46}^-, and a_{67}^-, while we add it to

	*				*		*	*
	P_0	P_1	P_2	P_3	P_4	P_5	P_6	P_7
P_0		2	1	2	3^-			
P_1	1		3			2	2	
P_2	7	1				0	3	
P_3	2				2	5		4
P_4	3^+			2			2^-	
P_5		4	6	0			1	0
P_6		2	4		3^+	0		3^-
P_7				4		7	2^+	

a_{40}^+, a_{64}^+, and a_{76}^+, which yields the table

	P_0	P_1	P_2	P_3	P_4	P_5	P_6	P_7
P_0		2	1	2	1			
P_1	1		3			2	2	
P_2	7	1				0	3	
P_3	2				2	5		4
P_4	5			2			0	
P_5		4	6	0			1	0
P_6		2	4		5	0		1
P_7				4		7	4	

.

In the next four steps we obtain the paths

$$\mu_3(P_0, P_1, P_6, P_7) \text{ c } \theta_3 = 1, \ \mu_4(P_0, P_3, P_7) \text{ c } \theta_4 = 2,$$
$$\mu_5(P_0, P_4, P_3, P_7) \text{ c } \theta_5 = 1, \ \mu_6(P_0, P_2, P_6, P_4, P_3, P_7)$$

where $\theta_6 = 1$.

In the table at the top of p. 189 that is obtained in the sixth step of the problem we can no longer find a path from P_0 to P_7, so we need only find the flows x_{ij} over the links of the network, and the maximal flow z.

From the elements of the first table we subtract the corresponding elements of the last table, and in the table we enter only the positive differences thus obtained. This yields the second table on p. 189 .

	P_0	P_1	P_2	P_3	P_4	P_5	P_6	P_7
P_0		1	0	0	0			
P_1	2		3			2	1	
P_2	8	1				0	2	
P_3	4				4	5		0
P_4	6			0			1	
P_5		4	6	0			1	0
P_6		3	5		4	0		0
P_7				8		7	5	

	P_0	P_1	P_2	P_3	P_4	P_5	P_6	P_7
P_0		1	5	2	3			
P_1							1	
P_2						4	1	
P_3								4
P_4				2			1	
P_5								4
P_6								3
P_7								

which shows that the maximal flow is

$$z^* = x^*_{37} + x^*_{57} + x^*_{67} = 4 + 4 + 3 = 11.$$

5

Linear Programming and Chebyshev Approximation

In this chapter we consider application of the methods of linear programming to problems on Chebyshev approximation.

In Sections 1-3 we study Chebyshev approximation problems that reduce to linear programming problems, even though they are problems in convex piecewise linear programming.*

Section 4 considers a Chebyshev approximation problem that reduces to a nonlinear programming problem.** To solve this problem, we present a convergent algorithm in which each step is the solution to a linear programming problem.

Finally, in Section 5 we solve a problem in minimizing the sum of the absolute values of linear functions by reducing this problem in convex piecewise linear programming to a linear programming problem.

In keeping with the plan of the remainder of the book, here we consider only algorithms that reduce the problems given below to linear programming problems that can be solved by means of the simplex method. This leads to a considerable increase in the number of constraints, and, as a result, to increase in the size of the tables required.

However, there exist other algorithms that, because their rules for choosing resolvent elements are more complex than that of the simplex method, do not require introduction of auxiliary constraints and make it possible to compute with much smaller tables. For the case of Chebyshev approximation, we should note the algorithms given in [4a] and [35], while for the problem of Section 5, we should note the algorithms given in [3] and [4b].

---

*That is, problems in which the minimized (target) function is convex (below) and is constructed of "pieces" of linear functions.

**That is, it is a problem in which the minimized (target) function or some of its constraints are not linear.

1. THE CHEBYSHEV APPROXIMATION PROBLEM FOR AN INCONSISTENT SYSTEM OF LINEAR EQUATIONS

1. Statement of the Problem. Geometric Interpretation. A Uniqueness Condition

Assume that we are given an inconsistent system of m linear equations in n unknowns

$$\eta_i(x) \equiv a_{i1}x_1 + \ldots + a_{in}x_n + a_i = 0 \quad (i = 1, \ldots, m). \tag{5.1}$$

The Chebyshev approximation problem for system (5.1) consists in finding a Chebyshev point for this system, i.e., a point x^* (x_1^*, , ..., x_n^*) for which

$$\max_{1 \leqslant i \leqslant m} |\eta_i(x^*)| = \inf_x \max_{1 \leqslant i \leqslant m} |\eta_i(x)| = L^*. \tag{5.2}$$

Geometrically, the Chebyshev point x^* is a point with least deviation (see Chapter 1, Paragraph 2, Section 1) from the entire system of planes (5.1) in the sense that any other point will be further than x^* from some of the planes in system (5.1), i.e., any other point will have deviation greater than L.

If each n planes of (5.1) intersect at a point, i.e., if all the minors of the nth order matrix $\|a_{ij}\|_{m,n}$ are nonzero (Haar's condition), then, as we can easily see, the Chebyshev point x^* lies inside some n-dimensional simplex bounded by $n + 1$ planes of (5.1) from which x^* is maximally and equally distant (the deviation is L), and the deviation of x^* from the remaining planes of system (5.1) has absolute value no greater than L.

Figure 16 shows the Chebyshev point x^* for the case $n = 2$, $m = 6$. Here the Chebyshev point lies inside a two-dimensional simplex — the triangle bounded by the heavy lines — from which x^* is maximally and equally distant.

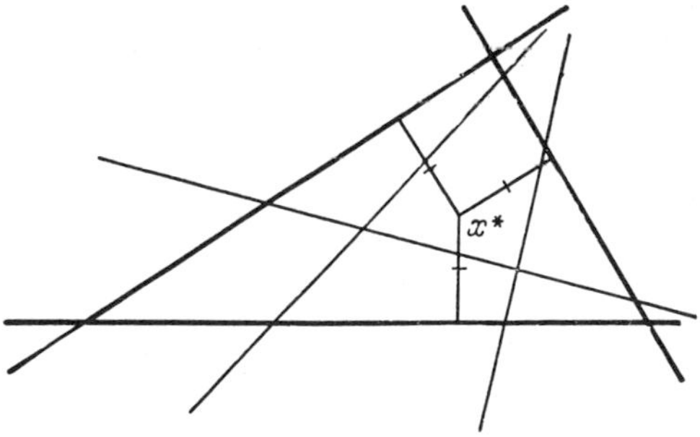

Fig. 16.

* Instead of the Chebyshev approximation for inconsistent system (5.1), we may consider the Chebyshev approximation problem for a system of linear functions $\eta_1(x)$, ..., $\eta_m(x)$.

This is the only case in which a Chebyshev point of system (5.1) is unique for any system of constant terms a_i.

It is desirable to use the notion of an r-dimensional prism to explain the geometrical characteristics of the problem when Haar's condition is not satisfied. By an r-dimensional prism we mean the set of points in n-dimensional space bounded by $r+1$ planes of (5.1) such that each r planes intersect to form a linear manifold — an $(n-r)$dimensional edge of the prism — and the remaining $(r+1)$-st plane (the face of the prism) is parallel to this edge. In particular an n-dimensional prism is a (n-dimensional) simplex. In 3-dimensional space, a 2-dimensional prism is an ordinary 3-faced prism, except that it is infinite, i.e., has no bases. When $r=1$, a prism (1-dimensional) is the layer in n-dimensional space that is bounded by two parallel planes that are simultaneously the edges and faces of the prism.

It can be seen that when Haar's condition is not satisfied, the Chebyshev points x^* of system (5.1) lie inside some r-dimensional prism $(1 \leqslant r \leqslant n)$ that is bounded by $r+1$ planes from which it is maximally and equally distant (where the absolute value of the deviation is L), while the absolute value of its deviation from the remaining planes of system (5.1) is no greater than L. Under these circumstances, Chebyshev points need not be unique and depend essentially on the constant terms a_i of system (5.1).

Another geometric interpretation (this one due to Fourier) is obtained if, in $(n+1)$-dimensional space, we consider the convex surface

$$z = \max_{1 \leqslant i \leqslant m} |\eta_i(x)| \tag{5.3}$$

with its convexity directed downward, i.e., toward the (horizontal) plane $z=0$, and consisting of sections of planes, i.e., this surface is a convex piecewise-linear surface. Now the Chebyshev point x^* is the "lowest" point (vertex) (x^*, z^*) of the surface.

Surface (5.3) may have an area parallel to the plane $z=0$, at which time problem (5.1) - (5.2) does not have a unique solution. [Each of the points (x, z) is a Chebyshev point.]

2. The Associated Linear Programming Problem

Introducing an additional variable x_{n+1} and considering the system of linear inequalities

$$|\eta_i(x)| \leqslant x_{n+1} \qquad (i=1, \ldots, m),$$

i.e., the system

$$\left.\begin{aligned} y_i &\equiv \eta_i + x_{n+1} \equiv a_{i1}x_1 + \ldots + a_{in}x_n + x_{n+1} + a_i \geqslant 0, \\ y_i^* &\equiv -\eta_i + x_{n+1} \equiv -a_{i1}x_1 - \ldots - a_{in}x_n + x_{n+1} - a_i \geqslant 0 \end{aligned}\right\} \tag{5.4}$$
$$(i = 1, \ldots, m).$$

We consider the problem of minimizing the linear form

$$z = x_{n+1} \tag{5.5}$$

under constraints (5.4). This linear programming problem is called the associated problem of the Chebyshev approximation problem for system (5.1).

It is not difficult to see that *theChebyshev approximation problem (5.1) - (5.2) is equivalent to the linear programming problem (5.4) -(5.5).*

Indeed, let $z' = \min x_{n+1}$ under the constraints $|\eta_i(x)| \leqslant x_{n+1}$ $(i = 1, \ldots, m)$ and assume that this minimum is achieved at the point (x', x'_{n+1}), which is therefore a solution of problem (5.4) - (5.5). Now

$$z' = x'_{n+1} = \max_i |\eta_i(x')| \geqslant \min_x \max_i |\eta_i(x)| = L.$$

On the other hand, at the Chebyshev point x^*, i.e., at a solution of problem (5.1) - (5.2), we have $|\eta_i(x^*)| \leqslant L$ $(i = 1, \ldots, m)$i.e.,$(x^*, x_{n+1} = L)$ satisfies constraints (5.4), so z' as the smallest value of x_{n+1} for which constraints (5.4) are satisfied, is no greater than L:

$$z' \leqslant L.$$

It follows from the two inequalities that

$$L = z',$$

so that

$$L = \max_i |\eta_i(x')| = \min_x \max_i |\eta_i(x)|,$$

i.e., x' is a Chebyshev point of system (5.1) and $L = x'_{n+1}$.

Now let x^* be a Chebyshev point of a system (5.1), i.e.,

$$\max_i |\eta_i(x^*)| = \min_x \max_i |\eta_i(x)| = L.$$

Then

$$L \geqslant |\eta_i(x^*)| \qquad (i = 1, \ldots, m),$$

i.e., $(x^*, x_{n+1} = L)$ satisfies constraints (5.4); as a result $z' \leqslant L$.

On the other hand, as we have already noted, we have

$$z' = x'_{n+1} = \max_i |\eta_i(x')| \geqslant \min_x \max_i |\eta_i(x)| = L$$

for the solution (x', x'_{n+1}) of problem (5.4) - (5.5), so that $z' \geqslant L$; as a result, $z' = L$, i.e., (x^*, L) is a solution of problem (5.4) - (5.5).

Thus, the Chebyshev approximation problem (5.1) - (5.2) reduces to the associated problem (5.4) - (5.5), which, as a typical linear programming problem, can be solved by means of the simplex method.

3. A Technique for Simplex Solution

To solve the Chebyshev approximation problem for the system

$$\eta_i(x) \equiv a_{i1}x_1 + \ldots + a_{in}x_n + a_i = 0 \quad (i = 1, \ldots, m) \tag{5.1}$$

we consider the associated problem (5.4) - (5.5), which yields the table

$$\begin{array}{r|ccccc|c|} & -x_1 & \ldots & -x_n & -x_{n+1} & & 1 \\ \hline y_1 = & -a_{11} & \ldots & -a_{1n} & -1 & & a_1 \\ \ldots & \ldots & \ldots & \ldots & \ldots & & \ldots \\ y_m = & -a_{m1} & \ldots & -a_{mn} & -1 & & a_m \\ y_1^* = & a_{11} & \ldots & a_{1n} & -1 & & -a_1 \\ \ldots & \ldots & \ldots & \ldots & \ldots & & \ldots \\ y_m^* = & a_{m1} & \ldots & a_{mn} & -1 & & -a_m \\ \hline z = & 0 & \ldots & 0 & -1 & & 0 \\ \hline \end{array} \tag{5.6}$$

We use modified Jordan eliminations to eliminate only the coordinates $x_1, \ldots, x_n$ (since $x_{n+1} \geqslant 0$) and write out their values separately.*

We now apply the simplex method to find a basic solution (Chapter 2, Section 2,), i.e., to eliminate negative slack terms, and then to minimize z (Chapter 2, Sections 3 and 5).

After we obtain a solution, we compute the coordinates $x_1^*, \ldots, x_n^*$ of the corresponding Chebyshev point. The deviation L is the value of the z obtained in this manner.

Example. Solve the Chebyshev approximation problem for the system

$$\begin{aligned} \eta_1 &= 2x_1 - x_2 - 3 = 0, \\ \eta_2 &= x_1 + x_2 + 2 = 0, \\ \eta_3 &= x_1 - 3x_2 + 1 = 0, \\ \eta_4 &= x_1 - 2x_2 + 2 = 0. \end{aligned}$$

* However, it would also be convenient to eliminate x_n+1, since the table contains $z \equiv x_{n+1}$.

We immediately pass to the associated problem of minimizing the form $z = x_3$ under the constraints

$$
\begin{aligned}
y_1 &= 2x_1 - x_2 + x_3 - 3 \geqslant 0,\\
y_2 &= x_1 + x_2 + x_3 + 2 \geqslant 0,\\
y_3 &= x_1 - 3x_2 + x_3 + 1 \geqslant 0,\\
y_4 &= x_1 - 2x_2 + x_3 + 2 \geqslant 0,\\
y_1^* &= -2x_1 + x_2 + x_3 + 3 \geqslant 0,\\
y_2^* &= -x_1 - x_2 + x_3 - 2 \geqslant 0,\\
y_3^* &= -x_1 + 3x_2 + x_3 - 1 \geqslant 0,\\
y_4^* &= -x_1 + 2x_2 + x_3 - 2 \geqslant 0.
\end{aligned}
$$

We first construct the table

	$-x_1$	$-x_2$	$-x_3$	1
$y_1 =$	-2	1	$\boxed{-1}$	-3
$y_2 =$	-1	-1	-1	2
$y_3 =$	-1	3	-1	1
$y_4 =$	-1	2	-1	2
$y_1^* =$	2	-1	-1	3
$y_2^* =$	1	1	-1	-2
$y_3^* =$	1	-3	-1	-1
$y_4^* =$	1	-2	-1	-2
$z =$	0	0	-1	0

.

Eliminating the variables x_1, x_2, x_3, we obtain the table

	$-y_2^*$	$-y_3$	$-y_1$	1
$y_2 =$	$-\frac{2}{3}$	1	$-\frac{4}{3}$	$\frac{25}{3}$
$y_4 =$	$-\frac{1}{6}$	$-\frac{1}{2}$	$-\frac{1}{3}$	$\frac{17}{6}$
$y_1^* =$	$-\frac{5}{3}$	1	$-\frac{1}{3}$	$\frac{25}{3}$
$y_3^* =$	$-\frac{5}{3}$	2	$-\frac{4}{3}$	$\frac{25}{3}$
$y_4^* =$	$-\frac{3}{2}$	$\boxed{\frac{3}{2}}$	-1	$\frac{11}{2}$
$z =$	$-\frac{5}{6}$	$\frac{1}{2}$	$-\frac{2}{3}$	$\frac{25}{6}$

,

and the expressions

$$
\begin{aligned}
x_3 &= -2x_1 + x_2 + y_1 + 3,\\
x_1 &= -\frac{1}{3} y_2^* + \frac{1}{3} y_1 + \frac{1}{3},\\
x_2 &= \frac{1}{6} y_2^* - \frac{1}{2} y_3 + \frac{1}{3} y_1 + \frac{11}{6}.
\end{aligned}
$$

Since all the slack terms in the last table are positive, the solution

$$y_2^* = y_3 = y_1 = 0$$

is basic, but not optimal, because there are positive entries in the z-row. To find $\min z$, we must execute a modified Jordan elimination over the resolvent element shown in the square. This yields

	$-y_2^*$	$-y_4^*$	$-y_1$	1
$y_2 =$				$\frac{14}{3}$
$y_4 =$				$\frac{14}{3}$
$y_1^* =$				$\frac{14}{3}$
$y_3^* =$				1
$y_3 =$				$\frac{11}{3}$
$z =$	$-\frac{1}{3}$	$-\frac{1}{3}$	$-\frac{1}{3}$	$\frac{7}{3}$

Thus, $\min z = \frac{7}{3}$ is achieved when

$$y_2^* = y_4^* = y_1 = 0, \quad y_2 = \frac{14}{3}, \quad y_4 = \frac{14}{3}, \quad y_1^* = \frac{14}{3},$$
$$y_3^* = 1, \quad y_3 = \frac{11}{3},$$

i.e., when

$$x_2 = 0, \quad x_1 = \frac{1}{3}, \quad x_3 = \frac{7}{3}.$$

Substituting the values we have obtained for x_1, x_2, and x_3 into the initial system, we obtain the deviations:

$$\eta_1 = -\frac{7}{3}, \quad \eta_2 = \frac{7}{3}, \quad \eta_3 = \frac{4}{3}, \quad \eta_4 = \frac{7}{3}, \quad L = \frac{7}{3}.$$

4. Application of the Dual Simplex Method

Since the coefficients in the z-row of table (5.6) do not change after the coordinates $x_1, \ldots, x_n$ are eliminated, it is desirable to proceed by means of the dual simplex method. In this case the coefficients of the z-row remain nonpositive, and the first basic solution is optimal.

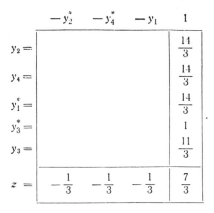

We illustrate this by means of the above example:

	$-x_1$	$-x_2$	$-x_3$	1
$y_1=$	-2	1	-1	-3
$y_2=$	-1	-1	-1	2
$y_3=$	-1	3	-1	1
$y_4=$	-1	2	-1	2
$y_1^*=$	2	-1	-1	3
$y_2^*=$	$\boxed{1}$	1	-1	-2
$y_3^*=$	1	-3	-1	-1
$y_4^*=$	1	-2	-1	-2
$z=$	0	0	-1	0

→

	$-y_2^*$	$-x_2$	$-x_3$	1
$y_1=$	2	$\boxed{3}$	-3	-7
$y_2=$	1	0	-2	0
$y_3=$	1	4	-2	-1
$y_4=$	1	3	-2	0
$y_1^*=$	-2	-3	1	7
$x_1=$	1	1	-1	-2
$y_3^*=$	-1	-4	0	1
$y_4^*=$	-1	-3	0	0
$z=$	0	0	-1	0

$$x_1=-y_2^*-x_2+x_3-2$$

→

	$-y_2^*$	$-y_1$	$-x_3$	1
$x_2=$	$\frac{2}{3}$	$\frac{1}{3}$	-1	$-\frac{7}{3}$
$y_2=$	1	0	-2	0
$y_3=$	$-\frac{5}{3}$	$-\frac{4}{3}$	2	$\frac{25}{3}$
$y_4=$	-1	-1	1	7
$y_1^*=$	0	1	-2	0
$y_3^*=$	$\frac{5}{3}$	$\frac{4}{3}$	-4	$-\frac{25}{3}$
$y_4^*=$	1	1	$\boxed{-3}$	-7
$z=$	0	0	-1	0

→

	$-y_2^*$	$-y_1$	$-y_4^*$	1
$y_2=$				$\frac{14}{3}$
$y_3=$				$\frac{11}{3}$
$y_4=$				$\frac{14}{3}$
$y_1^*=$				$\frac{14}{3}$
$y_3^*=$				1
$x_3=$				$\frac{7}{3}$
$z=$	$-\frac{1}{3}$	$-\frac{1}{3}$	$-\frac{1}{3}$	$\frac{7}{3}$

$$x_2=-\frac{2}{3}y_2^*-\frac{1}{3}y_1+x_3-\frac{7}{3}.$$

The last table shows that $\min z=\frac{7}{3}$ and is achieved when $x_1=\frac{1}{3}$, $x_2=0$.

2. THE CHEBYSHEV APPROXIMATION PROBLEM FOR A SYSTEM OF LINEAR FUNCTIONS (EQUATIONS) IN THE PRESENCE OF CONSTRAINTS

1. Linear Inequality Constraints

Assume that we are given a system of linear functions

$$\eta_i(x)\equiv a_{i1}x_1+\dots+a_{in}x_n+a_i \qquad (i=1,\dots,m) \tag{5.7}$$

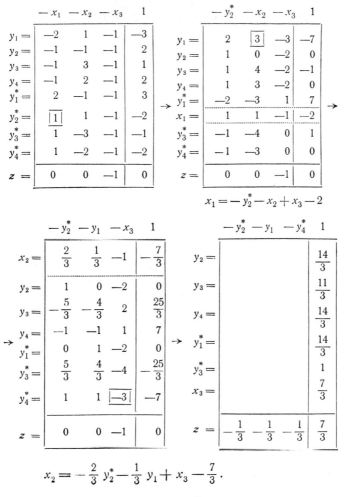

and a system of linear inequalities (constraints)

$$\delta_k(x) \equiv b_{k1}x_1 + \dots + b_{kn}x_n + b_k \geqslant 0 \qquad (k = 1, \dots, p) \tag{5.8}$$

defining some bounded polyhedron Ω. Now, consider a piecewise-linear convex function

$$u(x) = \max_i |\eta_i(x)|.$$

The problem of minimizing the function $u(x)$ under constraints (5.8), i.e., the problem of finding a point $x^* \in \Omega$ such that

$$u(x^*) = \max_i |\eta_i(x^*)| = \min_{x \in \Omega} \max_i |\eta_i(x)| \tag{5.9}$$

is a problem in convex piecewise-linear programming and provides a generalization of the Chebshev approximation problem, discussed in Section 1 for system (5.7), to the case in which additional constraints of the form (5.8) are given.

To solve the problem, we introduce, as in Paragraph 2 of Section 1, an additional variable x_{n+1}, and set

$$|\eta_i(x)| \leqslant x_{n+1} \qquad (i = 1, \dots, m). \tag{5.10}$$

We thus obtain the following linear programming problem: Minimize the function

$$z = x_{n+1}$$

under constraints (5.10) and (5.8), i.e., under the constraints

$$\left.\begin{aligned} y_i(x) &\equiv a_{i1}x_1 + \dots + a_{in}x_n + x_{n+1} + a_i \geqslant 0, \\ y_i^*(x) &\equiv -a_{i1}x_1 - \dots - a_{in}x_n + x_{n+1} - a_i \geqslant 0 \end{aligned}\right\}$$
$$(i = 1, \dots, m),$$
$$\delta_k(x) \equiv b_{k1}x_1 + \dots + b_{kn}x_n + b_k \geqslant 0$$
$$(k = 1, \dots, p).$$

Example. Minimize the function

$$u(x) = \max_{1 \leqslant i \leqslant 3} |\eta_i(x)|,$$

where

$$\eta_1(x) \equiv x_1 - 2x_2, \quad \eta_2(x) \equiv 2x_1 - x_2 - 4,$$
$$\eta_3(x) \equiv 3x_1 + x_2 - 3,$$

under the constraints

$$\delta_1(x) \equiv -x_1 - x_2 + 1 \geqslant 0,$$
$$x_1 \geqslant 0, \quad x_2 \geqslant 0.$$

The equivalent linear programming problem may be stated as follows:

Minimize the function

$$z = x_3$$

under the constraints

$$\begin{aligned} y_1 &= x_1 - 2x_2 + x_3 \geqslant 0, \\ y_2 &= 2x_1 - x_2 + x_3 - 4 \geqslant 0, \\ y_3 &= 3x_1 + x_2 + x_3 - 3 \geqslant 0, \\ y_1^* &= -x_1 + 2x_2 + x_3 \geqslant 0, \\ y_2^* &= -2x_1 + x_2 + x_3 + 4 \geqslant 0, \\ y_3^* &= -3x_1 - x_2 + x_3 + 3 \geqslant 0, \\ \delta_1 &= -x_1 - x_2 + 1 \geqslant 0, \\ & x_1 \geqslant 0, \quad x_2 \geqslant 0. \end{aligned}$$

After negative slack terms are eliminated, the table for the problem takes the form

	$-x_1$	$-x_2$	$-y_2$	1
$y_1 =$	1	1	−1	4
$y_3 =$	−1	−2	−1	1
$y_1^* =$	3	−3	−1	4
$y_2^* =$	4	−2	−1	8
$y_3^* =$	5	0	−1	7
$\delta_1 =$	[1]	1	0	1
$z =$	2	−1	−1	4

,

where

$$x_3 = -2x_1 + x_2 + y_2 + 4.$$

Modified Jordan elimination yields the table

	$-\delta_1$	$-x_2$	$-y_2$	1
$y_1 =$				3
$y_3 =$				2
$y_1^* =$				1
$y_2^* =$				4
$y_3^* =$				2
$x_1 =$				1
$z =$	-2	-3	-1	2

,

from which we find that

$$\min z = 2, \quad \delta_1 = x_2 = y_2 = 0,$$
$$y_1 = 3, \quad y_3 = 2, \quad y_1^* = 1, \quad y_2^* = 4, \quad y_3^* = 2, \quad x_1 = 1,$$

and

$$x_1 = 1, \quad x_2 = 0, \quad x_3 = 2,$$
$$\eta_1 = 1, \quad \eta_2 = -2, \quad \eta_3 = 0.$$

2. Linear Equality Constraints

We again consider the system of linear functions

$$\eta_i(x) \equiv a_{i1}x_1 + \ldots + a_{in}x_n + a_i \quad (i = 1, \ldots, m), \tag{5.7}$$

and assume that, in contrast to Paragraph 1, the constraints are given in the form of linear equations (links):

$$\delta_k(x) \equiv b_{k1}x_1 + \ldots + b_{kn}x_n + b_k = 0 \ (k = 1, \ldots, p). \tag{5.11}$$

The Chebyshev approximation problem for system (5.7) with constraints (5.11) consists in finding, among the set of solutions $X = \{x\}$ of system (5.11), a solution x^* such that

$$\max_i |\eta_i(x^*)| = \min_{x \in X} \max_i |\eta_i(x)|$$

(this problem is due to V. A. Markov [11]).

It is obvious that the method of Paragraph 1 can be applied verbatim to the solution of this problem, except that here there is a mixed system of constraints: the inequalities

$$\left.\begin{aligned} y_i(x) &\equiv a_{i1}x_1 + \ldots + a_{in}x_n + x_{n+1} + a_i \geqslant 0, \\ y_i^*(x) &\equiv -a_{i1}x_1 - \ldots - a_{in}x_n + x_{n+1} - a_i \geqslant 0 \end{aligned}\right\}$$
$$(i = 1, \ldots, m)$$

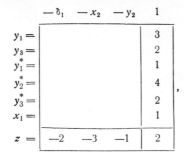

and the equations

$$\delta_k(x) \equiv b_{k1}x_1 + \ldots + b_{kn}x_n + b_k = 0 \qquad (k = 1, \ldots, p).$$

As a result the simplex method must be applied as in Paragraph 2, Section 4, Chapter 2.

Example. Find the Chebyshev approximation for the system

$$\begin{aligned}
\eta_1(x) &\equiv x_1 - x_2 - 2x_3 - 1,\\
\eta_2(x) &\equiv 2x_1 + x_2 + 2,\\
\eta_3(x) &\equiv -x_2 + 3x_3
\end{aligned}$$

under the constraints

$$\begin{aligned}
\delta_1(x) &\equiv -x_1 + x_3 + 4 = 0,\\
\delta_2(x) &\equiv 2x_1 - x_2 - 3x_3 = 0.
\end{aligned}$$

As we noted above, this problem reduces to minimization of the function

$$z = x_4$$

under the following mixed system of constraints:

$$\begin{aligned}
y_1 &= x_1 - x_2 - 2x_3 + x_4 - 1 \geqslant 0,\\
y_2 &= 2x_1 + x_2 + x_4 + 2 \geqslant 0,\\
y_3 &= -x_2 + 3x_3 + x_4 \geqslant 0,\\
y_1^* &= -x_1 + x_2 + 2x_3 + x_4 + 1 \geqslant 0,\\
y_2^* &= -2x_1 - x_2 + x_4 - 2 \geqslant 0,\\
y_3^* &= x_2 - 3x_3 + x_4 \geqslant 0,\\
\delta_1 &= -x_1 + x_3 + 4 = 0,\\
\delta_2 &= 2x_1 - x_2 - 3x_3 = 0.
\end{aligned}$$

The table for the problem is

	$-x_1$	$-x_2$	$-x_3$	$-x_4$	1
$y_1 =$	–1	1	2	–1	–1
$y_2 =$	–2	–1	0	–1	2
$y_3 =$	0	1	–3	–1	0
$y_1^* =$	1	–1	–2	–1	1
$y_2^* =$	2	1	0	–1	–2
$y_3^* =$	0	–1	3	–1	0
$0 = \delta_1 =$	[1]	0	–1	0	4
$0 = \delta_2 =$	–2	1	3	0	0
$z =$	0	0	0	–1	0

and, in accordance with Chapter 2, Section 4, Chapter 2,

	$-x_2$	$-x_3$	$-x_4$	1
$y_1 =$	1	1	−1	3
$y_2 =$	−1	−2	−1	10
$y_3 =$	1	−3	−1	0
$\overset{*}{y}_1 =$	−1	−1	−1	−3
$\overset{*}{y}_2 =$	1	2	−1	−10
$\overset{*}{y}_3 =$	−1	3	−1	0
$x_1 =$	0	−1	0	4
$0 =$	1	1	0	8
$z =$	0	0	−1	0

→

	$-x_2$	$-x_4$	1
$y_1 =$	0	−1	−5
$y_2 =$	1	−1	26
$y_3 =$	4	−1	24
$\overset{*}{y}_1 =$	0	−1	5
→ $\overset{*}{y}_2 =$	1	−1	−26
$\overset{*}{y}_3 =$	−4	−1	−24
$x_3 =$	1	0	8
$z =$	0	−1	0

→

	$-\overset{*}{y}_2$	$-x_4$	1
$y_1 =$	0	−1	−5
$y_2 =$	1	−2	0
$y_3 =$	4	−5	−80
→ $\overset{*}{y}_1 =$	0	−1	5
$x_2 =$	−1	1	26
$\overset{*}{y}_3 =$	−4	3	80
$z =$	0	−1	0

→

	$-\overset{*}{y}_2$	$-y_3$	1
$y_1 =$			11
$y_2 =$			32
$x_4 =$			16
→ $\overset{*}{y}_1 =$			21
$\overset{*}{y}_3 =$			32
$z =$	$-\frac{4}{5}$	$-\frac{1}{5}$	16

$$x_1 = x_3 + 4, \qquad x_3 = -x_2 + 8, \qquad x_2 = \overset{*}{y}_2 - x_4 + 26$$

Thus,

$$\min z = 16$$

and is achieved at the point

$$x_1 = 2, \quad x_2 = 10, \quad x_3 = -2.$$

3. CHEBYSHEV POINTS FOR SYSTEMS OF LINEAR INEQUALITIES

1. Statement of the Problem. Geometric Interpretation

Assume that we are given a system of linear inequalities

$$\eta_i \equiv \eta_i(x) \equiv a_{i1}x_1 + \ldots + a_{in}x_n + a_i \leqslant 0 \quad (i = 1, \ldots, m) \tag{5.12}$$

and let

$$L = \min_{x} \max_{1 \leqslant i \leqslant m} \eta_i(x). \tag{5.13}$$

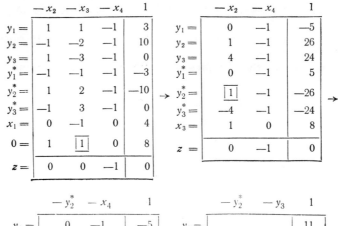

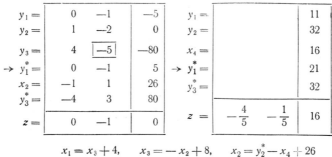

System (5.12) is clearly consistent (solvable) if and only if $L \leqslant 0$. In this case $|L|$ is a measure of the ***stability of the solution*** of this system in the sense that there exists a solution x^* that is stable with respect to some variation in the coefficients of the system (5.12), i.e., this new system has the same solution as long as the deviations $\eta_i\ (x^*)\ (i=1, \ldots, m)$ do not change by more than $|L|$.

If, however, $L > 0$, system (5.12) is inconsistent and L is its minimal deviation.

A point $x^*(x_1^*, \ldots, x_n^*)$ at which the minmax (5.13) is achieved when $L \neq -\infty$, i.e., a point at which

$$\max_{1 \leqslant i \leqslant m} \eta_i(x^*) = \min_x \max_{1 \leqslant i \leqslant m} \eta_i(x) = L, \tag{5.14}$$

is said to be a Chebyshev solution of system (5.12) if $L \leqslant 0$ (x^* is a stable solution), and a Chebyshev approximation if $L > 0$. In either of these cases, x^* is said to be a Chebyshev point of system (5.12).

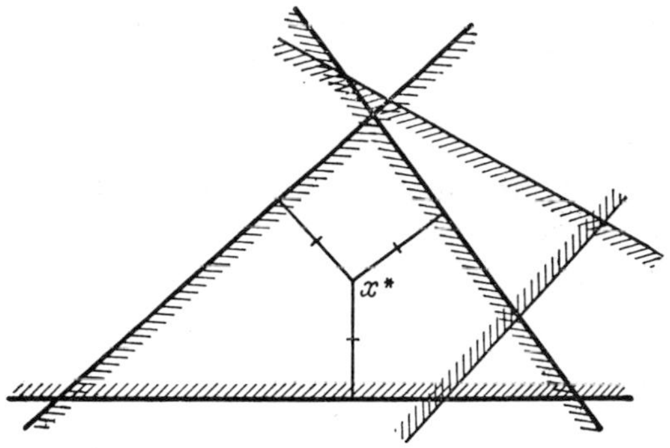

Fig. 17.

It is easiest to interpret Chebyshev points x^* of (5.12) geometrically when every set of n planes $\eta_i = 0\ (i=1, \ldots, m > n)$ has a non-empty intersection, i.e., when Haar's condition is satisfied. In this case, if x^* is a Chebyshev solution of a consistent system (5.12), the point x^* has equal deviation $L < 0$ from $n+1$ of these planes. These planes bound an n-dimensional simplex, x^* lies inside this simplex, since it is a member of the set of solutions of the system (5.12),and x^* has deviation no greater than L from the remaining $m-n-1$ planes. Figure 17 illustrates the case $n=2$, $m=5$. The crosshatching shows the half-planes for the x such that $\eta_i(x) \leqslant 0$. The point x^* is a Chebyshev solution of the system of linear inequalities.

If, however, x^* is a Chebyshev approximation of an inconsistent system (5.12), the geometric interpretation is the same, except that x^* is not a solution (there are no solutions) (Fig. 18).

While the problem of finding Chebyshev points for a system of linear inequalities is also of independent interest, it is of considerable value in the problem considered below in Section 4 and in Chapter 6.

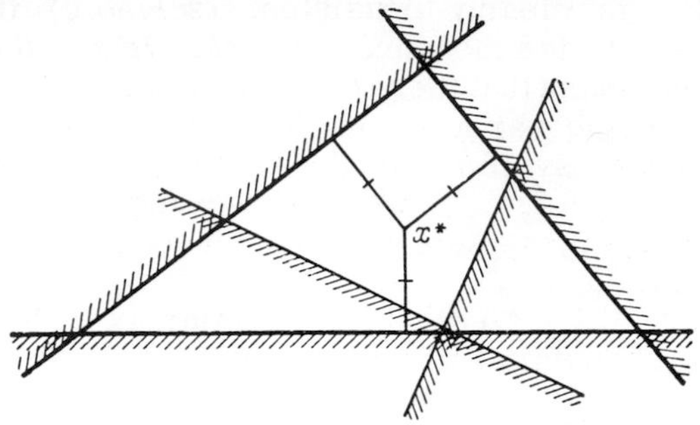

Fig. 18.

2. Reduction to Linear Programming Problems. Examples

We introduce an auxilliary variable x_{n+1} into all constraints, and require satisfaction of the inequalities

$$\eta_i(x) \equiv a_{i1}x_1 + \ldots + a_{in}x_n + a_i \leqslant x_{n+1} \quad (i = 1, \ldots, m).$$

Then, as in Section 1, problem (5.12)-(5.14) reduces to the following equivalent linear programming problem:

Minimize the linear form

$$z = x_{n+1} \tag{5.15}$$

under the constraints

$$\eta_i(x) \equiv a_{i1}x_1 + \ldots + a_{in}x_n + a_i \leqslant x_{n+1} \quad (i = 1, \ldots, m).$$

Rewriting the constraints in the form

$$y_i(x) = -a_{i1}x_1 - \ldots - a_{in}x_n + x_{n+1} - a_i \geqslant 0 \quad (i = 1, \ldots, m), \tag{5.16}$$

we can solve problem (5.15)-(5.16) with the simplex method.

Example 1. Find a Chebyshev point for the system of linear inequalities

$$\begin{aligned}
\eta_1 &= x_1 - x_2 + 3 \leqslant 0,\\
\eta_2 &= -2x_1 - x_2 - 2 \leqslant 0,\\
\eta_3 &= x_1 + x_2 - 2 \leqslant 0,\\
\eta_4 &= -x_1 + 2x_2 - 8 \leqslant 0,\\
\eta_5 &= -x_1 + x_2 - 6 \leqslant 0.
\end{aligned}$$

By introducing the auxiliary variable x_3, we reduce the problem to minimizing the form

$$z = x_3$$

under the constraints

$$\begin{aligned} y_1 &= -x_1 + x_2 + x_3 - 3 \geqslant 0, \\ y_2 &= 2x_1 + x_2 + x_3 + 2 \geqslant 0, \\ y_3 &= -x_1 - x_2 + x_3 + 2 \geqslant 0, \\ y_4 &= x_1 - 2x_2 + x_3 + 8 \geqslant 0, \\ y_5 &= x_1 - x_2 + x_3 + 6 \geqslant 0. \end{aligned}$$

By constructing a table for the problem and eliminating variables, we obtain the table

	$-y_1$	$-y_4$	$-y_3$	1
$y_2 =$	$-\frac{7}{4}$	$\boxed{-\frac{3}{2}}$	$\frac{9}{4}$	$-\frac{1}{4}$
$y_5 =$	$-\frac{1}{2}$	-1	$\frac{1}{2}$	$\frac{1}{2}$
$z =$	$-\frac{3}{4}$	$-\frac{1}{2}$	$\frac{1}{4}$	$-\frac{5}{4}$

and the following expressions for x_1, x_2, and x_3:

$$\begin{aligned} x_1 &= -y_1 + x_2 + x_3 - 3, \\ x_2 &= -y_1 - y_4 + 2x_3 + 5, \\ x_3 &= \frac{3}{4}y_1 + \frac{1}{2}y_4 - \frac{1}{4}y_3 - \frac{5}{4}. \end{aligned}$$

There is still one negative slack term in the table, $-\frac{1}{4}$. Modified Jordan elimination over $-\frac{3}{2}$ leads to the table

	$-y_1$	$-y_2$	$-y_3$	1
$y_4 =$				$\frac{1}{6}$
$y_5 =$				$\frac{2}{3}$
$z =$	$-\frac{1}{6}$	$-\frac{1}{3}$	$-\frac{1}{2}$	$-\frac{7}{6}$

in which all the entries of the z-row are nonpositive. Consequently,

$$\min z = -\frac{7}{6} < 0,$$

so that the system is consistent. Here

$$y_1 = y_2 = y_3 = 0, \quad y_4 = \frac{1}{6}, \quad y_5 = \frac{2}{3},$$

so that

$$x_1 = -\frac{5}{3}, \; x_2 = \frac{5}{2}, \; x_3 = -\frac{7}{6},$$

i.e., $(-\frac{5}{3}, \frac{5}{2})$ is a Chebyshev point (solution) and its deviations from the planes $\eta_i = 0$ ($i = 1, \ldots, 5$) are

$$\eta_1 = -\frac{7}{6}, \; \eta_2 = -\frac{7}{6}, \; \eta_3 = -\frac{7}{6}, \; \eta_4 = -\frac{8}{6}, \; \eta_5 = -\frac{11}{6}.$$

Example 2. Find a Chebyshev point for the system

$$\begin{aligned}
\eta_1 &= x_1 + x_2 - 1 \leqslant 0,\\
\eta_2 &= -x_2 + 1 \leqslant 0,\\
\eta_3 &= -x_1 + 1 \leqslant 0,\\
\eta_4 &= -x_1 - 2x_2 + 2 \leqslant 0,\\
\eta_5 &= 2x_1 + x_2 - 3 \leqslant 0.
\end{aligned}$$

We replace this problem by the problem of minimizing the function

$$z = x_3$$

under the constraints

$$\begin{aligned}
y_1 &= -x_1 - x_2 + x_3 + 1 \geqslant 0,\\
y_2 &= x_2 + x_3 - 1 \geqslant 0,\\
y_3 &= x_1 + x_3 - 1 \geqslant 0,\\
y_4 &= x_1 + 2x_2 + x_3 - 2 \geqslant 0,\\
y_5 &= -2x_1 - x_2 + x_3 + 3 \geqslant 0.
\end{aligned}$$

Constructing the appropriate table and eliminating x_1, x_2, and x_3, we find that

$$\begin{aligned}
x_1 &= y_3 - x_3 + 1,\\
x_2 &= y_2 - x_3 + 1,\\
x_3 &= \frac{1}{2}y_3 + y_2 - \frac{1}{4}y_4 + \frac{1}{2}
\end{aligned}$$

and we obtain the table

	$-y_3$	$-y_2$	$-y_4$	1
$y_1 =$	$-\frac{1}{2}$	-2	$\boxed{\frac{3}{2}}$	$\frac{1}{2}$
$y_5 =$	0	-3	2	2
$z =$	$-\frac{1}{2}$	-1	$\frac{1}{2}$	$\frac{1}{2}$

,

in which all the slack terms are nonnegative, so that the solution

$$y_3 = y_2 = y_4 = 0$$

is basic.

We now proceed to finding an optimal solution. Modified Jordan elimination over $\frac{3}{2}$ yields the table

	$-y_3$	$-y_2$	$-y_1$	1
$y_4 =$				$\frac{1}{3}$
$y_5 =$				$\frac{4}{3}$
$z =$	$-\frac{1}{3}$	$-\frac{1}{3}$	$-\frac{1}{3}$	$\frac{1}{3}$

All the entries in the z-row are negative, so

$$y_1 = y_2 = y_3 = 0$$

leads to the optimal solution

$$x_1 = \frac{2}{3}, \quad x_2 = \frac{2}{3}, \quad x_3 = \frac{1}{3},$$

for which $\min z = \frac{1}{3} > 0$. This means the system is inconsistent and that the Chebyshev point $(\frac{2}{3}, \frac{2}{3})$ is a Chebyshev approximation.

4. CHEBYSHEV APPROXIMATION IN TERMS OF LINEAR FORMS

1. Origin and Statement of the Problem

Assume that for a function $f(t)$ continuous on the segment $[a, b]$, we are asked to find a Chebyshev approximation in terms of a rational fraction of the form

$$\frac{\xi_1 t^{m-1} + \xi_2 t^{m-2} + \dots + \xi_m}{\eta_1 t^{n-1} + \eta_2 t^{n-2} + \dots + \eta_n},$$

or in terms of the more general function

$$\frac{\xi_1 \varphi_1(t) + \xi_2 \varphi_2(t) + \dots + \xi_m \varphi_m(t)}{\eta_1 \psi_1(t) + \eta_2 \psi_2(t) + \dots + \eta_n \psi_n(t)},$$

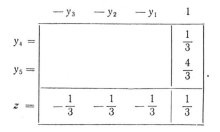

where $\varphi_1(t), \ldots, \varphi_m(t), \psi_1(t), \ldots, \psi_n(t)$ are given functions that are continuous on $[a, b]$. In other words, assume that we are asked to find coefficients $(\xi_1, \ldots, \xi_m; \eta_1, \ldots, \eta_n) = [x, y]$ for which

$$\min_{[x, y]} \max_{t \in [a, b]} \left| \frac{\xi_1\varphi_1(t) + \ldots + \xi_m\varphi_m(t)}{\eta_1\psi_1(t) + \ldots + \eta_n\psi_n(t)} - f(t) \right|.$$

Because all the functions under discussion are continuous, we can obtain an approximate solution for the problem by considering the Chebyshev approximation on an ε-grid $\{t_1, \ldots, t_p\}$ instead of on the entire interval $[a, b]$. We use the notation

$$\varphi_j(t_i) = \alpha_{ij} \qquad (i = 1, \ldots, p;\ j = 1, \ldots, m);$$
$$\psi_j(t_i) = \beta_{ij} \qquad (i = 1, \ldots, p;\ j = 1, \ldots, n);$$
$$f(t_i) = \gamma_i \qquad (i = 1, \ldots, p); \qquad a_i = (\alpha_{i1}, \ldots, \alpha_{im}),$$
$$b_i = (\beta_{i1}, \ldots, \beta_{in}), \qquad (i = 1, \ldots, p);$$
$$x \equiv (\xi_1, \ldots, \xi_m), \qquad y \equiv (\eta_1, \ldots, \eta_n).$$

The problem of Chebyshev approximation on the grid $\{t_1, \ldots, t_p\}$ consists of finding a point $(\overset{*}{\xi_1}, \ldots, \overset{*}{\xi_m}; \overset{*}{\eta_1}, \ldots, \overset{*}{\eta_n}) \equiv [x^*, y^*]$ such that

$$\max_{1 \leqslant i \leqslant p} \left| \frac{(x^*, a_i)}{(y^*, b_i)} - \gamma_i \right| = \min_{[x, y]} \max_{1 \leqslant i \leqslant p} \left| \frac{(x, a_i)}{(y, b_i)} - \gamma_i \right|. \qquad (5.17)$$

Assume that [independently of the approximation origin of problem (5.17)] we require that the point (x^*, y^*) belong to the polyhedron defined by the following inequalities:

$$(y, b_i) > 0 \quad (i = 1, \ldots, p) \text{ and } |\eta_i| \leqslant 1 \quad (i = 1, \ldots, n). \qquad (5.18)$$

The first p inequalities guarantee the existence of a solution for (5.17), while the remaining inequalities are introduced for normalization, since multiplication of x and y by the same number does not effect $\frac{(x, a_i)}{(y, b_i)}$. Now the problem of Chebyshev approximation in terms of linear forms is the problem of finding a point $[x^*, y^*] \in \Omega$ such that

$$\max_{1 \leqslant i \leqslant p} \left| \frac{(x^*, a_i)}{(y^*, b_i)} - \gamma_i \right| = \min_{[x, y] \in \Omega} \max_{1 \leqslant i \leqslant p} \left| \frac{(x, a_i)}{(y, b_i)} - \gamma_i \right|. \qquad (5.19)$$

2. Reduction to a Nonlinear Programming Problem

We introduce an auxiliary variable M and consider the inequalities

$$\left| \frac{(x, a_i)}{(y, b_i)} - \gamma_i \right| \leqslant M \qquad (i = 1, \ldots, p).$$

It is not difficult to show that our problem is equivalent to the following nonlinear programming problem.

Minimize the function

$$z = M \tag{5.20}$$

under the constraints

$$M \geqslant 0, \quad \left| \frac{(x, a_i)}{(y, b_i)} - \gamma_i \right| \leqslant M, \quad (y, b_i) > 0 \qquad (i = 1, \ldots, p),$$
$$|\eta_i| \leqslant 1 \qquad (i = 1, \ldots, n)$$

or, equivalently, under the constraints

$$\left.\begin{array}{c} \delta_0(x, y, M) \equiv M \geqslant 0, \\ \delta_i(x, y, M) \equiv (x, a_i) - (M + \gamma_i)(y, b_i) \leqslant 0 \\ (i = 1, \ldots, 2p), \end{array}\right\} \tag{5.21}$$

$$\left.\begin{array}{ll} \delta_{2p+j}(x, y, M) \equiv -(y, b_j) < 0 & (j = 1, \ldots, p), \\ |\eta_i| \leqslant 1 & (i = 1, \ldots, n), \end{array}\right\} \tag{5.22}$$

where we have set

$$a_{i+p} = -a_i, \; b_{i+p} = b_i, \; \gamma_{i+p} = -\gamma_i \qquad (i = 1, \ldots, p).$$

3. An Algorithm and Convergence

We choose some value $M_1 > 0$ of the variable M for which the linear system (5.21_1) obtained from (5.21) by substitution of M_1 for M is consistent, say, $M_1 = \max\{|\gamma_1|, \ldots, |\gamma_p|\}$. Using the method considered in Section 3, we find a Chebyshev point $[x^{(1)}, y^{(1)}]$ of system (5.21) under constraints (5.22), i.e., a point for which

$$\min_{[x, y] \in \mathfrak{L}} \max_{1 \leqslant i \leqslant 2p} \delta_i(x, y, M_1) = \max_{1 \leqslant i \leqslant 2p} \delta_i(x^{(1)}, y^{(1)}, M_1) = L_1.$$

After we find $[x^{(1)}, y^{(1)}]$, we continuously decrease M, beginning with M_1. In this case each plane

$$\begin{array}{c} \delta_i(x, y, M) \equiv (x, a_i) - (M + \gamma_i)(y, b_i) = 0 \\ (i = 1, \ldots, 2p) \end{array} \tag{5.23}$$

continuously rotates about the coordinate origin and, at some value of M, may pass through $[x^{(1)}, y^{(1)}]$. The first planes (5.23) (say those with $i = i_1$) meet the point $[x^{(1)}, y^{(1)}]$ at $M = M_2$, where M_2 is the largest positive value of M less than M_1 and among the $2p$ values

$$M = \frac{(x^{(1)}, a_i)}{(y^{(1)}, b_i)} - \gamma_i \qquad (i = 1, \ldots, 2p). \tag{5.24}$$

The first step in the algorithm ends when $M_2 < M_1$ is found.

The second step is a repetition of the first, except that we now use the system of inequalities (5.21_2) obtained from (5.21) with $M = M_2$ instead of system (5.21_1).

By continuing the process we construct a sequence of systems $\{(5.21_n)\}$, Chebyshev points $\{[x^{(n)}, y^{(n)}]\}$, maximal deviations $\{L_n\}$, and a monotonically decreasing sequence $\{M_n\}$, where

$$L_n = \min_{[x, y] \in \mathfrak{L}} \max_{1 \leqslant k \leqslant 2p} \delta_k (x, y, M_n) = \\ = \max_{1 \leqslant k \leqslant 2p} \delta_k (x^{(n)}, y^{(n)}, M_n) \qquad (n = 1, 2, \ldots),$$

and M_{n+1} is the largest positive value of M less than M_n and among the $2p$ values

$$M = \frac{(x^{(n)}, a_i)}{(y^{(n)}, b_i)} - \gamma_i \qquad (i = 1, \ldots, 2p, n = 1, 2, \ldots).$$

We show now that

$$L_n \to L_0 = 0. \tag{5.25}$$

To do so, we subtract the equation

$$(x^{(n)}, a_i) - (M_n + \gamma_i)(y^{(n)}, b_i) = \delta_i (x^{(n)}, y^{(n)}, M_n) = \delta_i^{(n)}$$

from the equation

$$(x^{(n)}, a_i) - (M_{n+1} + \gamma_i)(y^{(n)}, b_i) = \delta_i (x^{(n)}, y^{(n)}, M_{n+1}) = \delta_i^{(n+1)}$$

and substitute $L_n = \max\limits_{1 \leqslant i \leqslant 2p} \delta_i^{(n)}$ for $\delta_i^{(n)}$. We thus obtain the following inequality, which holds for all $i = 1, \ldots, 2p$:

$$(M_n - M_{n+1}) (y^{(n)}, b_i) = \delta_i^{(n+1)} - \delta_i^{(n)} \geqslant \delta_i^{(n+1)} + |L_n|.$$

But for some $i = i_n$ we have

$$\delta_{i_n} (x^{(n)}, y^{(n)}, M_{n+1}) = \delta_{i_n}^{(n+1)} = 0$$

(the plane $\delta_{i_n} (x, y, M_{n+1}) = 0$ passes through the point $[x^{(n)}, y^{(n)}]$), so

$$|L_n| \leqslant (M_n - M_{n+1}) (y^{(n)}, b_{i_n}). \tag{5.26}$$

It remains only to note that $|(y^{(n)}, b_i)| \leqslant K$ and that the existence of a limit M_0 for the monotonic sequence $\{M_n\}$ implies that $M_n - M_{n+1} \to 0$.

Since problem (5.18)-(5.19) has the solution $M^* [x^*, y^*]$, the stability of the solution of the system (5.21_0) obtained from (5.21) by setting $M = M_0$ with $M_0 = M^*$, i.e., the quantity $|L_0|$, is larger than zero, which is a contradiction. As a result, $M_0 = M^*$ and $[x^{(0)}, y^{(0)}]$ is one of the points $[x^*, y^*]$ for which (5.19) holds.

4. Example

Find

$$\min_{\xi_i,\,\eta_i} \max \left\{ \left| \frac{2\xi_2}{-\eta_1+\eta_2} + 10 \right|, \left| \frac{-\xi_1 - 3\xi_2}{-2\eta_1+\eta_2} - 2 \right|, \left| \frac{\xi_1 - \xi_2}{\eta_1} - 2 \right| \right\}$$

under the constraints

$$-\eta_1 + \eta_2 > 0, \quad -2\eta_1 + \eta_2 > 0, \quad \eta_1 > 0, \quad |\eta_1| \leqslant 1, \quad |\eta_2| \leqslant 1.$$

By introducing an auxiliary variable $M \geqslant 0$ we reduce the problem to the following nonlinear programming problem:

Minimize the function

$$z = M$$

under the constraints

$$M \geqslant 0, \quad \left| \frac{2\xi_2}{-\eta_1+\eta_2} + 10 \right| \leqslant M,$$
$$\left| \frac{-\xi_1 - 3\xi_2}{-2\eta_1+\eta_2} - 2 \right| \leqslant M, \quad \left| \frac{\xi_1 - \xi_2}{\eta_1} - 2 \right| \leqslant M,$$
$$-\eta_1 + \eta_2 > 0, \quad -2\eta_1 + \eta_2 > 0, \quad \eta_1 > 0,$$
$$\eta_1 \leqslant 1, \quad -\eta_1 \leqslant 1, \quad \eta_2 \leqslant 1, \quad -\eta_2 \leqslant 1,$$

i.e., under the constraints

$$\left.\begin{array}{ll}
\delta_0 = M \geqslant 0, & \\
\delta_1 = 2\xi_2 - (M-10)(-\eta_1+\eta_2) & \leqslant 0, \\
\delta_2 = -\xi_1 - 3\xi_2 - (M+2)(-2\eta_1+\eta_2) & \leqslant 0, \\
\delta_3 = \xi_1 - \xi_2 - (M+2)\,\eta_1 & \leqslant 0, \\
\delta_4 = -2\xi_2 - (M+10)(-\eta_1+\eta_2) & \leqslant 0, \\
\delta_5 = \xi_1 + 3\xi_2 - (M-2)(-2\eta_1+\eta_2) & \leqslant 0, \\
\delta_6 = -\xi_1 + \xi_2 - (M-2)\,\eta_1 & \leqslant 0,
\end{array}\right\} \quad (1)$$

$$\left.\begin{array}{ll}
\delta_7 = \eta_1 - \eta_2 & < 0, \\
\delta_8 = 2\eta_1 - \eta_2 & < 0, \\
\delta_9 = -\eta_1 & < 0, \\
\delta_{10} = \eta_1 - 1 & \leqslant 0, \\
\delta_{11} = -\eta_1 - 1 & \leqslant 0, \\
\delta_{12} = \eta_2 - 1 & \leqslant 0, \\
\delta_{13} = -\eta_2 - 1 & \leqslant 0.
\end{array}\right\} \quad (2^*)$$

---

* Elementary analysis of the constraints shows that δ_7, δ_9, δ_{10}, δ_{11}, and δ_{13}cannot be included in the table, and that the coordinates $\eta_1 > 0$ and $\eta_2 > 0$ cannot be eliminated.

First step. We set

$$M = M_1 = \max_{1 \leqslant i \leqslant 3} |\gamma_i| = 10,$$

substitute in constraints (1) and find a Chebyshev point of the system (1_1) thus obtained with constraints (2). To do so, we must solve the problem of minimizing the function $u = \zeta$ under the constraints

$$\delta_i(x, y, M_1) \leqslant \zeta \qquad (i = 1, \ldots, 6) \quad (\zeta \leqslant 0) \text{ and } (2),$$

i.e., under the constraints

$$\begin{aligned}
\bar{\delta}_1 &= \qquad -2\xi_2 + \zeta \geqslant 0,\\
\bar{\delta}_2 &= \xi_1 + 3\xi_2 - 24\eta_1 + 12\eta_2 + \zeta \geqslant 0,\\
\bar{\delta}_3 &= -\xi_1 + \xi_2 + 12\eta_1 + \zeta \geqslant 0,\\
\bar{\delta}_4 &= 2\xi_2 - 20\eta_1 + 20\eta_2 + \zeta \geqslant 0,\\
\bar{\delta}_5 &= -\xi_1 - 3\xi_2 - 16\eta_1 + 8\eta_2 + \zeta \geqslant 0,\\
\bar{\delta}_6 &= \xi_1 - \xi_2 + 8\eta_1 + \zeta \geqslant 0,\\
\bar{\delta}_7 &= -\eta_1 + \eta_2 \geqslant 0,\\
\bar{\delta}_8 &= -2\eta_1 + \eta_2 \geqslant 0,\\
\bar{\delta}_9 &= \eta_1 \geqslant 0,\\
\bar{\delta}_{10} &= -\eta_1 + 1 \geqslant 0,\\
\bar{\delta}_{11} &= \eta_1 + 1 \geqslant 0,\\
\bar{\delta}_{12} &= -\eta_2 + 1 \geqslant 0,\\
\bar{\delta}_{13} &= \eta_2 + 1 \geqslant 0.
\end{aligned}$$

We construct the table

	$-\xi_1$	$-\xi_2$	$-\eta_1$	$-\eta_2$	$-\zeta$	1
$\bar{\delta}_1 =$	0	2	0	0	−1	0
$\bar{\delta}_2 =$	−1	−3	24	−12	−1	0
$\bar{\delta}_3 =$	1	−1	−12	0	−1	0
$\bar{\delta}_4 =$	0	−2	20	−20	−1	0
$\bar{\delta}_5 =$	1	3	16	−8	−1	0
$\bar{\delta}_6 =$	−1	1	−8	0	−1	0
$\bar{\delta}_7 =$	0	0	1	−1	0	0
$\bar{\delta}_8 =$	0	0	2	−1	0	0
$\bar{\delta}_9 =$	0	0	−1	0	0	0
$\bar{\delta}_{10} =$	0	0	1	0	0	1
$\bar{\delta}_{11} =$	0	0	−1	0	0	1
$\bar{\delta}_{12} =$	0	0	0	1	0	1
$\bar{\delta}_{13} =$	0	0	0	−1	0	1
$u =$	0	0	0	0	−1	0

.

Eliminating the variables ξ_1, ξ_2, η_1, η_2, and ζ, we obtain the expressions

$$\eta_1 = \bar{\delta}_{11} - 1, \quad \eta_2 = -\bar{\delta}_{12} + 1,$$
$$\xi_1 = -\bar{\delta}_3 + \xi_2 + 12\bar{\delta}_{11} + \zeta - 12, \quad \zeta = 2\xi_2 + \bar{\delta}_1,$$
$$\xi_2 = \frac{1}{4}\bar{\delta}_3 + \frac{1}{4}\bar{\delta}_6 - 5\bar{\delta}_{11} - \frac{1}{2}\bar{\delta}_1 + 5$$

for the eliminated variables and the table

	$-\bar{\delta}_3$	$-\bar{\delta}_6$	$-\bar{\delta}_{11}$	$-\bar{\delta}_{12}$	$-\bar{\delta}_1$	1
$\bar{\delta}_2 =$	−1	−2	$\boxed{52}$	12	2	64
$\bar{\delta}_4 =$	−1	−1	40	20	1	60
$\bar{\delta}_5 =$	0	1	8	8	−2	16
$\bar{\delta}_7 =$	0	0	1	1	0	2
$\bar{\delta}_8 =$	0	0	2	1	0	3
$\bar{\delta}_9 =$	0	0	−1	0	0	−1
$\bar{\delta}_{10} =$	0	0	1	0	0	2
$\bar{\delta}_{13} =$	0	0	0	1	0	2
$u =$	$-\frac{1}{2}$	$-\frac{1}{2}$	10	0	0	10

.

To find a basic solution, we execute a modified Jordan elimination over the entry 52, which yields the table

	$-\bar{\delta}_3$	$-\bar{\delta}_6$	$-\bar{\delta}_2$	$-\bar{\delta}_{12}$	$-\bar{\delta}_1$	1
$\bar{\delta}_{11} =$						$\frac{16}{13}$
$\bar{\delta}_4 =$						$\frac{140}{13}$
$\bar{\delta}_5 =$						$\frac{80}{13}$
$\bar{\delta}_7 =$						$\frac{10}{13}$
$\bar{\delta}_8 =$						$\frac{7}{13}$
$\bar{\delta}_9 =$						$\frac{3}{13}$
$\bar{\delta}_{10} =$						$\frac{10}{13}$
$\bar{\delta}_{13} =$						2
$u =$	$-\frac{4}{13}$	$-\frac{3}{26}$	$-\frac{5}{26}$	$-\frac{30}{13}$	$-\frac{5}{13}$	$-\frac{30}{13}$

,

in which all of the coefficients of the u-row are negative, so that

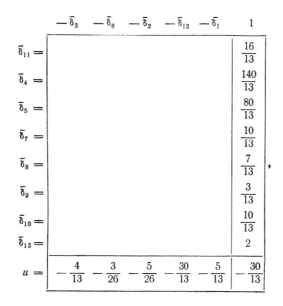

$$\min u = -\frac{30}{13},$$

which is achieved when

$$\bar{\delta}_3 = \bar{\delta}_6 = \bar{\delta}_2 = \bar{\delta}_{12} = \bar{\delta}_1 = 0,$$
$$\bar{\delta}_{11} = \frac{16}{13}, \quad \bar{\delta}_4 = \frac{140}{13}, \quad \bar{\delta}_5 = \frac{80}{13}, \quad \bar{\delta}_7 = \frac{10}{13},$$
$$\bar{\delta}_8 = \frac{7}{13}, \quad \bar{\delta}_9 = \frac{3}{13}, \quad \bar{\delta}_{10} = \frac{10}{13}, \quad \bar{\delta}_{13} = 2,$$

i.e., when

$$\xi_1 = -\frac{9}{13}, \quad \xi_2 = -\frac{15}{13}, \quad \eta_1 = \frac{3}{13}, \quad \eta_2 = 1, \quad \zeta = -\frac{30}{13}.$$

The point

$$[x^{(1)}, y^{(1)}] = \left(\xi_1^{(1)} = -\frac{9}{13}, \ \xi_2^{(1)} = -\frac{15}{13}; \ \eta_1^{(1)} = \frac{3}{13}, \ \eta_2^{(1)} = 1\right)$$

is a Chebyshev point system (1) under constraints (2).

We now compute M_2 — the largest positive value of M less than M_1 and among the values

$$M = \frac{(x^{(1)}, a_i)}{(y^{(1)}, b_i)} - \gamma_i \qquad (i = 1, \ldots, 6).$$

Thus, $M_2 = 7$, which is achieved at $i = 1$.

Second step. We substitute $M = M_2 = 7$ into constraints (1) and find a Chebyshev point of the system (1_2) obtained in this manner with constraints (2). To do so, we solve the problem of minimizing the function

$$u = \zeta$$

under the constraints

$$\begin{aligned}
\bar{\delta}_1 &= - 2\xi_2 + 3\eta_1 - 3\eta_2 + \zeta \geqslant 0,\\
\bar{\delta}_2 &= \xi_1 + 2\xi_2 - 18\eta_1 + 9\eta_2 + \zeta \geqslant 0,\\
\bar{\delta}_3 &= -\xi_1 + \xi_2 + 9\eta_1 + \zeta \geqslant 0,\\
\bar{\delta}_4 &= 2\xi_2 - 17\eta_1 + 17\eta_2 + \zeta \geqslant 0,\\
\bar{\delta}_5 &= -\xi_1 - 3\xi_2 - 10\eta_1 + 5\eta_2 + \zeta \geqslant 0,\\
\bar{\delta}_6 &= \xi_1 - \xi_2 + 5\eta_1 + \zeta \geqslant 0,\\
\bar{\delta}_7 &= -\eta_1 + \eta_2 > 0,\\
\bar{\delta}_8 &= -2\eta_1 + \eta_2 > 0,\\
\bar{\delta}_9 &= \eta_1 > 0,\\
\bar{\delta}_{10} &= -\eta_1 + 1 \geqslant 0,
\end{aligned}$$

$$\begin{aligned} \bar{\delta}_{11} &= \eta_1 + 1 \geqslant 0, \\ \bar{\delta}_{12} &= -\eta_2 + 1 \geqslant 0, \\ \bar{\delta}_{13} &= \eta_2 + 1 \geqslant 0. \end{aligned}$$

The solution of the minimization problem yields the Chebyshev point

$$[x^{(2)}, y^{(2)}] = \left(\xi_1^{(2)} = -\frac{3}{2},\ \xi_2^{(2)} = -\frac{105}{62},\ \eta_1^{(2)} = \frac{3}{31},\ \eta_2^{(2)} = 1\right)$$

and the value

$$M_3 = 6\frac{1}{4}.$$

We should note that

$$\lim_{n\to\infty} M_n = M_0 = 6.$$

5. MINIMIZING THE SUM OF THE ABSOLUTE VALUES OF LINEAR FUNCTIONS

1. Statement of the Problem

Assume that we are again given a system of linear functions

$$\eta_i(x) \equiv a_{i1}x_1 + \ldots + a_{in}x_n + a_i \quad (i = 1, \ldots, m) \tag{5.7}$$

and a system of linear inequalities (constraints)

$$\delta_k(x) \equiv b_{k1}x_1 + \ldots + b_{kn}x_n + b_k \geqslant 0 \quad (k = 1, \ldots, p). \tag{5.8}$$

But, instead of the problem of minimizing the function $u(x) = \max_i |\eta_i(x)|$ under constraints (5.6) (see Paragraph 1, Section 2), we now consider the problem of minimizing the (convex piecewise-linear) function

$$v(x) \equiv \sum_{i=1}^{n} |\eta_i(x)| \tag{5.27}$$

under constraints (5.8). This problem is clearly also a problem on convex piecewise-linear programming, but this one generalizes the problem of finding an approximation $x^*(x_1^*, \ldots, x_n^*)$ of the inconsistent system

$$\eta_i(x) \equiv a_{i1}x_1 + \ldots + a_{in}x_n + a_i = 0 \qquad (i = 1, \ldots, m)$$

by minimizing the sum of the absolute values of all of the deviations:

$$\sum_{i=1}^{n} |\eta_i(x^*)| = \min_x \sum_{i=1}^{n} |\eta_i(x)|.$$

We introduce the auxiliary variables $y_1, \ldots, y_m$, by setting $|\eta_i(x)| \leqslant y_i$ $(i = 1, \ldots, m)$, i.e.,

$$y_i + \eta_i(x) \geqslant 0 \text{ and } y_i - \eta_i(x) \geqslant 0 \quad (i = 1, \ldots, m). \tag{5.28}$$

Now the problem of minimizing (5.27) under constraints (5.28) is equivalent to the following linear programming problem: Minimize the function

$$z = \sum_{i=1}^{m} y_i \tag{5.29}$$

under the constraints

$$\left.\begin{aligned} &\left.\begin{aligned} \gamma_i &\equiv y_i + a_{i1}x_1 + \ldots + a_{in}x_n + a_i \geqslant 0, \\ \gamma_i^* &\equiv y_i - a_{i1}x_1 - \ldots - a_{in}x_n - a_i \geqslant 0 \end{aligned}\right\} \quad (i = 1, \ldots, m), \\ &\delta_k \equiv b_{k1}x_1 + \ldots + b_{kn}x_n + b_k \geqslant 0 \qquad (k = 1, \ldots, p). \end{aligned}\right\} \tag{5.30}$$

Indeed, let $z'' = \min z$ under constraints (5.30) be achieved at the point (x'', y''), and let $v' = \min v$ under constraints (5.8) and be achieved at the point x'.

Clearly, $y_i'' = |\eta_i(x'')|$ $(i = 1, \ldots, m)$, since, by (5.30), $y_i'' \geqslant |\eta_i(x'')|$ $(i = 1, \ldots, m)$ and when equality does not hold, we can decrease the y_1'' for some i when we attempt to find $\min z$.

We have

$$z'' = \sum_{i=1}^{m} y_i'' = \sum_{i=1}^{m} |\eta_i(x'')| \geqslant v'$$

[the point x'', which satisfies constraints (5.30), simultaneously satisfies constraints (5.8)].

We now set $y_i' = |\eta_i(x')|$. Now the point (x', y') satisfies constraints (5.30), so

$$z'' \leqslant \sum_{i=1}^{m} y_1' = \sum_{i=1}^{m} |\eta_i(x')| = v'.$$

Thus, the $z'' = v'$ and x'' of the solution (x'', y'') of problem (5.29)-(5.30) is a solution of problem (5.27)-(5.8), and the point $[x', y' = \eta$

$(x')]$, where x' is a solution of problem (5.27)-(5.8), is also a solution of problem (5.29)-(5.30).

2. Examples

Example 1. Let

$$\begin{aligned} \eta_1(x) &\equiv x_1 + x_2 - 2, \\ \eta_2(x) &\equiv -x_1 + x_3 + 2, \\ \eta_3(x) &\equiv x_1 - 2x_2 + x_3, \\ \eta_4(x) &\equiv -x_2 + x_3 - 2 \end{aligned}$$

and

$$\left.\begin{aligned} \delta_1 &\equiv x_1 - x_3 \geqslant 0, \\ \delta_2 &\equiv x_1 - 4x_2 \geqslant 0, \\ & x_2 \geqslant 0. \end{aligned}\right\} \tag{5.31}$$

It is required to minimize the function

$$v(x) = \sum_{i=1}^{4} |\eta_i(x)|$$

under constraints (5.31).

Setting $|\eta_i(x)| \leqslant y_i$ $(i = 1, 2, 3, 4)$, we obtain the problem of minimizing the function

$$z = y_1 + y_2 + y_3 + y_4$$

under the constraints

$$\begin{aligned} \gamma_1^* &\equiv y_1 - x_1 - x_2 + 2 \geqslant 0, \\ \gamma_2^* &\equiv y_2 + x_1 - x_3 - 2 \geqslant 0, \\ \gamma_3^* &\equiv y_3 - x_1 + 2x_2 - x_3 \geqslant 0, \\ \gamma_4^* &\equiv y_4 + x_2 - x_3 + 2 \geqslant 0, \\ \gamma_1 &\equiv y_1 + x_1 + x_2 - 2 \geqslant 0, \\ \gamma_2 &\equiv y_2 - x_1 + x_3 + 2 \geqslant 0, \\ \gamma_3 &\equiv y_3 + x_1 - 2x_2 + x_3 \geqslant 0, \\ \gamma_4 &\equiv y_4 - x_2 + x_3 - 2 \geqslant 0, \\ \delta_1 &\equiv x_1 - x_3 \geqslant 0, \\ \delta_2 &\equiv x_1 - 4x_2 \geqslant 0, \\ & x_2 \geqslant 0, \end{aligned}$$

which we solve with the simplex method.

The table for the problem is

	$-x_1$	$-x_2$	$-x_3$	$-y_1$	$-y_2$	$-y_3$	$-y_4$	1
$\gamma_1^* =$	1	1	0	−1	0	0	0	2
$\gamma_2^* =$	$\boxed{-1}$	0	1	0	−1	0	0	−2
$\gamma_3^* =$	1	−2	1	0	0	−1	0	0
$\gamma_4^* =$	0	−1	1	0	0	0	−1	2
$\gamma_1 =$	−1	−1	0	−1	0	0	0	−2
$\gamma_2 =$	1	0	−1	0	−1	0	0	2
$\gamma_3 =$	−1	2	−1	0	0	−1	0	0
$\gamma_4 =$	0	1	−1	0	0	0	−1	−2
$\delta_1 =$	−1	0	1	0	0	0	0	0
$\delta_2 =$	−1	4	0	0	0	0	0	0
$z =$	0	0	0	−1	−1	−1	−1	0

After we eliminate x_1 and x_3 we obtain the table

	$-\gamma_2^*$	$-x_2$	$-\gamma_4$	$-y_1$	$-y_2$	$-y_3$	$-y_4$	1
$\gamma_1^* =$	1	2	1	−1	−1	0	−1	−2
$\gamma_3^* =$	1	0	2	0	−1	−1	−2	−6
$\gamma_4^* =$	0	0	1	0	0	0	−2	0
$\gamma_1 =$	−1	−2	−1	−1	1	0	$\boxed{1}$	2
$\gamma_2 =$	1	0	0	0	−2	0	0	0
$\gamma_3 =$	−1	0	−2	0	1	−1	2	6
$\delta_1 =$	−1	0	0	0	1	0	0	2
$\delta_2 =$	−1	3	−1	0	1	0	1	4
$z =$	0	0	0	−1	−1	−1	−1	0

and the following expressions for x_1 and x_2:

$$x_1 = \gamma_2^* + x_3 - y_2 + 2, \quad x_3 = x_2 + \gamma_4 - y_4 + 2.$$

We first find a basic solution, and then an optimal solution:

	$-\gamma_2^*$	$-x_2$	$-\gamma_4$	$-y_1$	$-y_2$	$-y_3$	$-\gamma_1$	1
$\gamma_1^* =$	0	0	0	−2	0	0	1	0
$\gamma_3^* =$	−1	−4	0	−2	1	$\boxed{-1}$	2	−2
$\gamma_4^* =$	−2	−4	−1	−2	2	0	2	4
$y_4 =$	−1	−2	−1	−1	1	0	1	2
$\gamma_2 =$	1	0	0	0	−2	0	0	0
$\gamma_3 =$	1	4	0	2	−1	−1	−2	2
$\delta_1 =$	−1	0	0	0	1	0	0	2
$\delta_2 =$	0	5	0	1	0	0	−1	2
$z =$	−1	−2	−1	−2	0	−1	1	2

→

	$-\gamma_2^*$	$-x_2$	$-\gamma_4$	$-y_1$	$-y_2$	$-\gamma_3^*$	$-\gamma_1$	1
$\gamma_1^* =$	0	0	0	−2	0	0	1	0
$y_3^* =$	1	4	0	2	−1	−1	−2	2
$\gamma_4^* =$	−2	−4	−1	−2	2	0	2	4
$y_4 =$	−1	−2	−1	−1	1	0	1	2
→ $\gamma_2 =$	1	0	0	0	−2	0	0	0 →
$\gamma_3 =$	2	8	0	4	−2	−1	−4	4
$\delta_1 =$	−1	0	0	0	1	0	0	2
$\delta_2 =$	0	5	0	1	0	0	−1	2
$z =$	0	2	−1	0	−1	−1	−1	4

	$-\gamma_2^*$	$-\delta_2$	$-\gamma_4$	$-y_1$	$-y_2$	$-\gamma_3^*$	$-\gamma_1$	1
$\gamma_1^* =$								0
$y_3 =$								$\frac{2}{5}$
$\gamma_4^* =$								$\frac{28}{5}$
$y_4 =$								$\frac{14}{5}$
→ $\gamma_2 =$								0
$\gamma_3 =$								$\frac{4}{5}$
$\delta_1 =$								2
$x_2 =$								$\frac{2}{5}$
$z =$	0	$-\frac{2}{5}$	−1	$-\frac{2}{5}$	−1	−1	$-\frac{3}{5}$	$\frac{16}{5}$

It follows from the last table that

$$\min z = \frac{16}{5};$$

this minimum is achieved at

$$x_2^* = \frac{2}{5},\ x_3^* = \frac{2}{5} - \frac{14}{5} + 2 = -\frac{2}{5},\ x_1^* = -\frac{2}{5} + 2 = \frac{8}{5}.$$

Example 2. Find an approximation of the inconsistent system

$$\begin{aligned} \eta_1(x) &\equiv x_1 - x_2 - 1 = 0, \\ \eta_2(x) &\equiv 2x_1 + x_2 - 2 = 0, \\ \eta_3(x) &\equiv x_1 - 2x_2 + 1 = 0, \end{aligned}$$

that will minimize the sum

$$v(x) = |\eta_1(x)| + |\eta_2(x)| + |\eta_3(x)|.$$

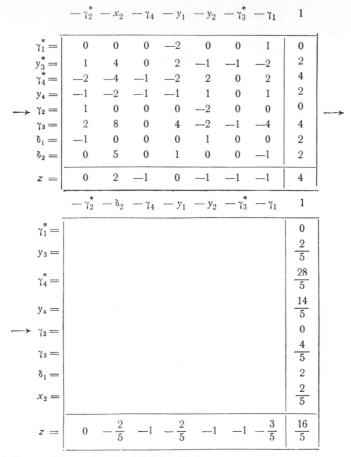

The problem under consideration reduces to the problem of minimizing the function

$$z = y_1 + y_2 + y_3$$

under the constraints

$$\eta_i(x) \leqslant y_i \qquad (i = 1, 2, 3),$$

i.e., under the constraints

$$\begin{aligned}
\gamma_1^* &\equiv y_1 - x_1 + x_2 + 1 \geqslant 0,\\
\gamma_2^* &\equiv y_2 - 2x_1 - x_2 + 2 \geqslant 0,\\
\gamma_3^* &\equiv y_3 - x_1 + 2x_2 - 1 \geqslant 0,\\
\gamma_1 &\equiv y_1 + x_1 - x_2 - 1 \geqslant 0,\\
\gamma_2 &\equiv y_2 + 2x_1 + x_2 - 2 \geqslant 0,\\
\gamma_3 &\equiv y_3 + x_1 - 2x_2 + 1 \geqslant 0.
\end{aligned}$$

Constructing the table for the problem and eliminating x_1 and x_2, we obtain the table

	$-\gamma_1$	$-\gamma_3^*$	$-y_1$	$-y_2$	$-y_3$	1
$\gamma_1^* =$	1	0	—2	0	0	0
$\gamma_2^* =$	5	3	|—5|	—1	—3	—6
$\gamma_2 =$	—5	—3	5	—1	3	6
$\gamma_3 =$	0	1	0	0	—2	0
$z =$	0	0	—1	—1	—1	0

and the following expressions for x_1 and x_2:

$$\begin{aligned}
x_1 &= \gamma_1 + x_2 - y_1 + 1,\\
x_2 &= \gamma_1 + \gamma_3^* - y_1 - y_3 + 2.
\end{aligned}$$

We now seek a basic solution:

	$-\gamma_1$	$-\gamma_3^*$	$-\gamma_2^*$	$-y_2$	$-y_3$	1
$\gamma_1^* =$						$\frac{12}{5}$
$y_1 =$						$\frac{6}{5}$
$\gamma_2 =$						0
$\gamma_3 =$						0
$z =$	—1	$-\frac{3}{5}$	$-\frac{1}{5}$	$-\frac{4}{5}$	$-\frac{2}{5}$	$\frac{6}{5}$

.

It is clear from the tables that the basic solution we have obtained is optimal, i.e.,

$$\min z = \frac{6}{5},$$

and is achieved after

$$\gamma_1 = \gamma_3^* = \gamma_2^* = y_2 = y_3 = \gamma_2 = \gamma_3 = 0, \quad \gamma_1^* = \frac{12}{5}, \quad y_1 = \frac{6}{5},$$

i.e., when

$$x_2 = \frac{4}{5}, \quad x_1 = \frac{3}{5}.$$

6

Convex Programming

The present chapter considers the general problem of convex programming, i.e., the problem of minimizing a nonlinear smooth convex function under constraints given by nonlinear inequalities defining a convex set in the space of variables.

An important example of the convex programming problem is the problem of complex Chebyshev approximation, particularly the problem of Chebyshev approximation for inconsistent systems of linear complex equations, both in the absence and the presence of constraints that define some convex set in the space of variables.

It turns out that this type of nonlinear problem can, when the minimized function and the constraints are smooth and convex, be solved by methods of steepest descent.

In Section 2 we present a convergent monotonic algorithm for solution of the general convex programming problems; this algorithm is also convenient for numerical computation.

In Section 3 this algorithm is applied to the solution of the Chebyshev approximation problem for an inconsistent system of linear complex equations.

In Section 4 we present an algorithm for finding points with minimal deviation from a system of points (on a plane) or a system of lines (in higher-dimensional spaces).

Section 5 is devoted to the quadratic programming problem, which we solve with the algorithm of Section 2; we also present another finite algorithm [5a].

Finally, in Section 6 the algorithm of Section 2 is applied to the general linear programming problem.

1. THE GENERAL CONVEX PROGRAMMING PROBLEM

1. Statement of the Problem and Nature of the Minimum

Assume that we are given a convex* smooth** function

$$f(x) \equiv f(x_1, \ldots, x_n) \qquad (6.1)$$

and a convex region Ω defined by the inequalities

$$\varphi_j(x) \equiv \varphi_j(x_1, \ldots, x_n) \leqslant 0 \qquad (j = 1, \ldots, q), \qquad (6.2)$$

where the $\varphi_j(x)$ are convex smooth functions and Ω contains x as an interior point, i.e., there exist points at which

$$\varphi_j(x) < 0 \qquad (j = 1, \ldots, q).$$

The convex programming problem consists in minimizing the function (6.1) under constraints (6.2), i.e., in finding, among the points of Ω, a point x^* for which

$$f(x^*) = \min_{x \in \Omega} f(x). \qquad (6.3)$$

We show that in convex programming problems a local minimum coincides with the absolute minimum, i.e., with the smallest value of the minimized function in Ω.

Indeed, assume that the function $f(x)$ has a local minimum $f(x^{(1)})$ at the point $x^{(1)}$, i.e.,

$$f(x^{(1)}) \leqslant f(x)$$

in some neighborhood $U(x^{(1)}) \subset \Omega$ and assume that

$$f(x^{(2)}) < f(x^{(1)})$$

at some point $x^{(2)} \in \Omega$. Now, consider the segment

$$x = (1 - t)\, x^{(1)} + t x^{(2)} \qquad (0 \leqslant t \leqslant 1).$$

Because β is convex, this segment is completely contained in Ω and it contains a point

$$x^{(0)} = (1 - t_0)\, x^{(1)} + t_0 x^{(2)} \in U(x^{(1)})$$

---

*A function $f(x)$ is said to be convex if

$$f[\lambda x' + (1 - \lambda)\, x''] \leqslant \lambda f(x') + (1 - \lambda)\, f(x'') \quad (0 \leqslant \lambda \leqslant 1)$$

for all x' and x''.

** A function is said to be smooth if its first derivatives are continuous.

that does not coincide with $x^{(1)}$. Because $f(x)$ is convex,

$$f(x^{(0)}) \leqslant (1-t_0) f(x^{(1)}) + t_0 f(x^{(2)}) =$$

$$= f(x^{(1)}) + t_0 [f(x^{(2)}) - f(x^{(1)})] < f(x^{(1)}),$$

which contradicts the assumption that $f(x^{(1)}) \leqslant f(x)$ in the neighborhood $U(x^{(1)})$. As a result $f(x^{(1)}) \leqslant f(x)$ at all points $x \in \Omega$.

Remark. When convexity is not present, local minima are encountered. These considerably complicate the problem, since descent methods sometimes lead to local minima and not necessarily to the desired absolute minimum.

2. Examples of Convex Programming Problems

Below we present four important concrete convex programming problems.

a) *Complex Chebyshev approximation.* Assume that it is required to find a Chebyshev approximation to some complex-valued continuous function $f(t)$ on a compact set Q and that the approximation is to be a polynomial

$$z_1 f_1(t) + \ldots + z_n f_n(t) \qquad (z_k = x_k + i y_k, \quad k = 1, \ldots, n),$$

where $f_1(t), \ldots, f_n(t)$ is a fixed set of continuous complex-valued linearly independent functions. Moreover, assume that the coefficients of the approximating polynomial satisfy certain constraints

$$\psi_j(z_1, \ldots, z_n) \leqslant c_j \qquad (j = 1, \ldots, q), \tag{6.4}$$

where the $\psi_j(z_1, \ldots, z_n)$ are real, smooth convex functions, so that (6.4) defines a convex set Ω in the $2n$-dimensional space of variables $x_1, \ldots, x_n, y_1, \ldots, y_n$. The constraints may be given, for example, in the form

$$\left| \sum_{k=1}^{n} \beta_{jk} z_k \right| \leqslant c_j \qquad (j = 1, \ldots, q).$$

By Chebyshev approximation of the function $f(t)$ in terms of the polynomial $z_1 f_1(t) + \ldots + z_n f_n(t)$ we mean finding, among the points $z(z_1, \ldots, z_n)$, satisfying (6.4), a point $z^*(z_1^*, \ldots, z_n)$, which is called a Chebyshev point, and for which

$$\max_{t \in Q} \left| \sum_{k=1}^{n} z_k^* f_k(t) - f(t) \right| = \inf_{z \in \Omega} \max_{t \in Q} \left| \sum_{k=1}^{n} z_k f_k(t) - f(t) \right|.$$

Since the function

$$F(z) = F(x_1, \ldots, x_n; y_1, \ldots, y_n) = \max_{t \in Q} \left| \sum_{k=1}^{n} z_k f_k(t) - f(t) \right|$$

is convex (as we can easily verify), the complex Chebyshev approximation problem under discussion is a convex programming problem.

Because the functions $f(t)$ and $f_1(t), \ldots, f_n(t)$ are continuous, we can obtain an approximate solution of the problem by solving it on an ε-grid $\{t_1, t_2, \ldots, t_m\}$ of the compact set Q, and the approximation improves as $\varepsilon > 0$ gets smaller.

If we write

$$f_k(t_\nu) = \alpha_{\nu k} = a_{\nu k} + ib_{\nu k}, \quad f(t_\nu) = \alpha_\nu$$
$$(\nu = 1, \ldots, m; \; k = 1, \ldots, n),$$

we obtain the following complex Chebyshev approximation problem:

For an inconsistent system of m linear complex equations

$$\Delta_\nu(z) \equiv \alpha_{\nu 1} z_1 + \ldots + \alpha_{\nu n} z_n + \alpha_\nu = 0 \quad (\nu = 1, \ldots, m) \tag{6.5}$$

and a system of inequalities (6.4), find Chebyshev approximation systems (6.5) under constraints (6.4), i.e., find a point $z^* \in \Omega$, for which

$$\max_\nu |\Delta_\nu(z^*)| = \min_{z \in \Omega} \max_\nu |\Delta_\nu(z)|. \tag{6.6}$$

We again note that $\max\limits_\nu |\Delta_\nu(z)|$ is a convex function, so that we can conclude that problem (6.4) - (6.6) is a convex programming problem.

b) *Points closest to a system of planes.* In n-dimensional Euclidean space, assume that we are given a system of m k-dimensional planes α_i defined by the systems

$$\alpha_i : \begin{cases} a_{11}^{(i)} x_1 + \ldots + a_{1n}^{(i)} x_n \quad + a_1^{(i)} = 0, \\ \cdots\cdots\cdots\cdots\cdots\cdots \\ a_{n-k,1}^{(i)} x_1 + \ldots + a_{n-k,n}^{(i)} x_n + a_{n-k}^{(i)} = 0 \end{cases} \tag{6.7}$$
$$(i = 1, \ldots, m),$$

and the individual hyperplanes in each system are mutually orthogonal and written in normal form. The quantity

$$\rho(x', \alpha_i) = \sqrt{\left(\sum_{j=1}^n a_{1j}^{(i)} x'_j + a_1^{(i)}\right)^2 + \ldots + \left(\sum_{j=1}^n a_{n-k,j}^{(i)} x'_j + a_{n-k}^{(i)}\right)^2}$$

is the distance from the point $x' \equiv (x'_1, \ldots, x'_n)$ to the plane α_i.

Consider the problem of finding the point with least distance from a system (6.7) of k-dimensional planes α_i, i.e., a point x^*, for which

$$\max_{1 \leqslant i \leqslant m} \rho(x^*, \alpha_i) = \inf_x \max_{1 \leqslant i \leqslant m} \rho(x, \alpha_i). \tag{6.8}$$

It is easy to show that the function

$$f(x) = \max_i \rho(x, \alpha_i)$$

is convex, so that problem (6.7)-(6.8) is also a convex programming problem.

When $k = n - 1$, the planes α_i become hyperplanes in the n-dimensional space under discussion and (6.7) consists of a single equation. In this case problem (6.7)-(6.8) degenerates into the problem of finding a point least distant from a given system of m hyperplanes in n-dimensional space, i.e., in the classical Chebyshev approximation problem for an inconsistent system of linear equations. This problem was considered in Section 1 of Chapter 5.

When $k = 0$, the plane α_i degenerates into a point in n-dimensional space. As a result, here problem (6.7)-(6.8) degenerates into the problem of finding a point with a minimal distance from the given system of points [4c].

c) *Convex Chebyshev approximation.* Problems a) and b) are special cases of the following convex Chebyshev approximation problem.

Assume that we are given a system of p convex smooth functions

$$f_i(x) \equiv f_i(x_1, \ldots, x_n) \qquad (i = 1, \ldots, p) \tag{6.9}$$

and a region Ω defined by q inequalities

$$\varphi_j(x) \equiv \varphi_j(x_1, \ldots, x_n) \leqslant 0 \qquad (j = 1, \ldots, q), \tag{6.10}$$

where $\varphi_1(x), \ldots, \varphi_q(x)$ are also convex smooth functions.

The convex Chebyshev approximation problem for system (6.9) under constraints (6.10) consists in finding a point $x^* \in \Omega$ for which

$$\max_i f_i(x^*) = \min_{x \in \Omega} \max_i f_i(x). \tag{6.11}$$

Since the function $\max_i f_i(x)$ is convex, the convex Chebyshev approximation problem is also a convex programming problem.

d) *Steiner's problem.* Assume that in n-dimensional Euclidean space we are given a system of m points $P_i(x_1^{(i)}, \ldots, x_n^{(i)})$ $(i = 1, 2, \ldots, m)$ and some convex set Ω. By Steiner's problem we mean the problem of finding a point P^* in Ω the sum of whose distances to all the points of the system is minimal:

$$\sum_{i=1}^{m} \rho(P^*, P_i) = \min_{P \in \Omega} \sum_{i=1}^{m} \rho(P, P_i).$$

Since the function

$$\rho(P, P_i) = \sqrt{\sum_{k=1}^{n} (x_k - x_k^{(i)})^2}$$

is convex and the sum of convex functions is also convex, Steiner's problem is a convex programming problem.

3. A Canonical Form for the General Problem

In the general convex programming problem (6.1) - (6.3) we introduce auxiliary variable x_{n+1} and the auxiliary constraints

$$f(x_1, \ldots, x_n) \leqslant x_{n+1}.$$

Now, as we can easily see, (see, for example, Paragraph 2, Section 1, Chapter 5), this problem is equivalent to the following problem: Minimize the linear form

$$z = x_{n+1}$$

under the constraints

$$f(x_1, \ldots, x_n) - x_{n+1} \leqslant 0,$$
$$\varphi_j(x_1, \ldots, x_n) \leqslant 0 \quad (j = 1, \ldots, q),$$

or, in more convenient notation minimize the linear form

$$z = p_1 x_1 + \ldots + p_n x_n \tag{6.12}$$

under the constraints

$$\psi_j(x_1, \ldots, x_n) \leqslant 0 \quad (j = 1, \ldots, q)^*. \tag{6.13}$$

We shall call the latter problem the canonical form of the general convex programming problem.

2. SOLUTION OF THE CONVEX PROGRAMMING PROBLEM

1. Fundamental Form of the Algorithm

a) *General description.* The algorithm consists of a preliminary step and an iterated step. The preliminary step consists in finding some point $x^0 \in \Omega$.

The iterated step consists of the following operations:

1) Determination of the direction $\zeta^{(k)} \equiv (\zeta_1^{(k)}, \ldots, \zeta_n^{(k)})$ of the fastest decrease of the function $z(x)$ at the point (approximation) $x^{(k-1)} (k = 1, 2, \ldots)$.

2) Computation of a new value for the parameter δ.

---

* The functions $\psi_j(x_1, \ldots, x_n)$ are smooth and convex but not necessarily strictly convex.

3) Computation of the number $t_k > 0$, characterizing the length of admissible travel from $x^{(k-1)}$ along $\zeta^{(k)}$.

4) Determination of a new approximation $x^{(k)}$ and new deviations.

b) *Preliminary step.* The initial approximation $x^{(0)}$ can be found, for example, by applying the convergent algorithm of Paragraph 3 to the following problem.

Minimize the linear form

$$u = \xi \tag{6.14}$$

under the constraints

$$\psi_j(x_1, \ldots, x_n) \leqslant \xi \qquad (j = 1, \ldots, q), \tag{6.15}$$

that define a region Ω'.

Since, by hypothesis, Ω contains an interior point,

$$\min_{(x, \xi) \in \Omega'} u < 0.$$

Thus, to obtain a preliminary approximation, we need not find min u under constraints (6.15); it is sufficient, beginning with an arbitrary point x', to execute only the iterated steps discussed below until we are led to a point $x^{(0)}$ such that the corresponding $u = \xi_0 \leqslant 0$.

c) *Iterated step.* Assume that an initial approximation $x^{(0)} \in \Omega$ has been found. Without loss of generality, we can assume that $x^{(0)}$ lies on the boundary of Ω, since otherwise it is sufficient to move from the point $x^{(0)}$ in the direction $\zeta = (-p_1, \ldots, -p_n)$, i.e., to increase t in the formula

$$x = x^{(0)} + t\zeta$$

until the boundary of Ω is reached. This reduces to finding the smallest positive root of the equations

$$\psi_j(x^{(0)} + t\zeta) = 0 \qquad (j = 1, \ldots, q),$$

say, with Newton's method.

To eliminate so-called 'jamming' (see [5b, 5c, 36]) and to establish a limit for the admissable computational error in each step, we establish a corresponding value of some positive parameter δ_k (k is the number of the iteration) for each step in our algorithm, beginning with some arbitrary, sufficiently small $\delta_1 > 0$ in the first iteration (after the preliminary step).

We assume that the point $x^{(0)}$ belongs to the surface $\psi_{j_0}(x) = 0$ if

$$-\delta_1 < \psi_{j_0}(x^{(0)}) \leqslant 0,$$

i.e., if the deviation of the point $x^{(0)}$ from the surface is nonpositive and larger that $-\delta_1$.

Let, for example,

$$-\delta_1 < \psi_{j_\nu}(x^{(0)}) \leqslant 0 \qquad (\nu = 1, \ldots, \nu_1),$$
$$\psi_j(x^{(0)}) \leqslant -\delta_1 \qquad (j \neq j_1, \ldots, j_{\nu_1}).$$

1) *Determination of the descent direction.* We determine the direction of descent $\zeta^{(1)} \equiv (\zeta_1^{(1)}, \ldots, \zeta_n^{(1)})$ from the point $x^{(0)}$, first from the requirement that the function

$$z(x) = p_1 x_1 + \ldots + p_n x_n$$

decrease in this direction, i.e., that

$$\frac{\partial z}{\partial \zeta} = p_1\zeta_1 + \ldots + p_n\zeta_n < 0, \tag{6.16}$$

and second from the condition that this direction lead strictly inside Ω, i.e., that all the functions $\psi_{j_\nu}(x)$, decrease in this direction, i.e., that all the inequalities

$$\frac{\partial \psi_{j_\nu}(x^{(0)})}{\partial \zeta} = \sum_{k=1}^{n} \frac{\partial \psi_{j_\nu}(x^{(0)})}{\partial x_k}\zeta_k < 0 \qquad (\nu = 1, 2, \ldots, \nu_1) \tag{6.17}$$

be satisfied.

The quantities

$$\frac{\partial z}{\partial \zeta} = \sum_{k=1}^{n} p_k\zeta_k \text{ and } \frac{\partial \psi_{j_\nu}(x^{(0)})}{\partial \zeta} = \sum_{k=1}^{n} \frac{\partial \psi_{j_\nu}(x^{(0)})}{\partial x_k}\zeta_k \qquad (\nu = 1, \ldots, \nu_1)$$

are the rates with which the functions $z(x)$ and $\psi_{j_\nu}(x)$ $(\nu = 1, \ldots, \nu_1)$ decrease in the direction $\zeta \equiv (\zeta_1, \ldots, \zeta_n)$.

To bring about steepest descent inside Ω, the smallest (in absolute value) of the quantities

$$\sum_{k=1}^{n} p_k\zeta_k, \quad \sum_{k=1}^{n} \frac{\partial \psi_{j_1}(x^{(0)})}{\partial x_k}\zeta_k, \ \ldots, \ \sum_{k=1}^{n} \frac{\partial \psi_{j_{\nu_1}}(x^{(0)})}{\partial x_k}\zeta_k, \tag{6.18}$$

must be maximal, i.e., the minimal absolute rate of decrease for the indicated functions must be maximal. Because these quantities are negative, the largest of the quantities (6.18) must be minimal.

In other words, the direction $\zeta^{(1)}$ must be the Chebyshev direction, i.e., must be a "Chebyshev point" of the system of linear inequalities

$$\sum_{k=1}^{n} p_k\zeta_k < 0,$$
$$\sum_{k=1}^{n} \frac{\partial \psi_{j_\nu}(x^{(0)})}{\partial x_k}\zeta_k < 0 \qquad (\nu = 1, 2, \ldots, \nu_1).$$

We now introduce one more auxiliary variable η as in Paragraph 2, Section 3, Chapter 5, and thus reduce the problem of determining the direction $\zeta^{(1)}$ to solution of the following linear programming problem:

Minimize the form

$$u = \eta$$

under the constraints

$$\sum_{k=1}^{n} p_k \zeta_k \leqslant \eta, \quad \sum_{k=1}^{n} \frac{\partial \psi_{j_\nu}(x^{(0)})}{\partial x_k} \zeta_k \leqslant \eta \qquad (\nu = 1, 2, \ldots, \nu_1).$$

The region D defined by these linear homogenous inequalities is not bounded, so the vector ζ must be normalized, e.g., by setting

$$|\zeta_1| \leqslant C, \ldots, |\zeta_n| \leqslant C.$$

Thus, determination of the direction of steepest descent $\zeta^{(1)}$ from the point $x^{(0)}$ reduces to the solution of the following linear programming problem:

Minimize the form

$$u = \eta \tag{6.19}$$

under the constraints

$$\left.\begin{array}{l} \sum_{k=1}^{n} p_k \zeta_k \leqslant \eta, \quad \sum_{k=1}^{n} \frac{\partial \psi_{j_\nu}(x^{(0)})}{\partial x_k} \zeta_k \leqslant \eta \quad (\nu = 1, 2, \ldots, \nu_1), \\ |\zeta_k| \leqslant C \quad (k = 1, \ldots, n). \end{array}\right\} \tag{6.20}$$

We will denote min u in constraints (6.20) by η.

2) *Computation of a new* δ. There are two cases: $\alpha)\ \eta_1 < -\delta_1$, $\beta)\ \eta_1 \geqslant -\delta_1$. In case α) we do not change the value of δ, i.e., we set

$$\delta_2 = \delta_1.$$

In case β) we change δ. If $-\delta_1 \leqslant \eta_1 < 0$, we set $\delta_2 = \frac{\delta_1}{2}$ and continue the process by moving in the direction $\zeta^{(1)}$ from the point $x^{(0)}$.

If, however, $\eta_1 = 0$ and

$$\psi_{j_\mu}(x^{(0)}) = 0 \ (\mu = 1, \ldots, \mu_1), \quad \psi_j(x^{(0)}) < 0 \ (j \neq j_1, \ldots, j_{\mu_1}),$$

we solve the following linear programming problem:

Minimize the form

$$u = \eta \tag{6.21}$$

under the constraints

$$\left.\begin{array}{l}\sum_{i=1}^{n} p_i\zeta_i \leqslant \eta, \quad \sum_{i=1}^{n} \frac{\partial\psi_{j_\mu}(x^{(0)})}{\partial x_i}\zeta_i \leqslant \eta \quad (\mu = 1, \ldots, \mu_1), \\ |\zeta_i| \leqslant C \quad (i = 1, \ldots, n).\end{array}\right\} \tag{6.22}$$

Here, if

$$\min u = \eta_1' = 0,$$

$x^{(0)}$ is a solution; if, however,

$$\min u = \eta_1' < 0,$$

we set $\delta_2 = \frac{\delta_1}{2}$ and continue the process by moving in the direction ζ, which is a solution of the linear programming problem (6.21)-(6.22) under discussion.

3) *Computation of the step* t_1. Assume that the direction $\zeta^{(1)}$ and the parameter δ_2 have been determined. Now we must move from the point $x^{(0)}$ in the direction $\zeta^{(1)}$, i.e., we must increase t in the formula

$$x = x^{(0)} + t\zeta^{(1)}$$

until the smallest of the positive roots of the equation

$$\psi_j(x^{(0)} + t\zeta^{(1)}) = 0 \qquad (j = 1, \ldots, q) \tag{6.23}$$

is reached. We will call t_1 the approximation step.

4) *Determination of a new point (approximation)* $x^{(1)}$ *and new deviations.* For the first approximation we take the point

$$x^{(1)} = x^{(0)} + t_1\zeta^{(1)},$$

and we now compute new deviations $\psi_j(x^{(1)}) (j = 1, \ldots, q)$.

The process now proceeds by taking $x^{(1)}$ for the initial point, and δ_2 for the value of the parameter; as above, we determine the direction $\zeta^{(2)}$, compute δ_3 and t_2, a new approximation $x^{(2)} = x^{(1)} + t_2\zeta^{(2)}$, and new deviations $\psi_j(x^{(2)}) (j = 1, \ldots, q)$, etc.

5) *Criteria for solution of the problem and estimation of the approximations.* Assume that we have obtained an approximation $x^{(k-1)}$, and, when the direction $\zeta^{(k)}$ of descent from the point $x^{(k-1)}$ is determined, assume that

$$\min u = \eta_k = 0.$$

Moreover, assume that in the linear programming problem (6.21)-(6.22)

$$\min u = \eta_k' = 0.$$

Then the approximation $x^{(k-1)}$ is a solution of problem of (6.12)-(6.13) and the process terminates.

Indeed, it does not follow from the fact that $\eta_k = 0$, i.e., from the fact that there is no direction of descent from the point $x^{(k-1)}$, that the point $x^{(k-1)}$ is a solution. The fact is that there may be no direction of descent because δ_k is too small, and η_k is equal to zero because one or more surfaces do not actually contain $x^{(k-1)}$, but are closer than δ_k to it, as a result of which they figure in (6.19)-(6.20).

If, in addition to $\eta_k = 0$, we have $\eta_k' = 0$, the absence of a direction of descent may be due only to the fact that $x^{(k-1)}$ is a solution, since only the surfaces containing $x^{(k-1)}$ take part in problem (6.21)-(6.22).

We now consider the problem of estimating the closeness of the $z^{(k)}$ obtained in each step to the value $z^* = \min_{x \in \Omega} z$ [36].

The equation of the plane tangent to the surface $y = \psi_j(x)$ $(j = 1, \ldots, q)$ at the point $x = x^{(k)}$ is of the form

$$Y - \psi_j(x^{(k)}) = \sum_{i=1}^{n} \frac{\partial \psi_j(x^{(k)})}{\partial x_i}(x_i - x_i^{(k)}).$$

Because $\psi_j(x)$ is convex, we have

$$\psi_j(x) \geqslant Y.$$

Substituting into the preceding equation, we obtain the inequality

$$\sum_{i=1}^{n} \frac{\partial \psi_j(x^{(k)})}{\partial x_i}(x_i - x_i^{(k)}) \leqslant \psi_j(x) - \psi_j(x^{(k)}),$$

which, for any point, $x \in \Omega$ $(\psi_j(x) \leqslant 0)$, becomes

$$\sum_{i=1}^{n} \frac{\partial \psi_j(x^{(k)})}{\partial x_i}(x_i - x_i^{(k)}) + \psi_j(x^{(k)}) \leqslant 0 \quad (j = 1, \ldots, q).$$

This shows that the region Ω is a proper subset of the polyhedron Ω_1 defined by the last set of inequalities.

Since $\Omega \subset \Omega_1$, we have the following inequality:

$$\min_{x \in \Omega_1}(z - z^{(k)}) \leqslant \min_{x \in \Omega}(z - z^{(k)}) \leqslant 0.$$

This means that

$$\left|\min_{x \in \Omega}(z - z^{(k)})\right| \leqslant \left|\min_{x \in \Omega_1}(z - z^{(k)})\right|.$$

Thus, to obtain an upper bound for the closeness of $z^{(k)}$ to $z^* = \min_{x \in \Omega} z$, it suffices to solve the following linear programming problems:

Minimize the function

$$z' = p_1 x_1 + \ldots + p_n x_n - z^{(k)}$$

under the constraints

$$\sum_{i=1}^{n} \frac{\partial \psi_j(x^{(k)})}{\partial x_i} (x_i - x_i^{(k)}) + \psi_j(x^{(k)}) \leqslant 0 \quad (j = 1, \ldots, q).$$

D) *Example.* Minimize the form

$$z = x_3$$

under the constraints

$$\begin{aligned} \psi_1(x) \equiv \psi_1(x_1, x_2, x_3) &= x_1^2 + 2x_1x_2 + \\ &\quad + 2x_2^2 - 2x_1 - x_2 - x_3 - 2 \leqslant 0, \\ \psi_2(x) \equiv \psi_2(x_1, x_2, x_3) &= x_1^2 + x_2^2 - x_1 + x_2 - x_3 - 3 \leqslant 0, \\ \psi_3(x) \equiv \psi_3(x_1, x_2, x_3) &= x_1^2 + x_1 - 4x_2 - x_3 + 3 \leqslant 0. \end{aligned}$$

For the initial approximation we can take the point $x^{(0)} = (1. - 1.9)$, since

$$\psi_1(x^{(0)}) = -11, \quad \psi_2(x^{(0)}) = -12, \quad \psi_3(x^{(0)}) = 0.$$

If we set

$$\delta_1 = 0.5,$$

we find that

$$\psi_1(x^{(0)}) = -11 < -\delta_1, \quad \psi_2(x^{(0)}) = -12 < -\delta_1,$$
$$-\delta_1 < \psi_3(x^{(0)}) = 0.$$

First step. 1) Determination of $\zeta^{(1)}$.

$$\frac{\partial z}{\partial \zeta} = \zeta_3, \quad \frac{\partial \psi_3(x^{(0)})}{\partial \zeta} = 3\zeta_1 - 4\zeta_2 - \zeta_3.$$

To find the direction $\zeta^{(1)} \equiv (\zeta_1^{(1)}, \zeta_2^{(1)}, \zeta_3^{(1)})$, we must solve the following linear programming problem:

Minimize the form

$$u = \eta$$

under the constraints

$$\zeta_3-\eta\leqslant 0,\quad 3\zeta_1-4\zeta_2-\zeta_3-\eta\leqslant 0,$$
$$\zeta_1-1\leqslant 0,\quad -\zeta_1-1\leqslant 0,\quad \zeta_2-1\leqslant 0,\quad -\zeta_2-1\leqslant 0.$$

We should note that the constraint $|\zeta_3|\leqslant 1$ is superfluous, because the variable ζ_3 is, in view of the first two inequalities, obviously bounded.

Solving this problem, we find that

$$\zeta_1^{(1)}=-1;\quad \zeta_2^{(1)}=1;\quad \zeta_3^{(1)}=-3.5.$$

2) Computation of δ_2. We have $\eta_1=-3.5<-\delta_1$, so that

$$\delta_2=\delta_1=0.5.$$

3) Determination of t_1. The motion must be along the ray

$$x_1=1-t;\quad x_2=-1+t;\quad x_3=9-3.5t;\quad t>0.$$

The smallest positive root of the equations

$$\psi_1(x^{(0)}+t\zeta^{(1)})=0;\quad \psi_2(x^{(0)}+t\zeta^{(1)})=0;\quad \psi_3(x^{(0)}+t\zeta^{(1)})=0$$

is $t_1=2.1$.

4) Determination of a new point and new deviations. The new approximation $x^{(1)}$ is given by the formula

$$x^{(1)}=x^{(0)}+t_1\zeta^{(1)}=(-1.1;\ 1.1;\ 1.65),$$

and for the new deviations we have

$$\psi_1(x^{(1)})=-1.34<-\delta_2;\quad -\delta_2<\psi_2(x^{(1)})=0;$$
$$\psi_3(x^{(1)})=-2.94<-\delta_2.$$

Second step. 1) Determination of $\zeta^{(2)}$.

$$\frac{\partial z}{\partial\zeta}=\zeta_3;\quad \frac{\partial\psi_2}{\partial\zeta}=-3.2\zeta_1+3.2\zeta_2-\zeta_3.$$

To find the direction of descent, we solve the following linear programming problem:

Minimize the form

$$u=\eta$$

under the constraints

$$\zeta_3-\eta\leqslant 0;\quad -3.2\zeta_1+3.2\zeta_2-\zeta_3-\eta\leqslant 0;$$
$$|\zeta_i|\leqslant 1\quad (i=1,\ 2).$$

Solving this problem, we find that

$$\zeta_1^{(2)} = 1; \quad \zeta_2^{(2)} = -1; \quad \zeta_3^{(2)} = -3.2.$$

2) Determination of δ_3. We have $\eta_2 = -3.2 < -\delta_3$. Thus,

$$\delta_3 = \delta_2 = 0.5.$$

3) Determination of t_2. The movement must be along the ray

$$x_1 = -1.1 + t; \quad x_2 = 1.1 - t; \quad x_3 = 1.65 - 3.2t; \quad t > 0.$$

The smallest of the roots of the equations

$$\psi_j(x^{(1)} + t\zeta^{(2)}) = 0 \qquad (j = 1,\ 2,\ 3)$$

is $t_2 = 0.45$.

4) Determination of a new point and new deviations. The new approximation $x^{(2)}$ is given by the formula

$$x^{(2)} = x^{(1)} + t_2\zeta^{(2)} = (-0.65;\ 0.65;\ 0.21).$$

The new deviations are

$$\psi_1(x^{(2)}) = -1.14 < -\delta_3; \quad \psi_2(x^{(2)}) = -1.07 < -\delta_3;$$
$$-\delta_3 < \psi_3(x^{(2)}) = 0.$$

Third step.

$$\zeta^{(3)} = (1;\ 1;\ -2.15); \quad \delta_4 = \delta_3 = 0.5; \quad t_3 = 0.36;$$
$$x^{(3)} = (-0.29;\ 1.01;\ -0.57).$$

Fourth step.

$$\zeta^{(4)} = (1;\ -1;\ -1.51); \quad \delta_5 = \delta_4 = 0.5; \quad t_4 = 0.12;$$
$$x^{(4)} = (-0.17;\ 0.89;\ -0.75).$$

Fifth step. Determination of $\zeta^{(5)}$.

$$\frac{\partial z}{\partial \zeta} = \zeta_3; \quad \frac{\partial \psi_1(x^{(4)})}{\partial \zeta} = 0.56\zeta_1 + 2.22\zeta_2 - \zeta_3;$$
$$\frac{\partial \psi_2(x^{(4)})}{\partial \zeta} = -1.34\zeta_1 + 2.78\zeta_2 - \zeta_3; \quad \frac{\partial \psi_3(x^{(4)})}{\partial \zeta} = 0.66\zeta_1 - 4\zeta_2 - \zeta_3.$$

To find the direction of descent, we solve the following linear programming problem:

Minimize the form

$$u = \eta$$

under the constraints

$$\zeta_3-\eta\leqslant 0;\quad 0.56\zeta_1+2.22\zeta_2-\zeta_3-\eta\leqslant 0;$$
$$-1.34\zeta_1+2.78\zeta_2-\zeta_3-\eta\leqslant 0;$$
$$0.66\zeta_1-4\zeta_2-\zeta_3-\eta\leqslant 0;\qquad |\zeta_i|\leqslant 1\qquad (i=1,\ 2).$$

Solving this problem, we find that $\eta_5 = 0$.

2) Determination of δ_6. We have $\eta_5 = 0$, and thus we apply the solution criterion for the problem.

We have

$$\psi_1(x^{(4)})=-0.49;\quad \psi_2(x^{(4)})=-0.37;\quad \psi_3(x^{(4)})=0.$$

We now solve the linear programming problem of minimizing the form

$$u=\eta$$

under the constraints

$$\zeta_3-\eta\leqslant 0,$$
$$\frac{\partial\psi_3(x^{(4)})}{\partial\zeta}-\eta=0.66\zeta_1-4\zeta_2-\zeta_3-\eta\leqslant 0,$$
$$|\zeta_i|\leqslant 1\quad (i=1,\ 2).$$

We find that

$$\zeta^{(5)}=(-1;\ 1;\ -2.33).$$

We now set

$$\delta_6=\frac{\delta_5}{2}=0.25.$$

3) Determination of t_5. We move along the ray

$$x_1=-0.17-t;\ x_2=0.89+t;\ x_3=-0.75-2.33t;\ t>0.$$

The smallest of the positive roots of the equations

$$\psi_j(x^{(4)}+t\zeta^{(5)})=0\quad (j=1,\ 2,\ 3)$$

is $t_5 = 0.06$.

4) Determination of a new point and new deviations.

$$x^{(5)}=x^{(4)}+t_5\zeta^{(5)}=(-0.23;\ 0.95;\ -0.88);$$
$$\psi_1(x^{(5)})=-0.19>-\delta_6;\quad \psi_2(x^{(5)})=0;$$
$$\psi_3(x^{(5)})=-0.1>-\delta_6.$$

Sixth step. 1) Determination of $\zeta^{(6)}$.

$$\frac{\partial z}{\partial \zeta} = \zeta_3; \quad \frac{\partial \psi_1(x^{(5)})}{\partial \zeta} = -0.56\zeta_1 + 2.34\zeta_2 - \zeta_3;$$
$$\frac{\partial \psi_2(x^{(5)})}{\partial \zeta} = -1.46\zeta_1 + 2.90\zeta_2 - \zeta_3;$$
$$\frac{\partial \psi_3(x^{(5)})}{\partial \zeta} = 0.54\zeta_1 - 4\zeta_2 - \zeta_3.$$

To find the direction of descent, we solve the linear programming problem of minimizing the form

$$u = \eta$$

under the constraints

$$\zeta_3 - \eta \leqslant 0; \quad -0.56\zeta_1 + 2.34\zeta_2 - \zeta_3 - \eta \leqslant 0;$$
$$-1.46\zeta_1 + 2.90\zeta_2 - \zeta_3 - \eta \leqslant 0; \quad 0.54\zeta_1 - 4\zeta_2 - \zeta_3 - \eta \leqslant 0$$
$$|\zeta_i| \leqslant 1 \quad (i = 1,\ 2).$$

Solving this problem, we find that

$$\zeta_1^{(6)} = 1; \quad \zeta_2^{(6)} = 0.18; \quad \zeta_3^{(6)} = -0.08.$$

2) Determination of δ_7. We have $\eta_6 = -0.08 > -0.25$, so that

$$\delta_7 = \frac{\delta_6}{2} = 0.12.$$

3) Determination of t_6. Movement is along the ray

$$x_1 = -0.23 + t; \quad x_2 = 0.95 + 0.18t;$$
$$x_3 = -0.88 - 0.08t; \quad t > 0.$$

The smallest of the positive roots of the equations

$$\psi_j(x^{(5)} + t\zeta^{(6)}) = 0 \qquad (j = 1,\ 2,\ 3)$$

is $t_6 = 0.34$.

4) Determination of a new point and new deviations.

$$x^{(6)} = x^{(5)} + t_6\zeta^{(6)} = (0.11;\ 1.01;\ -0.91);$$
$$\psi_1(x^{(6)}) = -0.05; \quad \psi_2(x^{(6)}) = -0.16; \quad \psi_3(x^{(6)}) = 0.$$

Seventh step.

$$\zeta^{(7)} = (-1;\ -0.15;\ -0.26); \quad \delta_8 = \delta_7 = 0.12; \quad t_7 = 0.2;$$
$$x^{(7)} = (-0.09;\ 0.98;\ -0.96).$$

Eighth step.

$$\zeta^{(8)}=(0.3;\ -0.03;\ -0.18);\quad \delta_9=\delta_8=0.12;\quad t_8=0.09;$$
$$x^{(8)}=(-0.06;\ 0.98;\ -0.98).$$

5) Application of the solution criterion. Here we consider the point x^* = (0, 1, -1) and we show it is a solution to the problem.

We have

$$\psi_1(x^*)=0,\quad \psi_2(x^*)=0,\quad \psi_3(x^*)=0,$$

i.e., x^* belongs to all the surfaces.

We now determine the direction of steepest descent from the point x^*. To do so, we find

$$\frac{\partial z}{\partial \zeta}=\zeta_3,\quad \frac{\partial \psi_1(x^*)}{\partial \zeta}=3\zeta_2-\zeta_3,\quad \frac{\partial \psi_2(x^*)}{\partial \zeta}=-\zeta_1+3\zeta_2-\zeta_3,$$
$$\frac{\partial \psi_3(x^*)}{\partial \zeta}=\zeta_1-4\zeta_2-\zeta_3$$

and minimize the form

$$u=\eta$$

under the constraints

$$\begin{aligned}\zeta_3-\eta\leqslant 0,\ 3\zeta_2-\zeta_3-\eta&\leqslant 0,\\ -\zeta_1+3\zeta_2-\zeta_3-\eta&\leqslant 0,\\ \zeta_1-4\zeta_2-\zeta_3-\eta&\leqslant 0,\\ |\zeta_1|\leqslant 1,\quad |\zeta_2|&\leqslant 1.\end{aligned}$$

We find that

$$\min u=\eta^*=0.$$

In virtue of the solution criterion, the point (0, 1, -1) is a solution of the problem.

e) Convergence of the algorithm. Assuming that Ω is bounded and closed we prove that the algorithm converges. The monotonically increasing sequence of approximations $\{z(x^{(k)})\}$ has a finite limit α.

First we show that

$$\lim_{k\to\infty} z(x^{(k)})=\alpha>-\infty$$

implies that the nonnegative monotonically decreasing sequence $\{\delta_k\}$ approaches zero:

$$\lim_{k\to\infty}\delta_k=\delta=0.$$

Assume that this is not so. Then there exists a K_0 such that for all $k > K_0$ we have

$$\delta_k = \delta \text{ and } \eta_k < -\delta.$$

Now, consider the limit $\tilde{x}$ of the sequence $\{x^{(k)}\}$ and let $x^{(k_i)} \to \tilde{x}$. It is clear that $\tilde{x}$ is a boundary point. Assume that at this point

$$\left.\begin{array}{ll} -\delta < \psi_{j_\nu}(\tilde{x}) \leqslant 0 & (\nu = 1, \ldots, \nu_1), \\ \psi_j(\tilde{x}) \leqslant -\delta & (j \neq j_1, \ldots, j_{\nu_1}). \end{array}\right\} \qquad (6.24)$$

Because the functions $\psi_j(x)$ are continuous, there exists a neighborhood $U(\tilde{x})$ such that for all $x \in U(\tilde{x}) \cap \Omega$ we have

$$-\delta < \psi_{j_\nu}(x) \leqslant 0 \qquad (\nu = 1, \ldots, \nu_1). \qquad (6.25)$$

Since $x^{(k_i)} \to \tilde{x}$, there exists a $K_1 \geqslant K_0$ such that, beginning with $k > K_1$, all points $x^{(k_i)}$ lie in $U(\tilde{x}) \cap \Omega$, since all the functions $\psi_{j_1}(x), \ldots, \psi_{j_{\nu_1}}(x)$take part in the determination of the direction of descent from $x^{(k_i)}$.

Moreover, for all $x^{(k_i)} \in U(\tilde{x}) \cap \Omega$,

$$\left.\begin{array}{c} \sum_{i=1}^{n} p_i \zeta_i^{(k_i+1)} \leqslant \eta_{k_i} < -\delta, \\ \sum_{i=1}^{n} \frac{\partial \psi_{j_\nu}\left(x^{(k_i)}\right)}{\partial x_i} \zeta_i^{(k_i+1)} \leqslant \eta_{k_i} < -\delta \\ (\nu = 1, \ldots, \nu_1). \end{array}\right\} \qquad (6.26)$$

Since the sequence $\{\zeta^{(k_i+1)}\}$ is bounded, it contains a convergent subsequence. We can assume that $\lim_{i \to \infty} \zeta^{(k_i)} = \tilde{\zeta}$. Passing to the limit inequalities (6.26) as $i \to \infty$, we find that

$$\sum_{i=1}^{n} p_i \tilde{\zeta}_i \leqslant -\delta, \quad \sum_{i=1}^{n} \frac{\partial \psi_{j_\nu}(\tilde{x})}{\partial x_i} \tilde{\zeta}_i \leqslant -\delta \qquad (\nu = 1, \ldots, \nu_1).$$

Thus, the direction $\tilde{\zeta}$ is a direction of descent from the point $\tilde{x}$. The size of the step in this direction is $\tilde{t} > 0$. Thus,

$$\psi_j\left(\tilde{x} + \frac{\tilde{t}}{2}\tilde{\zeta}\right) < 0 \qquad (j = 1, \ldots, q),$$

which means that for sufficiently largely k_i we have

$$\psi_j\left(x^{(k_i)} + \frac{\tilde{t}}{2}\zeta^{(k_i+1)}\right) < 0 \qquad (j = 1, \ldots, q),$$

i.e., for sufficiently large k_i we have $t_{k_i} > \frac{\tilde{t}}{2}$.

Finally, we have

$$\begin{aligned} z(x^{(k_i)}) &= z(x^{(k_i-1)} + t_{k_i}\zeta^{(k_i)}) = z(x^{(k_i-1)}) + z(t_{k_i}\zeta^{(k_i)}) = \\ &= z(x^{(k_i-2)}) + z(t_{k_i-1}\zeta^{(k_i-1)}) + z(t_{k_i}\zeta^{(k_i)}) = \\ &\dots\dots\dots\dots\dots\dots\dots\dots \\ &= z(x^{(0)}) + \sum_{j=1}^{k_i} z(t_j\zeta^{(j)}) = z(x^{(0)}) + \sum_{j=1}^{k_i} t_j \sum_{\mu=1}^{n} p_\mu \zeta_\mu^{(j)} \leqslant \\ &\leqslant z(x^{(0)}) + \sum_{j=1}^{i} t_{k_j} \sum_{\mu=1}^{n} p_\mu \zeta_\mu^{(k_j)} \leqslant z(x^{(0)}) - \frac{\gamma}{2} i\delta, \end{aligned}$$

i.e.,

$$\lim_{i\to\infty} z(x^{(k_i)}) = -\infty.$$

But this contradicts the assumption that

$$\lim_{i\to\infty} z(x^{(k_i)}) > -\infty,$$

so $\delta = 0$.

We now show that $z(x^{(k)})$ converges to a minimal α.

Let k_i' be the index of a step in which δ_k must be changed. Then, by the construction of $\{\delta_k\}$

$$\lim_{k_i'\to\infty} \eta_{k_i'} = 0.$$

Let x^* be the limit of some subsequence of $\left\{x^{(k_i')}\right\}$. It can be assumed that

$$\lim_{k_i'\to\infty} x^{(k_i')} = x^*.$$

Now, assume that x^* is not a solution of problem (6.12) - (6.13), and let

$$\left.\begin{aligned} \psi_{j_\mu}(x^*) &= 0 \qquad (\mu = 1, 2, \dots, \mu_1), \\ \psi_j(x^*) &< 0 \qquad (j \neq j_1, \dots, j_{\mu_1}). \end{aligned}\right\} \tag{6.27}$$

Then there exists a direction ζ^* of steepest descent from the point x^*, and it satisfies the system of inequalities

$$\left.\begin{aligned} &\sum_{i=1}^{n} p_i \zeta_i^* \leqslant \eta^*, \\ &\sum_{i=1}^{n} \frac{\partial \psi_{j_\mu}(x^*)}{\partial x_i} \zeta_i^* \leqslant \eta^* \qquad (\mu = 1, 2, \dots, \mu_1), \end{aligned}\right\} \tag{6.28}$$

where $\eta^* < 0$.

It follows from (6.28) that

$$\left.\begin{aligned} \sum_{i=1}^{n} p_i \zeta_i^* < \frac{\eta^*}{2}, \\ \sum_{i=1}^{n} \frac{\partial \psi_{j_\mu}(x^*)}{\partial x_i} \zeta_i^* < \frac{\eta^*}{2}. \end{aligned}\right\} \tag{6.29}$$

We now show that for sufficiently large k_i' only functions of the form $\psi_{j_1}(x), \ldots, \psi_{j_{\mu_1}}(x)$ (and not necessarily all such) can take part in the determination of the direction of descent from the point $x^{(k_i')}$.

Indeed, (6.27) is satisfied at the point x^*. Let

$$\min_{j \neq j_\mu} |\psi_j(x^*)| = \sigma.$$

Now

$$\psi_j(x^*) < -\frac{\sigma}{2} \qquad (j \neq j_1, \ldots, j_{\mu_1}).$$

Thus, for all points x of some neighborhood $U(x^*) \cap \Omega$ of the point x^*

$$\psi_j(x) < -\frac{\sigma}{2} \qquad (j \neq j_1, \ldots, j_{\mu_1}).$$

And since

$$\delta_k < \frac{\sigma}{2}$$

for sufficiently large k, functions other than $\psi_{j_1}(x), \ldots, \psi_{j_{\mu_1}}(x)$ cannot take part in the determination of the direction of descent at points $x \in U(x^*) \cap \Omega$, and consequently at points $x^{(k_i')}$ for sufficiently large k_i'.

It follows from the continuity of the partial derivatives of the functions $\psi_j(x)$ and from inequalities (6.29) that for sufficiently large k_j' we have

$$\sum_{\nu=1}^{n} p_\nu \zeta_\nu^* < \frac{\eta^*}{2},$$

$$\sum_{\nu=1}^{n} \frac{\partial \psi_{j_\mu}\left(x^{(k_i')}\right)}{\partial x_\nu} \zeta_\nu^* < \frac{\eta^*}{2}.$$

As a result ζ^* is a direction of descent (possibly the steepest) from the point $x^{(k_i')}$. For the steepest descent we have the inequality

$$\eta_{k_i'} \leqslant \frac{\eta^*}{2},$$

which contradicts the fact that $\eta_{k_i'} \to 0$.

Thus, the assumption that x^* is not a solution of problem (6.12) - (6.13) leads to a contradiction. Consequently, $\{z(x^{(k)})\}$ converges to $z(x^*)$, i.e., to the smallest value of the function $z(x)$ in Ω.

2. A Second Form of the Algorithm

The second form of the algorithm differs from the first, as presented in Paragraph 1, only in the method of finding the direction of descent ζ.

In the above method for finding a direction of descent, inequalities (6.16) - (6.17) were "equally justified," which is not always desirable, since the object of the problem is to make the function $z(x) = p_1x_1 + \ldots + p_nx_n$ decrease as fast as possible under constraints (6.13). As a result, it is natural to find the direction of descent in the following manner.

After $x^{(0)}$ is found, we choose, together with $\delta_1 > 0$, an arbitrary sufficiently small $\lambda_1 > 0$. Now the direction $\zeta^{(1)}$ is determined by solving the following linear programming problem:

Minimize the form

$$u = p_1\zeta_1 + \ldots + p_n\zeta_n \tag{6.30}$$

under the constraints

$$\left.\begin{aligned} &\sum_{i=1}^{n} \frac{\partial \psi_{j_\nu}(x^{(0)})}{\partial x_i} \zeta_i \leqslant -\lambda_1 \qquad (\nu = 1, 2, \ldots, \nu_1), \\ &|\zeta_i| \leqslant C. \end{aligned}\right\} \tag{6.31}$$

If

$$\min u = \eta_1 < -\delta_1,$$

we proceed in the direction $\zeta^{(1)}$ until the boundary of Ω is first encountered. We thus obtain the point

$$x^{(1)} = x^{(0)} + t_0\zeta^{(1)},$$

which we take as the initial point, and we set

$$\delta_2 = \delta_1, \quad \lambda_2 = \lambda_1$$

etc., until

$$\min u = \eta_k \geqslant -\delta_k.$$

at some kth step.

When $0 > \eta_k \geqslant -\delta_k$ we determine t_k, $x^{(k)}$, new deviations, and continue the process at the point $x^{(k)}$ by setting

$$\delta_{k+1} = \frac{\delta_k}{2} \text{ and } \lambda_{k+1} = \frac{\lambda_k}{2}.$$

When $\eta_k \geqslant 0$, we set $\delta_{k+1} = \frac{\delta_k}{2}$, and choose λ_k in the following manner. Let

$$\psi_{j_\mu}(x^{(k-1)}) = 0 \qquad (\mu = 1, \ldots, \mu_1);$$
$$\psi_j(x^{(k-1)}) < 0 \qquad (j \neq j_1, \ldots, j_{\mu_1}).$$

Then we minimize the function

$$u = p_1\zeta_1 + \ldots + p_n\zeta_n$$

under the constraints

$$\sum_{i=1}^{n} \frac{\partial\psi_{j_\mu}(x^{(k-1)})}{\partial x_i}\zeta_i \leqslant 0 \qquad (\mu = 1, \ldots, \mu_1);$$
$$|\zeta_i| \leqslant C \qquad (i = 1, \ldots, n).$$

If

$$\min u = \eta'_k = 0,$$

$x^{(k-1)}$ is a solution of problem (6.12) - (6.13) and the process terminates.

If, however, $\eta'_k < 0$, we solve the linear programming problem of maximizing the form

$$v = \lambda$$

under the constraints

$$\sum_{i=1}^{n} p_i\zeta_i - \frac{\eta'_k}{2} \leqslant 0,$$
$$\sum_{i=1}^{n} \frac{\partial\psi_{j_\mu}(x^{(k-1)})}{\partial x_i}\zeta_i \leqslant -\lambda \quad (\mu = 1, \ldots, \mu_1);$$
$$|\zeta_i| \leqslant C \quad (i = 1, \ldots, n).$$

We obtain the direction of descent $\zeta^{(k)}$ and let $\max v = v_k$. We now set

$$\lambda_{k+1} = \min\left\{\frac{\lambda_k}{2},\ v_k\right\}$$

and continue the process, using δ_{k+1} instead of δ_k and λ_{k+1} instead of λ_k.

3. COMPLEX CHEBYSHEV APPROXIMATION

As we noted in Paragraph 2, a of Section 1, one of the major convex programming problems is the Chebyshev approximation problem for an inconsistent system of complex linear equations

$$\left.\begin{array}{l}\Delta_\nu(z) \equiv \alpha_{\nu 1} z_1 + \ldots + \alpha_{\nu n} z_n + \alpha_\nu = 0 \quad (\nu = 1, \ldots, m), \\ z \equiv (z_1, \ldots, z_n), \quad z_k = x_k + i y_k, \quad \alpha_{\nu k} = a_{\nu k} + i b_{\nu k}, \\ \alpha_\nu = a_\nu + i b_\nu \quad (k = 1, \ldots, n;\ \nu = 1, \ldots, m)\end{array}\right\} \tag{6.32}$$

under inequality constraints

$$\psi_j(z) = \psi_j(x_1, \ldots, x_n;\ y_1, \ldots, y_n) \leqslant 0 \quad (j = 1, \ldots, q), \tag{6.33}$$

which define some convex set in Ω in the $2n$-dimensional space of variables $x_1, \ldots, x_n;\ y_1, \ldots, y_n$ (the $\psi_j(z)$ are assumed to be real, convex, and smooth), i.e., the problem of finding a point $z^* \in \Omega$ such that

$$\max_\nu |\Delta_\nu(z^*)| = \min_{z \in \Omega} \max_\nu |\Delta_\nu(z)|. \tag{6.34}$$

Of course, the algorithm described in Section 2 provides a solution to problem (6.32) - (6.34), but to eliminate the extremely large number of constraints, we apply the algorithm directly to the problem (6.32) - (6.34) (see [5b]) instead of passing to canonical form. The following examples explain the various changes that must be made in the algorithm.

1. The Case of No Constraints

We first consider Chebyshev approximation of a linear inconsistent complex system of equations with no constraints, i.e., the case in which Ω is the entire space.

Example. Given an inconsistent system of linear complex equations

$$\begin{array}{l}\Delta_1(z) = z_1 - z_2 = 0, \\ \Delta_2(z) = z_1 - 1 + i = 0, \\ \Delta_3(z) = z_2 + 1 - i = 0, \\ \Delta_4(z) = z_1 + z_2 = 0, \\ \Delta_5(z) = z_1 - 2z_2 - 1 + i = 0, \\ z_1 = x_1 + i y_1, \quad z_2 = x_2 + i y_2, \quad z = (z_1, z_2),\end{array}$$

find a point z^* for which

$$\max_{1 \leqslant i \leqslant 5} |\Delta_i(z^*)|^2 = \min_z \max_{1 \leqslant i \leqslant 5} |\Delta_i(z)|^2.$$

We have

$$|\Delta_1(z)|^2 = f_1(x;\ y) = (x_1 - x_2)^2 + (y_1 - y_2)^2,$$
$$|\Delta_2(z)|^2 = f_2(x;\ y) = (x_1 - 1)^2 + (y_1 + 1)^2,$$
$$|\Delta_3(z)|^2 = f_3(x;\ y) = (x_2 + 1)^2 + (y_2 - 1)^2,$$
$$|\Delta_4(z)|^2 = f_4(x;\ y) = (x_1 + x_2)^2 + (y_1 + y_2)^2,$$
$$|\Delta_5(z)|^2 = f_5(x;\ y) = (x_1 - 2x_2 - 1)^2 + (y_1 - 2y_2 + 1)^2,$$

where $x = (x_1,\ x_2)$, $y = (y_1,\ y_2)$, and $f_i(x^{(0)},\ y^{(0)})$ is the deviation of the point $(x^{(0)},\ y^{(0)})$ from the surface $f_i(x;\ y) = 0$.

Thus, the problem consists of finding a point $(x^*;\ y^*)$ such that

$$\max_{1 \leqslant i \leqslant 5} f_i(x^*;\ y^*) = \min_{(x;\ y)} \max_{1 \leqslant i \leqslant 5} f_i(x;\ y).$$

For the initial approximation we take the point $(x^{(0)};\ y^{(0)}) = (1{,}0;\ 0{,}1)$, and for the initial value of the parameter δ we take $\delta_1 = 0.2$.

Substituting into $f_i(x;\ y)$, we find that

$$\max_{1 \leqslant i \leqslant 5} f_i(x^{(0)};\ y^{(0)}) = f_1(x^{(0)};\ y^{(0)}) = f_4(x^{(0)};\ y^{(0)}) = 2,$$
$$f_i(x^{(0)};\ y^{(0)}) - 2 < -\delta_1 \qquad (i = 2,\ 3,\ 5).$$

First step. 1) Determination of the direction of steepest descent. We have

$$\frac{1}{2}\frac{\partial f_1(x^{(0)};\ y^{(0)})}{\partial \zeta} = \zeta_1 - \zeta_2 - \zeta_3 + \zeta_4;$$
$$\frac{1}{2}\frac{\partial f_4(x^{(0)};\ y^{(0)})}{\partial \zeta} = \zeta_1 + \zeta_2 + \zeta_3 + \zeta_4.$$

Along the direction $\zeta^{(1)}$ of steepest descent, these derivatives must be negative and the derivative with the smallest absolute value must be as large as possible, i.e., $\zeta^{(1)}$ is a solution of the following linear programming problem:

Minimize the form

$$u = \xi$$

under the constraints

$$\zeta_1 - \zeta_2 - \zeta_3 + \zeta_4 \leqslant \xi; \quad \zeta_1 + \zeta_2 + \zeta_3 + \zeta_4 \leqslant \xi$$

and the auxiliary constraints

$$|\zeta_i| \leqslant 1 \qquad (i = 1,\ 2,\ 3,\ 4),$$

which, as we noted in Paragraph 1 of Section 2, must be introduced in order to normalize the vector ζ.

We obtain

$$\zeta^{(1)} = (-1, 1; -1, -1).$$

2) Computation of δ_2. We have $\min u = \xi_1 = -2 < -\delta_1$, so that $\delta_2 = \delta_1 = 0.2$.

3) Determination of t_1. The motion must be along the ray

$$x_1 = 1 - t; \quad x_2 = t; \quad y_1 = -t; \quad y_2 = 1 - t; \quad t > 0.$$

For the maximal deviations along this ray we find

$$f_1(x; y) = 1 + (1 - 2t)^2, \quad f_4(x; y) = 1 + (1 - 2t)^2.$$

We obtain t_1 from the formula

$$t_1 = \min\{t'; t''\},$$

where t' minimizes $f_1(x; y) = f_4(x; y)$, and t'' is the smallest positive root of the equations

$$f_1(x; y) = f_i(x; y) \qquad (i = 2, 3, 5).$$

We find that

$$t' = 0.5, \quad t'' = 0.18, \text{ so } \quad t_1 = 0.18.$$

4) Determination of a new point and new maximal deviations. For the new approximation

$$(x^{(1)}; y^{(1)}) = (x^{(0)}; y^{(0)}) + t_1\zeta^{(1)} = (0.82; 0.18; -0.18; 0.82),$$

the new maximal deviations are

$$f_1(x^{(1)}; y^{(1)}) = f_3(x^{(1)}; y^{(1)}) = f_4(x^{(1)}; y^{(1)}) = 1.4,$$
$$f_i(x^{(1)}; y^{(1)}) - 1.4 < -\delta_2 \qquad (i = 2, 5).$$

Second step. 1) Determination of $\zeta^{(2)}$.

$$\frac{1}{2} \cdot \frac{\partial f_1(x^{(1)}; y^{(1)})}{\partial \zeta} = 0.64\zeta_1 - 0.64\zeta_2 - \zeta_3 + \zeta_4,$$
$$\frac{1}{2} \cdot \frac{\partial f_3(x^{(1)}; y^{(1)})}{\partial \zeta} = 1.18\zeta_2 - 0.18\zeta_4,$$
$$\frac{1}{2} \cdot \frac{\partial f_4(x^{(1)}; y^{(1)})}{\partial \zeta} = \zeta_1 + \zeta_2 + 0.64\zeta_3 + 0.64\zeta_4.$$

We minimize the form

$$u = \xi$$

under the constraints

$$\begin{gathered}
0.64\zeta_1 - 0.64\zeta_2 - \zeta_3 + \zeta_4 - \xi \leqslant 0, \\
1.18\zeta_2 - 0.18\zeta_4 - \xi \leqslant 0, \\
\zeta_1 + \zeta_2 + 0.64\zeta_3 + 0.64\zeta_4 - \xi \leqslant 0, \\
|\zeta_i| \leqslant 1 \quad (i = 1, 2, 3, 4).
\end{gathered}$$

We find that $\zeta^{(2)} = (-1; -1; 1; -0.15)$.

2) Determination of δ_3. We have $\xi_2 = -1.15 < -\delta_2$, so $\delta_3 = \delta_2 = 0.2$.

3) Determination of t_2. The motion must be along the ray

$$x_1 = 0.82 - t; \quad x_2 = 0.18 - t; \quad y_1 = -0.18 + t;$$
$$y_2 = 0.82 - 0.15t; \quad t > 0.$$

For the maximal deviations along this ray we have

$$\begin{gathered}
f_1(x;\ y) = 0.41 + (1 - 1.15t)^2, \\
f_3(x;\ y) = (1.18 - t)^2 + (0.18 + 0.15t)^2, \\
f_4(x;\ y) = (1 - 2t)^2 + (0.64 + 0.85t)^2.
\end{gathered}$$

Of these functions, the one that decreases most slowly in the direction $\zeta^{(2)}$ is $f_1(x;\ y)$, since, of the three derivatives

$$\left.\frac{df_1(x;\ y)}{dt}\right|_{t=0} = -1.15 = \left.\frac{df_3(x;\ y)}{dt}\right|_{t=0},$$
$$\left.\frac{df_4(x;\ y)}{dt}\right|_{t=0} = -1.46,$$

the first has the smallest absolute value for small, positive t.

We determine t_1 with the formula

$$t_1 = \min\{t',\ t''\},$$

where t' minimizes $f_1(x;\ y)$ and t'' is the smallest positive root of the equations

$$f_1(x;\ y) = f_i(x;\ y) \qquad (i = 2, 3, 4, 5).$$

4) Determination of a new point and new maximal deviations.

$$(x^{(2)};\ y^{(2)}) = (x^{(1)};\ y^{(1)}) + t_2\zeta^{(2)} = (0.66;\ 0.02;\ -0.02;\ 0.80),$$
$$\max_{1 \leqslant i \leqslant 5} f_i(x^{(2)};\ y^{(2)}) = f_1(x^{(2)};\ y^{(2)}) = f_2(x^{(2)};\ y^{(2)}) =$$
$$= f_3(x^{(2)},\ y^{(2)}) = 1.08.$$

Moreover, since

$$-\delta_3 < f_4(x^{(2)};\ y^{(2)}) - 1.08 < 0,$$
$$f_5(x^{(2)};\ y^{(2)}) - 1.08 < -\delta_3,$$

the maximal deviations are

$$f_1(x^{(2)};\ y^{(2)});\quad f_2(x^{(2)};\ y^{(2)});\quad f_3(x^{(2)};\ y^{(2)});\quad f_4(x^{(2)};\ y^{(2)}).$$

Third step.

$$\zeta^{(3)}=(-1;\ -0.6;\ -0.8;\ -1);\quad \delta_4=\delta_3=0.2;\quad t_3=0.30;$$
$$x^{(3)}=(0.36;\ -0.16;\ -0.26;\ 0.50).$$

Fourth step.

$$\zeta^{(4)}=(1;\ -0.85;\ 0.55;\ -1);\quad \delta_5=\delta_4=0.2;\quad t_4=0.13;$$
$$(x^{(4)};\ y^{(4)})=(0.49;\ -0.27;\ -0.19;\ 0.37);$$
$$\max f_i(x^{(4)};\ y^{(4)})=0.93.$$

5) *Application of the solution criterion.* We consider the points $(x^*;\ y^*)=\left(\frac{1}{3},\ -\frac{1}{3};\ -\frac{1}{3},\ \frac{1}{3}\right)$ and let $\delta^*=0$. We have $\max\limits_{1\leqslant i\leqslant 5} f_i(x^*;\ y^*)=f_1(x^*;\ y^*)=f_2(x^*;\ y^*)=f_3(x^*;\ y^*)=0{,}889$. Moreover,

$$\frac{1}{2}\cdot\frac{\partial f_1(x^*;\ y^*)}{\partial\zeta}=\frac{2}{3}\zeta_1-\frac{2}{3}\zeta_2-\frac{2}{3}\zeta_3+\frac{2}{3}\zeta_4,$$
$$\frac{1}{2}\cdot\frac{\partial f_2(x^*;\ y^*)}{\partial\zeta}=-\frac{2}{3}\zeta_1+\frac{2}{3}\zeta_3,$$
$$\frac{1}{2}\cdot\frac{\partial f_3(x^*;\ y^*)}{\partial\zeta}=\frac{2}{3}\zeta_2-\frac{2}{3}\zeta_4.$$

We now minimize the form

$$u=\xi$$

under the constraints

$$\frac{2}{3}\zeta_1-\frac{2}{3}\zeta_2-\frac{2}{3}\zeta_3+\frac{2}{3}\zeta_4-\xi\leqslant 0,$$
$$-\frac{2}{3}\zeta_1+\frac{2}{3}\zeta_3-\xi\leqslant 0,$$
$$\frac{2}{3}\zeta_2-\frac{2}{3}\zeta_4-\xi\leqslant 0,$$
$$|\zeta_i|\leqslant 1\quad (i=1,\ 2,\ 3,\ 4).$$

It turns out that

$$\min u=0.$$

In virtue of the solution criterion in Paragraph 1 of Section 2, the point

$$(x^*;\ y^*)=\left(\frac{1}{3},\ -\frac{1}{3};\ -\frac{1}{3},\ \frac{1}{3}\right)$$

is a solution to the problem.

2. The Case in Which There Are Constraints

We now consider the problem of Chebyshev approximation for a linear inconsistent complex system of equations when there are constraints on the unknowns and the set of constraints defines a convex region Ω.

Example. Given an inconsistent system of linear complex equations

$$\begin{aligned}
\Delta_1(z) &= z_1 - 2z_2 + 1 - i = 0,\\
\Delta_2(z) &= z_1 + 1 - i = 0,\\
\Delta_3(z) &= z_1 + 3z_2 - 0.5i = 0,\\
\Delta_4(z) &= 0.5z_1 - z_2 = 0,\\
\Delta_5(z) &= 2z_1 + z_2 + 1 - i = 0
\end{aligned}$$

and the region Ω defined by the inequalities

$$\begin{aligned}
|2z_1 + 2z_2| &\leqslant \sqrt{2},\\
|2z_1 - 4z_2| &\leqslant \sqrt{2},
\end{aligned}$$

find a point $z^* \in \Omega$ such that

$$\max_{1\leqslant i\leqslant 5} |\Delta_i(z^*)|^2 = \min_{z\in\Omega} \max_{1\leqslant i\leqslant 5} |\Delta_i(z)|^2.$$

We have

$$\begin{aligned}
|\Delta_1(z)|^2 &= f_1(x;\ y) = (x_1 - 2x_2 + 1)^2 + (y_1 - 2y_2 - 1)^2,\\
|\Delta_2(z)|^2 &= f_2(x;\ y) = (x_1 + 1)^2 + (y_1 - 1)^2,\\
|\Delta_3(z)|^2 &= f_3(x;\ y) = (x_1 + 3x_2)^2 + (y_1 + 3y_2 - 0.5)^2,\\
|\Delta_4(z)|^2 &= f_4(x;\ y) = (0.5x_1 - x_2)^2 + (0.5y_1 - y_2)^2,\\
|\Delta_5(z)|^2 &= f_5(x;\ y) = (2x_1 + x_2 + 1)^2 + (2y_1 + y_2 - 1)^2
\end{aligned}$$

and the constraints

$$\begin{aligned}
\psi_1(x;\ y) &= (2x_1 + 2x_2)^2 + (2y_1 + 2y_2)^2 - 2 \leqslant 0,\\
\psi_2(x;\ y) &= (2x_1 - 4x_2)^2 + (2y_1 - 4y_2)^2 - 2 \leqslant 0.
\end{aligned}$$

The problem consists of finding a point $(x^*;\ y^*) \in \Omega$ such that

$$\max_{1\leqslant i\leqslant 5} f_i(x^*;\ y^*) = \min_{(x;\ y)\in\Omega} \max_{1\leqslant i\leqslant 5} f_i(x;\ y).$$

For the initial approximation we take the point $(x^{(0)};\ y^{(0)}) = (0,\ 0;\ 0,\ 0)$ and for the initial values of the parameters δ and λ we take $\delta_1 = 0.42$ and $\lambda_1 = 1$.

Substituting $(x^{(0)};\ y^{(0)})$ into $f_i(x;\ y)$ and $\psi_j(x;\ y)$, we find that

$$\max_{1\leqslant i\leqslant 5} f_i(x^{(0)};\ y^{(0)}) = f_1(x^{(0)};\ y^{(0)}) = f_2(x^{(0)};\ y^{(0)}) = \\ = f_5(x^{(0)};\ y^{(0)}) = 2,$$

$$f_i(x^{(0)};\ y^{(0)}) - 2 < -\delta_1 \qquad (i=3,\ 4),$$
$$\psi_1(x^{(0)};\ y^{(0)}) < -\delta_1,$$
$$\psi_2(x^{(0)};\ y^{(0)}) < -\delta_1.$$

First step. 1) Determination of the direction of steepest descent. We have

$$\frac{\partial f_1(x^{(0)};\ y^{(0)})}{\partial\zeta} = 2\zeta_1 - 4\zeta_2 - 2\zeta_3 + 4\zeta_4,$$
$$\frac{\partial f_2(x^{(0)};\ y^{(0)})}{\partial\zeta} = 2\zeta_1 \qquad - 2\zeta_3,$$
$$\frac{\partial f_5(x^{(0)};\ y^{(0)})}{\partial\zeta} = 4\zeta_1 + 2\zeta_2 - 4\zeta_3 - 2\zeta_4.$$

The direction of steepest descent $\zeta^{(1)}$ is a solution of the following linear programming problem:

Minimize the form

$$u = \xi$$

under the constraints

$$\begin{aligned} &2\zeta_1 - 4\zeta_2 - 2\zeta_3 + 4\zeta_4 - \xi \leqslant 0,\\ &2\zeta_1 \qquad\quad - 2\zeta_3 \qquad\quad - \xi \leqslant 0,\\ &4\zeta_1 + 2\zeta_2 - 4\zeta_3 - 2\zeta_4 - \xi \leqslant 0,\\ &|\zeta_i| \leqslant 1 \qquad (i=1,\ 2,\ 3,\ 4). \end{aligned}$$

We find that

$$\zeta^{(1)} = (-1,\ 1;\ 1,\ 1).$$

2) Computation of δ_2 *and* λ_2. We have $\min u = \xi_1 = -4 < -\delta_1$, so

$$\delta_2 \doteq \delta_1 = 0.42 \text{ and } \lambda_2 = \lambda_1 = 1.$$

3) Determination of t_1. The movement must be along the ray

$$x_1 = -t;\quad x_2 = t;\quad y_1 = t;\quad y_2 = t;\quad t > 0.$$

We obtain t_1 from the formula

$$t_1 = \min\{t',\ t'',\ t'''\},$$

where t' and t'' are computed as in the example of Paragraph 1, while t''' is the smallest positive root of the equations

$$\psi_1(x;\ y)=0;\quad \psi_2(x;\ y)=0.$$

We find that

$$t_1=\min\{t',\ t'',\ t'''\}=t'=0.20.$$

4) Determination of a new approximation and new maximal deviations.

$$(x_1^{(1)},\ x_2^{(1)};\ y_1^{(1)},\ y_2^{(1)})=(x^{(0)};\ y^{(0)})+t_1\zeta^{(1)}=(-0.20;\ 0.20;\ 0.20;\ 0.20).$$

For the new maximal deviations we obtain

$$\max_{1\leqslant i\leqslant 5} f_i(x^{(1)};\ y^{(1)})=f_1(x^{(1)};\ y^{(1)})=1.60.$$

Moreover,

$$-\delta_2 < f_2(x^{(1)};\ y^{(1)})-1.60<0,$$
$$f_i(x^{(1)};\ y^{(1)})-1{,}60<-\delta_2 \qquad (i=3,\ 4,\ 5),$$
$$\psi_1(x^{(1)};\ y^{(1)})<-\delta_2,$$
$$-\delta_2<\psi_2(x^{(1)};\ y^{(1)})<0.$$

Second step.

$$\zeta^{(2)}=(-1,\ -1;\ 1,\ -1);\quad \delta_3=\delta_2=0.42;\quad \lambda_3=\lambda_2=1;$$
$$t_2=0.20;\quad (x^{(2)};\ y^{(2)})=(-0{,}40;\ 0;\ 0.40;\ 0).$$

Third step.

$$\zeta^{(3)}=(-1,\ 1;\ 1,\ -1);\quad \delta_4=\delta_3=0{,}42;\quad \lambda_4=\lambda_3;\quad t_3=0{,}03;$$
$$(x^{(3)};\ y^{(3)})=(-0{,}43;\ 0.03;\ 0.43;\ -0{,}03).$$

Fourth step. 1) Determination of $\zeta^{(4)}$. We minimize

$$u=\xi$$

under the constraints

$$1{,}02\zeta_1-2{,}04\zeta_2-1{,}02\zeta_3+2{,}04\zeta_4-\xi\leqslant 0,$$
$$1{,}14\zeta_1 \qquad\qquad -1{,}14\zeta_3 \qquad\qquad -\xi\leqslant 0,$$
$$-3{,}92\zeta_1+7{,}84\zeta_2+3{,}92\zeta_3-7{,}84\zeta_4 \qquad \leqslant -1,$$
$$|\zeta_i|\leqslant 1 \qquad (i=1,\ 2,\ 3,\ 4);$$

we find that min u = 0.3 > 0.

2) Computation of δ_5 *and* λ_5. Since min $u > 0$, we find that $\delta_5 = \frac{\delta_4}{2} = 0.21$.

To compute λ_5 we solve the following two linear programming problems:

α) Minimize

$$u = \xi$$

under the constraints

$$\begin{aligned} 1.14\zeta_1 \qquad\qquad - 1.14\zeta_3 \qquad\qquad - \xi &\leqslant 0, \\ -3.92\zeta_1 + 7.84\zeta_2 + 3.92\zeta_3 - 7.84\zeta_4 \qquad &\leqslant 0, \\ |\zeta_i| \leqslant 1 \qquad (i = 1, 2, 3, 4). \end{aligned}$$

We find that min u = -2.28.

β) Maximize the form

$$v = \lambda$$

under the constraints

$$\begin{aligned} 1.14\zeta_1 \qquad\qquad - 1.14\zeta_3 \qquad\qquad + 1.14 &\leqslant 0, \\ -3.92\zeta_1 + 7.84\zeta_2 + 3.92\zeta_3 - 7.84\zeta_4 + \lambda \qquad &\leqslant 0. \end{aligned}$$

We find that max v = 11.76. Thus,

$$\lambda_5 = \min \{0.5;\ 11,76\} = 0.5.$$

For $\zeta^{(4)}$ we find

$$\zeta^{(4)} = (0, -1; 1, 1).$$

3) Determination of t_4. The movement must be along the ray

$$\begin{aligned} x_1 = -0.43; \quad x_2 = 0.03 - t; \\ y_1 = 0.43 + t; \quad y_2 = -0.03 + t; \quad t > 0. \end{aligned}$$

We find that t_4 = 0.03.

4) Determination of a new point and new deviations.

$$(x^{(4)};\ y^{(4)}) = (-0.43;\ 0;\ 0.46;\ 0).$$

For the new maximal deviations we find

$$\begin{aligned} \max_{1 \leqslant i \leqslant 5} f_i(x^{(4)};\ y^{(4)}) = f_1(x^{(4)};\ y^{(4)}) = f_2(x^{(4)};\ y^{(4)}) = 0.62, \\ f_i(x^{(4)};\ y^{(4)}) - 0.62 < -\delta_5 \qquad (i = 3, 4, 5), \\ \psi_1(x^{(4)};\ y^{(4)}) < -\delta_5; \quad \psi_2(x^{(4)};\ y^{(4)}) < -\delta_5. \end{aligned}$$

Fifth step.

$$\zeta^{(5)}=(-1,\ 1;\ 1,\ -1);\quad \delta_6=\delta_5=0.21;\quad \lambda_6=\lambda_5=0.5;$$
$$t_5=0.018,\quad (x^{(5)};\ y^{(5)})=(-0.448;\ 0.018;\ 0.478;\ -0.018).$$

It is easy to see that the point

$$(x^*;\ y^*)=(-0.5;\ 0;\ 0.5;\ 0)$$

provides a solution to the problem.

4. POINTS CLOSEST TO A SYSTEM OF PLANES

As we noted in Paragraph 2, b of Section 1, the general geometric problem of finding points closest to a given finite system of k-dimensional planes in n-dimensional Euclidean space is a convex programming problem. Below we consider two special cases of this problem that are of particular interest.

1. Points Closest to a Given System of Points on a Plane

For $k = 0$, the general geometric problem of Paragraph 2,b of Section 1 degenerates into the problem of finding a point closest to a given system of points in n-dimensional space [4c]. We consider the special case $n = 2$, i.e., the problem of finding a point closest to a given system of points in a plane, where we assume that the distances are weighted.

Assume that we are given the 5 points

$$M_1(-3,\ -1);\quad M_2(-1,\ -3);\quad M_3(-{}^3/_2,\ -{}^5/_2);$$
$$M_4(0,\ 0);\quad M_5(-2,\ -2)$$

in a plane and that they are assigned weights $\frac{1}{\sqrt{2}}$; $\frac{1}{\sqrt{2}}$; $\frac{2}{\sqrt{2}}$; $\frac{1}{2\sqrt{2}}$; $\frac{2}{\sqrt{2}}$, respectively, i.e., the distances from the points $M(x,\ y)$ to M_i are

$$\rho_1(x,\ y)=\rho(M,\ M_1)=\frac{1}{\sqrt{2}}\sqrt{(x+3)^2+(y+1)^2},$$

$$\rho_2(x,\ y)=\rho(M,\ M_2)=\frac{1}{\sqrt{2}}\sqrt{(x+1)^2+(y+3)^2},$$

$$\rho_3(x,\ y)=\rho(M,\ M_3)=$$
$$=\frac{2}{\sqrt{2}}\sqrt{\left(x+\frac{3}{2}\right)^2+\left(y+\frac{5}{2}\right)^2}=\frac{1}{\sqrt{2}}\sqrt{(2x+3)^2+(2y+5)^2},$$

$$\rho_4(x,\ y)=\rho(M,\ M_4)=\frac{1}{2\sqrt{2}}\sqrt{x^2+y^2}=\frac{1}{\sqrt{2}}\sqrt{\frac{x^2}{4}+\frac{y^2}{4}},$$

$$\rho_5(x,\ y)=\rho(M,\ M_5)=$$
$$=\frac{2}{\sqrt{2}}\sqrt{(x+2)^2+(y+2)^2}=\frac{1}{\sqrt{2}}\sqrt{(2x+4)^2+(2y+4)^2}.$$

The problem of determining points closest to the given system of points consists of finding a point $M^*(x^*, y^*)$ such that

$$\max_{1 \leqslant \nu \leqslant 5} \rho_\nu^2(x^*, y^*) = \min_{(x, y)} \max_{1 \leqslant \nu \leqslant 5} \rho_\nu^2(x, y).$$

This problem is obviously equivalent to a problem of finding a Chebyshev point for the following inconsistent system of linear complex equations:

$$\Delta_1(z) = \frac{1}{\sqrt{2}}(z + 3 + i) = 0,$$

$$\Delta_2(z) = \frac{1}{\sqrt{2}}(z + 1 + 3i) = 0,$$

$$\Delta_3(z) = \frac{1}{\sqrt{2}}(2z + 3 + 5i) = 0,$$

$$\Delta_4(z) = \frac{1}{2\sqrt{2}} z = 0,$$

$$\Delta_5(z) = \frac{1}{\sqrt{2}}(2z + 4 + 4i) = 0.$$

That is, this problem is equivalent to the problem of finding a point z^* such that

$$\max_{1 \leqslant \nu \leqslant 5} |\Delta_\nu(z^*)|^2 = \min_z \max_{1 \leqslant \nu \leqslant 5} |\Delta_\nu(z)|^2.$$

For the initial approximation we take $(x^{(0)}, y^{(0)}) = (-1, -1)$ and set $\delta_1 = 0.5$. We find that

$$\max_{1 \leqslant \nu \leqslant 5} \rho_\nu^2(x^{(0)}, y^{(0)}) = \rho_3^2(x^{(0)}, y^{(0)}) = 5.$$

First step. 1) Determination of $\zeta^{(1)}$. Since there is only one maximal deviation, the motion must be along the antigradient (i.e., in the direction opposite to that of the gradient)

$$-\operatorname{grad} \rho_3^2(x^{(0)}, y^{(0)}) = \left(-\frac{\partial \rho_3^2(x^{(0)}, y^{(0)})}{\partial x}, -\frac{\partial \rho_3^2(x^{(0)}, y^{(0)})}{\partial y}\right) = (-2, -6)$$

and we may set $\zeta^{(1)} = (-1/3, -1)$.

2) Computation of δ_2. We have

$$\frac{\partial \rho_3^2(x^{(0)}, y^{(0)})}{\partial \zeta^{(1)}} = -\frac{20}{3} = \xi_1 < -\delta_1,$$

so that $\delta_2 = \delta_1 = 0.5$.

3) Determination of t_1. The motion must be along the ray $x = -1 - {}^1/_3 t;\ y = -1 - t;\ t > 0$. The smallest of the positive roots of the equations

$$\rho_3^2[(x^{(0)}, y^{(0)}) + t\zeta^{(1)}] = \rho_\nu^2[(x^{(0)}, y^{(0)}) + t\zeta^{(1)}] \quad (\nu = 1, 2, 4, 5)$$

is $0.6 = t_1$.

4) Determination of a new point and new maximal deviations.

$$(x^{(1)}, y^{(1)}) = (x^{(0)}, y^{(0)}) + t_1\zeta^{(1)} = (-1.2; -1.6),$$
$$\max_{1 \leqslant \nu \leqslant 5} \rho_\nu^2 (x^{(1)}, y^{(1)}) = \rho_1^2 (x^{(1)}, y^{(1)}) = \rho_3^2 (x^{(1)}, y^{(1)}) = 1.8,$$
$$-\delta_1 < \rho_5^2 (x^{(1)}, y^{(1)}) - 1.8 < 0,$$
$$\rho_2^2 (x^{(1)}, y^{(1)}) - 1.8 < -\delta_1, \quad \rho_4^2 (x^{(1)}, y^{(1)}) - 1.8 < -\delta_1.$$

Second step. 1) Determination of $\zeta^{(2)}$.

$$\frac{1}{2} \cdot \frac{\partial \rho_1^2 (x^{(1)}, y^{(1)})}{\partial \zeta} = 0.9\zeta_1 - 0.3\zeta_2,$$
$$\frac{1}{2} \cdot \frac{\partial \rho_3^2 (x^{(1)}, y^{(1)})}{\partial \zeta} = 0.6\zeta_1 + 1.8\zeta_2,$$
$$\frac{1}{2} \cdot \frac{\partial \rho_5^2 (x^{(1)}, y^{(1)})}{\partial \zeta} = 1.6\zeta_1 + 0.8\zeta_2.$$

We now minimize the form

$$u = \xi$$

under the constraints

$$0.9\zeta_1 - 0.3\zeta_2 - \xi \leqslant 0,$$
$$0.6\zeta_1 + 1.8\zeta_2 - \xi \leqslant 0,$$
$$1.6\zeta_1 + 0.8\zeta_2 - \xi \leqslant 0,$$
$$|\zeta_i| \leqslant 1 \qquad (i = 1, 2).$$

We find that $\zeta^{(2)} = (-1; -0.14)$.

2) Determination of δ_3. We have $0 > \xi_2 = -0.85 < -\delta_2$, so we set $\delta_3 = \delta_2 = 0.5$.

3) Determination of t_2. The motion must be along the ray

$$x = -1.2 - t; \quad y = -1.6 - 0.14t; \quad t > 0.$$

For this step we find

$$t_2 = \min\{t', t''\} = t' = 0.42.$$

4) Determination of a new point and new maximal deviations.

$$(x^{(2)}, y^{(2)}) = (x^{(1)}, y^{(1)}) + t_2\zeta^{(2)} = (-1.62; -1.66),$$
$$\max_{1 \leqslant \nu \leqslant 5} \rho_\nu^2 (x^{(2)}, y^{(2)}) = \rho_3^2 (x^{(2)}, y^{(2)}) = 1.44,$$
$$-\delta_3 < \rho_i^2 (x^{(2)}, y^{(2)}) - 1.44 < 0 \qquad (i = 1, 2),$$
$$\rho_\nu^2 (x^{(2)}, y^{(2)}) - 1.44 < -\delta_3 \qquad (\nu = 4, 5).$$

Third step. 1) Determination of $\zeta^{(3)}$.

$$\frac{1}{2}\cdot\frac{\partial\rho_1^2(x^{(2)}, y^{(2)})}{\partial\zeta} = 0.69\zeta_1 - 0.33\zeta_2,$$
$$\frac{1}{2}\cdot\frac{\partial\rho_2^2(x^{(2)}, y^{(2)})}{\partial\zeta} = -0.31\zeta_1 + 0.67\zeta_2,$$
$$\frac{1}{2}\cdot\frac{\partial\rho_3^2(x^{(2)}, y^{(2)})}{\partial\zeta} = -0.24\zeta_1 + 1.68\zeta_2.$$

We minimize the form

$$u = \xi$$

under the constraints

$$\begin{aligned} 0.69\zeta_1 - 0.33\zeta_2 - \xi &\leqslant 0, \\ -0.31\zeta_1 + 0.67\zeta_2 - \xi &\leqslant 0, \\ -0.24\zeta_1 + 1.68\zeta_2 - \xi &\leqslant 0, \\ |\zeta_i| \leqslant 1 \qquad (i &= 1, 2). \end{aligned}$$

We find that $\zeta^{(3)} = (-1, -1)$.

2) Determination of δ_4. We have $\xi_3 = -0.36 > -\delta_3$, so $\delta_4 = \frac{\delta_3}{2} = 0.25$

3) Determination of t_3. The motion must be along the ray

$$x = -1.62 - t; \quad y = -1.66 - t; \quad t > 0.$$

For this step we find

$$t_3 = t' = 0.36.$$

4) Determination of a new point and new maximal deviations.

$$(x^{(3)}, y^{(3)}) = (x^{(2)}, y^{(2)}) + t_3\zeta^{(3)} \approx (-2, -2),$$
$$\max_{1\leqslant\nu\leqslant 5} \rho_\nu^2(x^{(3)}, y^{(3)}) = \rho_1^2(x^{(3)}, y^{(3)}) =$$
$$= \rho_2^2(x^{(3)}, y^{(3)}) = \rho_3^2(x^{(3)}, y^{(3)}) = \rho_4^2(x^{(3)}, y^{(3)}) = 1,$$
$$\rho_5^2(x^{(3)}, y^{(3)}) - 1 < -\delta_4.$$

Fourth step. 1) Determination of $\zeta^{(4)}$.

$$\frac{\partial\rho_1^2(x^{(3)}, y^{(3)})}{\partial\zeta} = \zeta_1 - \zeta_2,$$
$$\frac{\partial\rho_2^2(x^{(3)}, y^{(3)})}{\partial\zeta} = -\zeta_1 + \zeta_2,$$
$$\frac{\partial\rho_3^2(x^{(3)}, y^{(3)})}{\partial\zeta} = -2\zeta_1 + 2\zeta_2,$$
$$\frac{\partial\rho_4^2(x^{(3)}, y^{(3)})}{\partial\zeta} = -\zeta_1 - \zeta_2.$$

We minimize the form

$$u = \xi$$

under the constraints

$$\begin{aligned} \zeta_1 - \zeta_2 - \xi &\leqslant 0, \\ -\zeta_1 + \zeta_2 - \xi &\leqslant 0, \\ -2\zeta_1 + 2\zeta_2 - \xi &\leqslant 0, \\ -\zeta_1 - \zeta_2 - \xi &\leqslant 0, \\ |\zeta_i| &\leqslant 1 \ (i = 1, 2). \end{aligned}$$

we find that min $u = 0$.

2) Application of the solution criterion. Since the deviations entering into the determination of the direction of the steepest descent in the linear programming problem solved in the fourth step are all equal to each other, it follows from the solution criterion (Paragraph 1,c of Section 2), that the point $(x^{(3)}, y^{(3)}) =$ (-2, -2) is the desired solution.

Remark. We have considered the form of the problem in which the desired point M^* is sought anywhere in a plane. The somewhat more complex form in which M^* is sought in some convex set of points in a plane is solved with an algorithm analogous to that used in the example of Paragraph 2 of Section 3.

2. Points Closest to a Given System of Lines (in a Space)

We now consider the special case of the general geometric problem (6.7)-(6.8) with $k = 1$ and $n = 3$, i.e., the problem of finding a point closest to a system of lines in 3-space.

Example. In 3-space, assume that we are given the five lines

$$\alpha_1: \begin{cases} \dfrac{x_1 - x_2 - 1}{\sqrt{2}} = 0, \\ \dfrac{x_1 + x_2}{\sqrt{2}} = 0; \end{cases} \qquad \alpha_4: \begin{cases} x_2 = 0, \\ x_3 - 1 = 0; \end{cases}$$

$$\alpha_2: \begin{cases} x_1 - 1 = 0, \\ x_2 + 2 = 0; \end{cases} \qquad \alpha_5: \begin{cases} \dfrac{x_1 - 2x_2 - x_3 - 2}{\sqrt{6}} = 0, \\ \dfrac{x_1 + x_2 - x_3 + 1}{\sqrt{3}} = 0, \end{cases}$$

$$\alpha_3: \begin{cases} \dfrac{x_1 - x_3}{\sqrt{2}} = 0, \\ \dfrac{x_1 + x_3 - 2}{\sqrt{2}} = 0; \end{cases}$$

we also assume that these lines are given the weights $\sqrt{2}$, 1, $\sqrt{2}$, 1, $\sqrt{6}$, so that the distances $\rho_i(x)$ from the point $x=(x_1, x_2, x_3)$ to the lines α_i (i = 1, 2, 3, 4, 5) are given by the formula

$$\rho_1(x)=\sqrt{2}\sqrt{\left(\frac{x_1-x_2-1}{\sqrt{2}}\right)^2+\left(\frac{x_1+x_2}{\sqrt{2}}\right)^2}=$$
$$=\sqrt{(x_1-x_2-1)^2+(x_1+x_2)^2},$$
$$\rho_2(x)=\sqrt{(x_1-1)^2+(x_2+2)^2},$$
$$\rho_3(x)=\sqrt{2}\sqrt{\left(\frac{x_1-x_3}{\sqrt{2}}\right)^2+\left(\frac{x_1+x_3-2}{\sqrt{2}}\right)^2}=$$
$$=\sqrt{(x_1-x_3)^2+(x_1+x_3-2)^2},$$
$$\rho_4(x)=\sqrt{x_2^2+(x_3-1)^2},$$
$$\rho_5(x)=\sqrt{6}\sqrt{\left(\frac{x_1-2x_2-x_3-2}{\sqrt{6}}\right)^2+\left(\frac{x_1+x_2-x_3+1}{\sqrt{3}}\right)^2}=$$
$$=\sqrt{(x_1-2x_2-x_3-2)^2+2(x_1+x_2-x_3+1)^2}.$$

The problem of determining the points closest to the given system of lines consists in finding a point $x^* = (x_1^*, x_2^*, x_3^*)$ such that

$$\max_{1\leqslant i\leqslant 5}\rho_i^2(x^*)=\min_x\max_{1\leqslant i\leqslant 5}\rho_i^2(x).$$

For the initial approximation we take the point $x^{(0)}$ = (0,0,0) and set δ_1 = 0.50. We have

$$\max_{1\leqslant i\leqslant 5}\rho_i^2(x^{(0)})=\rho_5^2(x^{(0)})=6,$$
$$\rho_i^2(x^{(0)})-6<-\delta_1 \qquad (i=1,\ 2,\ 3,\ 4).$$

First step. *1) Determination of* $\zeta^{(1)}$. Since there is only one maximal distance, motion must be along the antigradient

$$-\operatorname{grad}\rho_5^2(x^{(0)})=(0,\ -12,\ 0)$$

and we must choose $\zeta^{(1)}=(0,\ -1,\ 0)$.

2) Computation of δ_2. We have

$$\frac{\partial\rho_5^2(x^{(0)})}{\partial\zeta^{(1)}}=-12<-\delta_1,$$

so that δ_2 = δ_1 = 0.50.

3) Determination of t_1. The motion must be along the ray

$$x_1=0;\ x_2=-t;\ x_3=0;\ t>0.$$

For t_1 we have

$$t_1 = \min\{t', t''\} = t'' = 0.14,$$

where t' minimizes the expression $\rho_5^2(x^{(0)} + t\zeta^{(1)})$ while t'' is the smallest positive root of the equations

$$\rho_5^2(x^{(0)} + t\zeta^{(1)}) = \rho_i^2(x^{(0)} + t\zeta^{(1)}) \qquad (i = 1, 2, 3, 4).$$

4) Determination of a new point and new maximal distances.

$$x^{(1)} = x^{(0)} + t_1\zeta^{(1)} = (0;\ -0.14;\ 0),$$
$$\max_{1 \leqslant i \leqslant 5} \rho_i^2(x^{(1)}) = \rho_2^2(x^{(1)}) = \rho_5^2(x^{(1)}) = 4.46,$$
$$-\delta_2 < \rho_3^2(x^{(1)}) - 4.46 < 0,$$
$$\rho_i^2(x^{(1)}) - 4.46 < -\delta_2 \qquad (i = 1, 4).$$

Second step. 1) Determination of $\zeta^{(2)}$. We minimize the form

$$u = \xi$$

under the constraints

$$\begin{aligned} -2\zeta_1 + 3.72\zeta_2 \qquad\qquad & - \xi \leqslant 0, \\ -4\zeta_1 \qquad\qquad - 4\zeta_3 & - \xi \leqslant 0, \\ 10.32\zeta_2 \qquad\qquad & - \xi \leqslant 0, \\ |\zeta_i| \leqslant 1 \quad (i = 1, 2, 3). & \end{aligned}$$

We find that

$$\zeta^{(2)} = (1, -1, 1).$$

2) Computation of δ_3. We have $\xi_2 = -5.72 < -\delta_2$, so that $\delta_3 = \delta_2 = 0.50$.

3) Determination of t_2. The motion must be along the ray

$$x_1 = t;\ x_2 = -0.14 - t;\ x_3 = t;\ t > 0.$$

For the step we find $t_2 = t'' = 0.86$.

4) Determination of a new approximation and new maximal distances.

$$x^{(2)} = (0.86;\ -1;\ 0.86),$$
$$\max_{1 \leqslant i \leqslant 5} \rho_i^2(x^{(2)}) = \rho_2^2(x^{(2)}) = \rho_4^2(x^{(2)}) = 1.02,$$
$$-\delta_3 < \rho_1^2(x^{(2)}) - 1.02 < 0,$$
$$\rho_i^2(x^{(2)}) - 1.02 < -\delta_3 \qquad (i = 3, 5).$$

Third step. 1) Determination of $\zeta^{(3)}$. We minimize the form

$$u = \xi$$

under the constraints

$$\begin{aligned} 3.44\zeta_1 - 2\zeta_2 \qquad\qquad & - \xi \leqslant 0, \\ -0.28\zeta_1 + 2\zeta_2 \qquad\qquad & - \xi \leqslant 0, \\ - 2\zeta_2 - 0.28\zeta_3 & - \xi \leqslant 0, \\ |\zeta_i| \leqslant 1 \qquad (i = 1,\ 2,\ 3). & \end{aligned}$$

We find that

$$\zeta^{(3)} = (-0.08;\ -0.08;\ 1).$$

2) Determination of δ_4. We have $\xi_3 = -0.12 > -\delta_3$, so that $\delta_4 = \frac{\delta_3}{2} = 0.25$.

3) Determination of t_3. The motion must be along the ray

$$x_1 = 0.86 - 0.08t;\ x_2 = -1 - 0.08t;\ x_3 = 0.86 + t;\ t > 0;$$
$$t_3 = t' = 0.06.$$

4) Determination of a new point and new maximal distances.

$$\begin{aligned} x^{(3)} &= (0.86;\ -1.00;\ 0.92), \\ \max_{1 \leqslant i \leqslant 5} \rho_i^2(x^{(3)}) &= \rho_2^2(x^{(3)}) = 1.02, \\ -\delta_4 &< \rho_4^2(x^{(3)}) - 1.02 < 0, \\ \rho_i^2(x^{(3)}) - 1.02 &< -\delta_4 \qquad (i = 1,\ 3,\ 5). \end{aligned}$$

Fourth step. 1) Determination of $\zeta^{(4)}$. We minimize the form

$$u = \xi$$

under the constraints

$$\begin{aligned} -0.28\zeta_1 + 2\zeta_2 \qquad\qquad & - \xi \leqslant 0, \\ - 2\zeta_2 - 0.16\zeta_3 & - \xi \leqslant 0, \\ |\zeta_i| \leqslant 1 \qquad (i = 1,\ 2,\ 3). & \end{aligned}$$

We have $\zeta^{(4)} = (1;\ 0.03;\ 1)$.

2) Computation of δ_5. We have $\xi_4 = -0.220 > -\delta_4$, so that $\delta_5 = \frac{\delta_4}{2} = 0.125$.

3) *Determination of* t_4. The motion must be along the ray

$$x_1 = 0.86 + t;\ x_2 = -1 + 0.03t;\ x_3 = 0.92 + t;\ t > 0;$$
$$t_4 = t' = 0.11.$$

4) *Determination of a new point.*

$$x^{(4)} = (0.97;\ -1;\ 1.03).$$

5) *Application of the solution criterion.* We consider the point x^* (1, -1, 1) and $\delta^* = 0$. We have

$$\max_{1 \leqslant i \leqslant 5} \rho_i^2(x^*) = \rho_1^2(x^*) = \rho_2^2(x^*) = \rho_4^2(x^*) = 1.$$

To determine the direction of steepest descent, we solve the following linear programming problem: Minimize the form

$$u = \xi$$

under the constraints

$$2\zeta_1 - 2\zeta_2 - \xi \leqslant 0,$$
$$2\zeta_2 - \xi \leqslant 0,$$
$$-2\zeta_2 - \xi \leqslant 0,$$
$$|\zeta_i| \leqslant 1 \qquad (i = 1,\ 2,\ 3).$$

We find min $u = 0$, and, in virtue of the solution criterion of Paragraph 1 of Section 2, the point x^* (1, -1, 1) is a solution of the problem.

5. QUADRATIC PROGRAMMING

1. Statement of the Problem

Assume that we are given a quadratic function

$$f(x) = f(x_1, \ldots, x_n) = \frac{1}{2}\sum_{i=1}^{n}\sum_{j=1}^{n} b_{ij}x_ix_j + \sum_{i=1}^{n} c_ix_i \tag{6.35'}$$

or, in matrix form,

$$f(x) = \frac{1}{2}x^TBx + c^Tx\ ^*, \tag{6.35}$$

---

* $x^T \equiv (x_1, \ldots, x_n)$, i.e., x^T is the row obtained by transposing the column $x \equiv \begin{pmatrix} x_1 \\ \vdots \\ x_n \end{pmatrix}$; $B = \| b_{ij} \|$.

and the linear inequalities

$$\psi_j(x) = \psi_j(x_1, \ldots, x_n) = \\ = a_{j1}x_1 + \ldots + a_{jn}x_n + a_j \leqslant 0 \quad (j = 1, \ldots, m), \tag{6.36'}$$

which take the matrix form

$$Ax + a \leqslant 0, \tag{6.36}$$

and assume that inequalities (6.36) define some region Ω containing an interior point.

We assume that the matrix $B = \|b_{ij}\|$ is symmetric and positive definite, so that $f(x)$ is a convex function.

The quadratic programming problem can be stated as follows: Find a point $x^* \in \Omega$ that minimizes the function (6.35) under constraints (6.36):

$$f(x^*) = \min_{x \in \Omega} f(x). \tag{6.37}$$

2. Application of the Convex Programming Algorithm

Preliminary step. The initial approximation $x^{(0)} \in \Omega$ can be computed, for example, with the simplex method.

Iterated step. Assume that we have already found an initial approximation $x^{(0)} \in \Omega$. Without loss of generality, we can assume that $x^{(0)}$ lies on the boundary of Ω.

As in the general algorithm of Paragraph 1, Section 2, in each step we find a value for the positive parameter δ_k (k is the number of the step). We begin with some arbitrary sufficiently small δ_1 in the first step (after the preliminary step), and we say that the point $x^{(0)}$ belongs to the plane $\psi_j(x) = 0$, if

$$-\delta_1 < \psi_j(x^{(0)}) \leqslant 0.$$

Let, for example,

$$-\delta_1 < \psi_{j_\nu}(x^{(0)}) \leqslant 0 \quad (\nu = 1, \ldots, \nu_1),$$
$$\psi_j(x^{(0)}) \leqslant -\delta_1 \quad (j \neq j_1, \ldots, j_{\nu_1}).$$

1) Determination of descent directions. We determine the direction $\zeta^{(1)} \equiv (\zeta_1^{(1)}, \ldots, \zeta_n^{(1)})$ of descent from the point $x^{(0)}$ by solving the following linear programming problem:

Minimize the linear form

$$u = (Bx^{(0)} + c)^T \zeta = \sum_{i=1}^{n} \frac{\partial f(x^{(0)})}{\partial x_i} \zeta_i$$

under the constraints

$$a_{j_\nu 1}\zeta_1 + \dots + a_{j_\nu n}\zeta_n \leqslant 0 \qquad (\nu = 1, \dots, \nu_1),$$
$$|\zeta_i| \leqslant C \qquad (i = 1, \dots, n).$$

We denote $\min u$ by u_1.

2) Computation of a new δ. There are two cases:

a) $u_1 < -\delta_1$, b) $u_1 \geqslant -\delta_1$.

In case a) the value of δ does not change, i.e., we set $\delta_2 = \delta_1$ and continue the process.

If $-\delta_1 \leqslant u_1 < 0$ in case b), we set $\delta_2 = \frac{\delta_1}{2}$ and continue the process; if, however, $u_1 = 0$, we check whether $x^{(0)}$ is a solution of the problem. Let, for example,

$$\psi_{j_\mu}(x^{(0)}) = 0 \qquad (\mu = 1, \dots, \mu_1).$$
$$\psi_j(x^{(0)}) < 0 \qquad (j \neq j_1, \dots, j_{\mu_1}).$$

Now we solve the following linear programming problem:

Minimize the form

$$u = \sum_{i=1}^{n} \frac{\partial f(x^{(0)})}{\partial x_i} \zeta_i$$

under the constraints

$$a_{j_\mu 1}\zeta_1 + \dots + a_{j_\mu n}\zeta_n \leqslant 0 \qquad (\mu = 1, \dots, \mu_1),$$
$$|\zeta_i| \leqslant C \qquad (i = 1, \dots, n).$$

If $\min u = u_1' = 0$, then $x^{(0)}$ is a solution of problem (6.36) - (6.37).

If, however, $u_1' < 0$, we again set $\delta_2 = \frac{\delta_1}{2}$ and continue the process by taking the solution of the linear programming problem under discussion as the direction of steepest descent.

3) Computation of t_1. Assume that we have already found the direction $\zeta^{(1)}$ of steepest descent from the point $x^{(0)}$. We now proceed to move in this direction, i.e., to increase t in the formula

$$x = x^{(0)} + t\zeta^{(1)}$$

until $t_1 = \min\{t', t''\}$, where

$$t' = -\frac{(Bx^{(0)} + c)^T \zeta^{(1)}}{(\zeta^{(1)})^T B\zeta^{(1)}}$$

minimizes the function $f(x^{(0)} + t\zeta^{(1)})$ and t'' is the smallest positive number in the set of numbers

$$\frac{-\psi_1(x^{(0)})}{\sum_{i=1}^{n} a_{1i}\zeta_i^{(1)}}, \ldots, \frac{-\psi_m(x^{(0)})}{\sum_{i=1}^{n} a_{mi}\zeta_i^{(1)}}.$$

4) Determination of a new point and new deviations. For the new approximation we take $x^{(1)} = x^{(0)} + t_1\zeta^{(1)}$ and compute new deviations. We proceed with the process, taking $x^{(1)}$ as the initial point and δ_2 as the value of the parameter.

5) A solution criterion and an estimate of the approximation quality. Assume that we have obtained the approximation $x^{(k-1)}$ and in determining the direction of descent $\zeta^{(k)}$ from the point $x^{(k-1)}$, we find that min $u = u_k = 0$. Then, as described above in 2), $x^{(k-1)}$ is the solution if $u'_k = 0$.

We now consider the problem of estimating the closeness of the approximation $f(x^{(k)})$ of the kth step to $f(x^*) = \min_{x \in \Omega} f(x)$. To do so, as in the general case of Paragraph 1 of Section 2, we consider the equation of the plane tangent to the surface $y = f(x)$ at the point $x^{(k)} \in \Omega$:

$$Y - f(x^{(k)}) = (Bx^{(k)} + c)^T (x - x^{(k)}).$$

Because $f(x)$ is convex, we have

$$f(x) \geqslant Y.$$

Substituting into the preceding equation, we obtain the inequality

$$(Bx^{(k)} + c)^T (x - x^{(k)}) \leqslant f(x) - f(x^{(k)}),$$

so that

$$\left|\min_{x \in \Omega} [f(x) - f(x^{(k)})]\right| \leqslant \left|\min_{x \in \Omega} (Bx^{(k)} + c)^T (x - x^{(k)})\right|.$$

Thus, in order to obtain an upper bound for the closeness of $f(x^{(k)})$ to $f(x^*) = \min_{x \in \Omega} f(x)$, it is sufficient to find $\min_{x \in \Omega} (Bx^{(k)} + c)^T (x - x^{(k)})$.

Example. Minimize the function

$$f(x) = x_1^2 + \frac{1}{2} x_2^2 + 2x_3^2$$

under the constraints

$$\begin{aligned}
\psi_1(x) &= x_1 + x_2 + x_3 - 2 \leqslant 0,\\
\psi_2(x) &= -2x_1 - x_2 - 3x_3 + 5 \leqslant 0,\\
\psi_3(x) &= x_1 - x_2 - 2 \leqslant 0,\\
\psi_4(x) &= x_1 + \frac{1}{2}x_2 - x_3 - 1 \leqslant 0,\\
\psi_5(x) &= -x_1 + 2x_2 - 2x_3 + 3 \leqslant 0,\\
\psi_6(x) &= x_2 - 3x_3 + 1 \leqslant 0.
\end{aligned}$$

For the initial approximation we take the point $x^{(0)} = (0, 0, 2)$, and for the initial value of δ we take $\delta_1 = 0.50$. We have

$$\psi_1(x^{(0)}) = 0; \ \psi_i(x^{(0)}) < -\delta_1 \qquad (i = 2, 3, 4, 5, 6).$$

First step. *1) Determination of* $\zeta^{(1)}$. To find the direction $\zeta^{(1)} = (\zeta_1^{(1)}, \zeta_2^{(1)}, \zeta_3^{(1)})$, we solve the following linear programming problem: Minimize the form

$$u = 8\zeta_3$$

under the constraints

$$\zeta_1 + \zeta_2 + \zeta_3 \leqslant 0,$$
$$|\zeta_i| \leqslant 1 \qquad (i = 1, 2, 3).$$

We find that

$$\zeta^{(1)} = (0, 0, -1).$$

2) Determination of δ_2. We have $u_1 = -8 < -\delta_1$, so that $\delta_2 = \delta_1 = 0.50$.

3) Determination of t_1. We move along the ray

$$x_1 = 0; \qquad x_2 = 0; \qquad x_3 = 2 - t; \qquad t > 0.$$

For t_1 we find

$$t_1 = t'' = 0.33.$$

4) Determination of a new point and new deviations.

$$x^{(1)} = x^{(0)} + t_1\zeta^{(1)} = (0;\ 0;\ 1.67),$$
$$\psi_2(x^{(1)}) = 0; \ -\delta_2 < \psi_1(x^{(1)}) < 0; \ -\delta_2 < \psi_5(x^{(1)}) < 0;$$
$$\psi_j(x^{(1)}) < -\delta_2 \qquad (j = 3, 4, 6).$$

Second step. 1) Determination of $\zeta^{(2)}$. To find $\zeta^{(2)}$, we solve the following linear programming problem:

Minimize the form

$$u = 6.65\zeta_3$$

under the constraints

$$\begin{aligned} \zeta_1 + \zeta_2 + \zeta_3 &\leqslant 0, \\ -2\zeta_1 - \zeta_2 - 3\zeta_3 &\leqslant 0, \\ -\zeta_1 + 2\zeta_2 - 2\zeta_3 &\leqslant 0, \\ |\zeta_i| \leqslant 1 \qquad (i = 1,\ 2,\ 3). \end{aligned}$$

We find that

$$\zeta^{(2)} = (1;\ -0.5;\ -0.5).$$

2) Determination of δ_3. We have $u_2 = -3.32 < -\delta_2$, so that $\delta_3 = \delta_2 = 0.50$.

3) Determination of t_2. We move along the ray

$$x_1 = t; \qquad x_2 = -0.5t; \qquad x_3 = 1.67 - 0.5t; \qquad t > 0.$$

For t_2 we find

$$t_2 = t' = 1.03.$$

4) Determination of a new point and new deviations.

$$x^{(2)} = (1.03;\ -0.52;\ 1.15),$$

$$-\delta_3 < \psi_1(x^{(2)}) < 0; \ -\delta_3 < \psi_2(x^{(2)}) = 0; \ -\delta_3 < \psi_3(x^{(2)}) < 0;$$

$$\psi_j(x^{(2)}) < -\delta_3 \qquad (j = 4,\ 5,\ 6).$$

Third step. 1) Determination of $\zeta^{(3)}$. We minimize

$$u = 2.06\zeta_1 - 0.52\zeta_2 + 4.6\zeta_3$$

under the constraints

$$\begin{aligned} \zeta_1 + \zeta_2 + \zeta_3 &\leqslant 0, \\ -2\zeta_1 - \zeta_2 - 3\zeta_3 &\leqslant 0, \\ \zeta_1 - \zeta_2 &\leqslant 0, \\ |\zeta_i| \leqslant 1 \qquad (i = 1,\ 2,\ 3). \end{aligned}$$

We find that

$$\zeta^{(3)} = (-1;\ 0.5;\ 0.5).$$

2) Determination of δ_4. We have $u_3 = -0.02 > -\delta_3$, so that $\delta_4 = \frac{\delta_3}{2} = 0.25$.

3) Determination of t_4. We move along the ray

$$x_1 = 1.03 - t; \qquad x_2 = -0.52 + 0.5t;$$
$$x_3 = 1.15 + 0.5t; \qquad t > 0.$$

For the step t_3 we have

$$t_3 = t' = 0.006 \approx 0.$$

4) Determination of a new point and new deviations.

$$x^{(3)} = x^{(2)} = (1.03;\ -0.52;\ 1.15);$$
$$-\delta_4 < \psi_2(x^{(4)}) = 0; \quad \psi_j(x^{(4)}) < -\delta_4 \qquad (j = 1,\ 3,\ 4,\ 5,\ 6).$$

Fourth step. 1) Determination of $\zeta^{(4}$. We minimize

$$u = 2.06\zeta_1 - 0.52\zeta_2 + 4.6\zeta_3$$

under the constraints

$$-2\zeta_1 - \zeta_2 - 3\zeta_3 \leqslant 0$$
$$|\zeta_i| \leqslant 1 \qquad (i = 1,\ 2,\ 3).$$

We find that

$$\zeta^{(4)} = (1,\ 1,\ -1).$$

2) Determination of δ_5. We have $u_4 = -3.06 < -\delta_4$, so that $\delta_5 = \delta_4 = 0.25$.

3) Determination of t_4. We move along the ray

$$x_1 = 1.03 + t; \qquad x_2 = -0.52 + t;$$
$$x_3 = 1.15 - t; \qquad t > 0.$$

For t_4 we have

$$t_4 = t'' = 0.34.$$

4) Determination of a new point and new deviations.

$$x^{(4)} = (1.37;\ -0.18;\ 0.81),$$
$$-\delta_5 < \psi_1(x^{(5)}) = 0; \quad -\delta_5 < \psi_2(x^{(5)}) = 0;$$
$$\psi_j(x^{(5)}) < -\delta_5 \qquad (j = 3,\ 4,\ 5,\ 6).$$

Fifth step. 1) Determination of $\zeta^{(5)}$. We minimize

$$u = 2.74\zeta_1 - 0.18\zeta_2 + 3.24\zeta_3$$

under the constraints

$$\zeta_1 + \zeta_2 + \zeta_3 \leqslant 0,$$
$$-2\zeta_1 - \zeta_2 - 3\zeta_3 \leqslant 0,$$
$$|\zeta_i| \leqslant 1 \qquad (i = 1,\ 2,\ 3).$$

We find that

$$\zeta^{(5)} = (-1;\ 0.5;\ 0.5).$$

2) *Determination of* δ_6. We have $u_5 = -1.21 < -\delta_5$, so that $\delta_6 = \delta_5 = 0.25$.

3) *Determination of* t_5. We move along the ray

$$x_1 = 1.37 - t; \qquad x_2 = -0.18 + 0.5t;$$
$$x_3 = 0.81 + 0.5t; \qquad t > 0.$$

For the step t_5 we have

$$t_5 = t'' = 0.35.$$

4) *Determination of a new point.*

$$x^{(5)} = (1.020;\ -0.005;\ 0.985).$$

5) It is easy to verify that the point $x^* = (1, 0, 1)$ is a solution.

3. A Finite Algorithm for Quadratic Programming

We will now present one finite algorithm for solving quadratic programming problem (6.35) – (6.37) [5a].

1) We construct a table of coefficients of the constants (6.36′) and of the partial derivatives of the function $f(x)$ (6.35′) whose minimum we seek:

	x_1	$\dots$	x_j	$\dots$	x_n	1
$\psi_1 =$	a_{11}	$\dots$	a_{1j}	$\dots$	a_{1n}	a_1
$\dots$	$\dots$	$\dots$	$\dots$	$\dots$	$\dots$	$\dots$
$\psi_i =$	a_{i1}	$\dots$	a_{ij}	$\dots$	a_{in}	a_i
$\dots$	$\dots$	$\dots$	$\dots$	$\dots$	$\dots$	$\dots$
$\psi_m =$	a_{m1}	$\dots$	a_{mj}	$\dots$	a_{mn}	a_m
$f'_{x_1} =$	b_{11}	$\dots$	b_{1j}	$\dots$	b_{1n}	c_1
$\dots$	$\dots$	$\dots$	$\dots$	$\dots$	$\dots$	$\dots$
$f'_{x_k} =$	b_{k1}	$\dots$	b_{kj}	$\dots$	b_{kn}	c_k
$\dots$	$\dots$	$\dots$	$\dots$	$\dots$	$\dots$	$\dots$
$f'_{x_n} =$	b_{n1}	$\dots$	b_{nj}	$\dots$	b_{nn}	c_n

.

We now find a point $\alpha^{(1)}$ that minimizes $f(x)$. If $\alpha^{(1)} \in \Omega$, then $\alpha^{(1)} = x^*$ and the problem is solved. If, however, $\alpha^{(1)} \notin \Omega$, we choose an arbitrary point $x^{(0)} \in \Omega$ (initial point) and a vector $\zeta^{(1)} = \alpha^{(1)} - x^{(0)}$, along which we move toward the point $\alpha^{(1)}$ until the boundary of the polyhedron is met at some point $x^{(1)}$, which we take for the initial approximation, i.e., we increase t in the formula

$$x = x^{(0)} + t\zeta^{(1)}$$

until it reaches a value t_1 equal to the smallest positive quantity in the set of numbers

$$\frac{-\psi_1(x^{(0)})}{\sum_{i=1}^{n} a_{1i}\zeta_i^{(1)}}, \ \ldots, \ \frac{-\psi_m(x^{(0)})}{\sum_{i=1}^{n} a_{mi}\zeta_i^{(1)}}, \ 1.$$

For convenience, assume that t_1 is reached at $j = 1, \ldots, \mu$, i.e.,

$$\psi_1(x^{(1)}) = \ldots = \psi_\mu(x^{(1)}) = 0.$$

By using the appropriate number of successive Jordan eliminations over arbitrarily chosen resolvent elements, we carry as many as possible of the annihilated ψ_j $(j = 1, \ldots, \mu)$ to the top of the table. Here each Jordan elimination is supplemented by the following operation (since on the right side we differentiate a composite function): If Jordan elimination exchanges ψ_i and x_j (a_{ij} is the resolvent element), we add, to each of the elements in the new row of f'_{x_k} $(k \neq j)$, the corresponding elements of the new row of f'_{x_j}, multiplied by the new value of a_{ik} (i.e., by $\frac{a_{ik}}{a_{ij}}$). We again denote the new row by f'_{x_k}. The elements in the new row f'_{x_j} are simply multiplied by the new value of a_{ij}, i.e., by $\frac{1}{a_{ij}}$, and the row is relabeled f'_{ψ_i}.

Indeed, if we exchange ψ_i and x_j (if the resolvent element is a_{ij}), then

$$x_j = \frac{\psi_i}{a_{ij}} - \frac{a_{i1}x_1}{a_{ij}} - \ldots - \frac{a_{i,j-1}x_{j-1}}{a_{ij}} - \frac{a_{i,j+1}x_{j+1}}{a_{ij}} - \ldots - \frac{a_{in}x_n}{a_{ij}} - \frac{a_i}{a_{ij}};$$

as a result,

$$\text{a)} \ \frac{\partial}{\partial x_k} f[x_1, \ldots, x_{j-1}, x_j(x_1, \ldots, x_{j-1}, \psi_i, x_{j+1}, \ldots, x_n), x_{j+1}, \ldots, x_n] =$$
$$= \frac{\partial f}{\partial x_k} + \frac{\partial f}{\partial x_j}\frac{\partial x_j}{\partial x_k} = f'_{x_k}(x_1, \ldots, x_{j-1}, \psi_i, x_{j+1}, \ldots, x_n) + f'_{x_j}(x_1, \ldots, x_{j-1}, \psi_i, x_{j+1}, \ldots, x_n)\left(-\frac{a_{ik}}{a_{ij}}\right),$$

where $f'_{x_k}(x_1, \ldots, x_{j-1}, \psi_i, x_{j+1}, \ldots, x_n)$ is the new row and $f'_{x_j}(x_1, \ldots, x_{j-1}, \psi_i, x_{j+1}, \ldots, x_n)$ is also a new row;

$$\text{b)}\ \frac{\partial}{\partial \psi_i} f\,[x_1, \ldots, x_{j-1}, x_j(x_1, \ldots, x_{j-1}, \psi_i, x_{j+1}, \ldots, x_n), x_{j+1}, \ldots, x_n] =$$

$$= \frac{\partial f}{\partial x_j}\frac{\partial x_j}{\partial \psi_i} = f'_{x_j}(x_1, \ldots, x_{j-1}, \psi_i, x_{j+1}, \ldots, x_n)\frac{1}{a_{ij}}.$$

Below we assume that this additional operation has been added to each Jordan elimination.

Assume that after $r \leqslant \mu$ successive Jordan eliminations we have obtained the table

$$\begin{array}{r|cccccc|c|}
 & \psi_1 & \ldots & \psi_r & x_{r+1} & \ldots & x_n & 1 \\
\hline
\psi_{r+1} = & a^{(r)}_{r+1,1} & \ldots & a^{(r)}_{r+1,r} & 0 & \ldots & 0 & 0 \\
\ldots & \ldots & \ldots & \ldots & \ldots & \ldots & \ldots & \ldots \\
\psi_\mu = & a^{(r)}_{\mu 1} & \ldots & a^{(r)}_{\mu r} & 0 & \ldots & 0 & 0 \\
\psi_{\mu+1} = & a^{(r)}_{\mu+1,1} & \ldots & a^{(r)}_{\mu+1,r} & a^{(r)}_{\mu+1,r+1} & \ldots & a^{(r)}_{\mu+1,n} & a^{(r)}_{\mu+1} \\
\ldots & \ldots & \ldots & \ldots & \ldots & \ldots & \ldots & \ldots \\
\psi_m = & a^{(r)}_{m1} & \ldots & a^{(r)}_{mr} & a^{(r)}_{m,r+1} & \ldots & a^{(r)}_{mn} & a^{(r)}_{m} \\
\hline
f'_{\psi_1} = & b^{(r)}_{11} & \ldots & b^{(r)}_{1r} & b^{(r)}_{1,r+1} & \ldots & b^{(r)}_{1n} & b^{(r)}_{1} \\
\ldots & \ldots & \ldots & \ldots & \ldots & \ldots & \ldots & \ldots \\
f'_{\psi_r} = & b^{(r)}_{r1} & \ldots & b^{(r)}_{rr} & b^{(r)}_{r,r+1} & \ldots & b^{(r)}_{rn} & b^{(r)}_{r} \\
f'_{x_{r+1}} = & b^{(r)}_{r+1,1} & \ldots & b^{(r)}_{r+1,r} & b^{(r)}_{r+1,r+1} & \ldots & b^{(r)}_{r+1,n} & b^{(r)}_{r+1} \\
\ldots & \ldots & \ldots & \ldots & \ldots & \ldots & \ldots & \ldots \\
f'_{x_n} = & b^{(r)}_{n1} & \ldots & b^{(r)}_{nr} & b^{(r)}_{n,r+1} & \ldots & b^{(r)}_{nn} & b^{(r)}_{n} \\
\hline
\end{array} \quad (*)$$

2) We now determine a single point $\alpha^{(2)}$ at which the function $f(x)$ has a relative minimum under the condition $\psi_1(x) = \ldots = \psi_\mu(x) = 0$. To do so, as usual, we solve the system of linear equations

$$(f'_{x_j})_{\psi_1 = \ldots = \psi_\mu = 0} = b^{(r)}_{j,r+1}x_{r+1} + \ldots + b^{(r)}_{jn}x_n + b^{(r)}_j = 0$$
$$(j = r+1, \ldots, n).$$

For the direction of descent from the point $x^{(1)}$ we choose the vector $\zeta^{(2)} = \alpha^{(2)} - x^{(1)}$ and move in this direction, i.e., we increase t in the formula

$$x = x^{(1)} + t\zeta^{(2)},$$

until we reach a value t_2 equal to the smallest of the positive member of the set

$$\frac{-\psi_{\mu+1}(x^{(1)})}{\sum\limits_{i=1}^{n} a_{\mu+1,i}\zeta_i^{(2)}}, \ldots, \frac{-\psi_m(x^{(1)})}{\sum\limits_{i=1}^{n} a_{mi}\zeta_i^{(2)}}, 1.$$

If $t_2 = 1$, then $\alpha^{(2)} \in \Omega$ and $x^{(2)} = \alpha^{(2)}$. We call such a point $x^{(2)}$ *stationary*.

If $\mu = 1$, the stationary point $\alpha^{(2)}$ is a solution.

Indeed, here the gradient of the function $f(x)$ is clearly orthogonal to only one face, say $\psi_1(x) = 0$, which contains the point $\alpha^{(2)}$, and is directed outside Ω, since the hyperplane $\psi_1(x) = 0$ separates Ω from $\alpha^{(1)}$. As a result, there is no direction from $\alpha^{(2)}$ that does not leave Ω, and is such that the function $f(x)$ decreases.

If, however, $\mu > 1$, the stationary point $\alpha^{(2)}$ is not a solution.

Indeed, here the gradient of the function $f(x)$ is orthogonal to the linear manifold that is the intersection of several hyperplanes $\psi_i = 0$, i.e., is orthogonal to a plane of dimension less than $n-1$ that does not separate Ω from $\alpha^{(1)}$. As a result, there may be a direction from $\alpha^{(2)}$ that does not leave Ω but is such that $f(x)$ decreases along it.

If, however, $0 < t_2 < 1$, no more than $n-r$ steps are needed to find a stationary point, or to obtain a point $x^{(\mu_1)}$ that is a vertex, i.e., that belongs to $\mu_1 \geqslant n$ boundary planes, among which there are n linearly independent planes, i.e., there is no x_j at the top of the table. We also call the point $x^{(\mu_1)}$ *stationary*.

3) We now determine the direction of motion from a stationary point. Assume that the stationary point $\tilde{x}(0, \ldots, 0, x_{r+1}, \ldots, x_n)$ belongs to the planes

$$\psi_1(x) = 0, \ \ldots, \ \psi_r(x) = 0, \ \psi_{r+1}(x) = 0, \ \ldots, \ \psi_\mu(x) = 0$$

[see Table (*)]. Then, if $\mu = 1$ the point $\tilde{x}$ is, as we have already proved, a solution of the problem.

If, however, $\mu > 1$, we find a direction of descent from the point $\tilde{x}$, i.e., a direction $\zeta(\psi_1, \ldots, \psi_r, x_{r+1}, \ldots, x_n)$, that does not leave Ω and is such that the function $f(x)$ decreases, so that if ζ leaves the planes $\psi_1(x) = 0, \ldots, \psi_\mu(x) = 0$, it enters Ω.

To obtain the direction of steepest descent, we solve the following linear programming problem:

Minimize the function

$$u = \frac{\partial f(\tilde{x})}{\partial \zeta} = \sum_{i=1}^{r} \frac{\partial f(\tilde{x})}{\partial \psi_i} \zeta_i + \sum_{i=r+1}^{n} \frac{\partial f(\tilde{x})}{\partial x_i} \zeta_i$$

under the constraints

$$\frac{\partial \psi_j}{\partial \zeta} = \sum_{i=1}^{r} \frac{\partial \psi_j}{\partial \psi_i} \zeta_i + \sum_{i=r+1}^{n} \frac{\partial \psi_j}{\partial x_i} \zeta_i \leqslant 0 \qquad (j = 1, \ldots, \mu),$$

$$-C \leqslant \zeta_i \leqslant C \qquad (i = 1, \ldots, n).$$

But $\psi_1, \ldots, \psi_r, x_{r+1}, \ldots, x_n$ are independent variables, so that [see Table (*)]

$$\frac{\partial\psi_1}{\partial\zeta}=\zeta_1\leqslant 0,\ \ldots,\ \frac{\partial\psi_r}{\partial\zeta}=\zeta_r\leqslant 0,$$

$$\frac{\partial\psi_{r+1}}{\partial\zeta}=a^{(r)}_{r+1,1}\zeta_1+\ \ldots\ +a^{(r)}_{r+1,r}\zeta_r\leqslant 0,$$

$$\cdots\cdots\cdots\cdots\cdots\cdots$$

$$\frac{\partial\psi_\mu}{\partial\zeta}=a^{(r)}_{\mu 1}\zeta_1+\ \ldots\ +a^{(r)}_{\mu r}\zeta_r\leqslant 0.$$

Also, the point $\tilde{x}$ is stationary, i.e.,

$$\left.\frac{\partial f(\tilde{x})}{\partial x_i}\right|_{\psi_1=\ldots=\psi_\mu=0}=0,$$

so that

$$\frac{\partial f(\tilde{x})}{\partial\zeta}=\sum_{i=1}^{r}\frac{\partial f(\tilde{x})}{\partial\psi_i}\zeta_i.$$

We thus obtain the following linear programming problem: Minimize the function

$$u=\sum_{i=1}^{r}\frac{\partial f(\tilde{x})}{\partial\psi_i}\zeta_i$$

under the constraints

$$-C\leqslant\zeta_i\leqslant 0 \qquad (i=1,\ \ldots,\ r),$$

$$\frac{\partial\psi_j}{\partial\zeta}=a^{(r)}_{j1}\zeta_1+\ \ldots\ +a^{(r)}_{jr}\zeta_r\leqslant 0 \qquad (j=r+1,\ \ldots,\ \mu)$$

(since $\zeta_{r+1},\ \ldots,\ \zeta_n$ do not enter into the present linear programming problem, we may assume that they are equal to zero).

If min $u = 0$, then $x^* = \tilde{x}$ and the problem is solved. If, however, min $u < 0$, we move from the point $\tilde{x}$ in the direction $\tilde{\zeta}$, i.e., we increase t in the formula $x = \tilde{x} + t\tilde{\zeta}$ until we reach a $\tilde{t}$ equal to the smallest positive term in the sequence

$$\frac{-\psi_{\mu+1}(\tilde{x})}{\sum_{i=1}^{r}a^{(r)}_{\mu+1,i}\tilde{\zeta}_i},\ \ldots,\ \frac{-\psi_m(\tilde{x})}{\sum_{i=1}^{r}a^{(r)}_{mi}\tilde{\zeta}_i},\ t',$$

where t' minimizes the function $f(\tilde{x}+t\tilde{\zeta})$.

After we obtain the point $x = \tilde{x}+\tilde{t}\,\tilde{\zeta}$, we carry as many as possible of the annihilated ψ_j among the numbers $\psi_{r+1},\ \ldots,\ \psi_m$ to the top of the table, and then apply the procedure of Paragraph 2 to the table thus obtained. We now continue the process until we obtain a new stationary point, to which we apply the operation of Paragraph 3, etc.

Since the algorithm is monotonic and there is a finite number of stationary points, we obtain a solution x^* after a finite number of steps.

Example. Minimize the function

$$f(x) = 2x_1^2 + x_2^2 + 3x_3^2 - x_1x_2 - 2x_1x_3 - x_2x_3 + \\ + 10x_1 + 9x_2 - 26x_3$$

under the constraints

$$\begin{aligned} \psi_1(x) &= -x_1 - 1 \leqslant 0, \\ \psi_2(x) &= -x_2 \leqslant 0, \\ \psi_3(x) &= -x_3 \leqslant 0, \\ \psi_4(x) &= x_1 + x_2 + x_3 - 4 \leqslant 0, \\ \psi_5(x) &= -x_1 - 2x_2 - x_3 + 3 \leqslant 0. \end{aligned}$$

Preliminary step. We construct the table

	x_1	x_2	x_3	1
$\psi_1 =$	−1	0	0	−1
$\psi_2 =$	0	−1	0	0
$\psi_3 =$	0	0	−1	0
$\psi_4 =$	1	1	1	−4
$\psi_5 =$	−1	−2	[−1]	3
$f'_{x_1} =$	4	−1	−2	10
$f'_{x_2} =$	−1	2	−1	9
$f'_{x_3} =$	−2	−1	6	−26

(1°)

First step. 1) Determination of a minimum. By solving the system of linear equations

$$\begin{aligned} f'_{x_1} &= 4x_1 - x_2 - 2x_3 + 10 = 0, \\ f'_{x_2} &= -x_1 + 2x_2 - x_3 + 9 = 0, \\ f'_{x_3} &= -2x_1 - x_2 + 6x_3 - 26 = 0, \end{aligned}$$

we obtain a point $\alpha^{(1)} = (-2, -4, 3) \notin \Omega$, at which $\min f(x)$ is achieved.

We now find some point $x^{(0)} \in \Omega$, say $x^{(0)} = (1, 1, 1)$. Indeed,

$$\psi_j(x^{(0)}) < 0 \qquad (j = 1, \ldots, 5).$$

2) Determination of $\zeta^{(1)}$.

$$\zeta^{(1)} = \alpha^{(1)} - x^{(0)} = (-3, -5, 2).$$

3) Determination of t_1. We move along the ray $x = x^{(0)} + t\zeta^{(1)}$, i.e.,

$$x_1 = 1 - 3t; \quad x_2 = 1 - 5t; \quad x_3 = 1 + 2t.$$

For t_1 we find

$$t_1 = \frac{1}{11}.$$

4) Determination of a new point and new deviations.

$$x^{(1)} = x^{(0)} + t_1\zeta^{(1)} = \left(\frac{8}{11}, \frac{6}{11}, \frac{13}{11}\right);$$
$$\psi_5(x^{(1)}) = 0; \quad \psi_j(x^{(1)}) < 0 \qquad (j \neq 5).$$

Second step. 1) Determination of a conditional minimum. We execute a Jordan elimination over the resolvent element a_{53} = -1 in Table (1°), which yields the table

	x_1	x_2	ψ_5	1
$\psi_1 =$	−1	0	0	−1
$\psi_2 =$	0	[−1]	0	0
$\psi_3 =$	1	2	1	−3
$\psi_4 =$	0	−1	−1	−1
$f'_{x_1} =$	14	16	8	12
$f'_{x_2} =$	16	30	13	22
$f'_{\psi_5} =$	8	13	6	8

(2°)

$$x_3 = -x_1 - 2x_2 - \psi_5 + 3.$$

By solving the system of linear equations

$$(f'_{x_1})_{\psi_5=0} = 14x_1 + 16x_2 + 12 = 0,$$
$$(f'_{x_2})_{\psi_5=0} = 16x_1 + 30x_2 + 22 = 0,$$

we find a conditional extremum of the function $f(x)$ (with the condition ψ_5 = 0) in the new coordinates (x_1, x_2, ψ_5):

$$\alpha^{(2)} = \left(-\frac{2}{41}, -\frac{29}{41}, 0\right) \notin \Omega.$$

2) Determination of $\zeta^{(2)}$.

$$\zeta^{(2)} = \alpha^{(2)} - x^{(1)} = \left(-\frac{350}{451}, -\frac{565}{451}, 0\right).$$

3) Determination of t_2. We move along the ray $x = x^{(1)} + t\zeta^{(2)}$, i.e.,

$$x_1 = \frac{8}{11} - \frac{350}{451}t; \quad x_2 = \frac{6}{11} - \frac{565}{451}t; \quad \psi_5 = 0.$$

For the step t_2 we obtain

$$t_2 = \frac{246}{565}.$$

4) Determination of a new point and new deviations.

$$x^{(2)} = \left(-\frac{44}{113},\ 0,\ 0\right);$$
$$\psi_2(x^{(2)}) = 0; \quad \psi_j(x^{(2)}) < 0 \qquad (j = 1, 3, 4).$$

Third step. 1) Determination of a conditional minimum. We execute a modified Jordan elimination over the resolvent element $a_{22} = -1$ in Table (2°), which yields the table

	x_1	ψ_2	ψ_5	1
$\psi_1 =$	-1	0	0	-1
$\psi_3 =$	1	-2	1	-3
$\psi_4 =$	0	1	-1	-1
$f'_{x_1} =$	14	-16	8	12
$f'_{\psi_2} =$	-16	30	-13	-22
$f'_{\psi_5} =$	8	-13	6	8

,

$$x_2 = -\psi_2.$$

By solving the equation

$$(f'_{x_1})_{\psi_2 = \psi_5 = 0} = 14x_1 + 12 = 0,$$

we find a conditional extremum of the function $f(x)$ (with the condition $\psi_2 = \psi_5 = 0$) in the new coordinates (x_1, ψ_2, ψ_5)

$$\alpha^{(3)} = (x_1, \psi_2, \psi_5) = \left(-\frac{6}{7},\ 0,\ 0\right) \in \Omega,$$

so that $x^{(3)} = \alpha^{(3)}$ is a stationary point.

We shall omit operations 2) and 3).

4) Determination of a new deviations.

$$\psi_j(x^{(3)}) < 0 \qquad (j = 1, 3, 4).$$

Fourth step. We omit operation 1).

2) Determination of $\zeta^{(4)}$. To leave the stationary point, we solve the following linear programming problem:

Minimize the form

$$u = \frac{\partial f(x^{(3)})}{\partial \zeta} = -8\frac{2}{7}\zeta_2 + 1\frac{1}{7}\zeta_3$$

under the constraints

$$\zeta_1 = 0,$$
$$-1 \leqslant \zeta_2 \leqslant 0,$$
$$-1 \leqslant \zeta_3 \leqslant 0.$$

For $\zeta^{(4)}$ we find that

$$\zeta^{(4)} = (0, 0, -1).$$

3) Determination of t_4. We move along the ray $x = x^{(3)} + t\zeta^{(4)}$, i.e.,

$$x_1 = -\frac{6}{7}; \quad \psi_2 = 0; \quad \psi_5 = -t.$$

For t_4 we obtain

$$t_4 = t' = \frac{4}{21},$$

where t' minimizes the function $f(x^{(3)} + t\zeta^{(4)})$.

4) Determination of a new point and new deviations.

$$x^{(4)} = x^{(3)} + t_4\zeta^{(4)} = \left(-\frac{6}{7}, 0, -\frac{4}{21}\right) \in \Omega,$$

and

$$\psi_j(x^{(4)}) < 0 \qquad (j = 1, 3, 4, 5).$$

Fifth step. 1) Determination of a conditional minimum. By solving the system of linear equations

$$(f'_{x_1})_{\psi_2=0} = 14x_1 + 8\psi_5 + 12 = 0,$$
$$(f'_{\psi_5})_{\psi_2=0} = 8x_1 + 6\psi_5 + 8 \quad = 0,$$

we find a conditional extremum point $\alpha^{(4)}$ of the function $f(x)$ (with the condition $\psi_2 = 0$) in the new coordinate system (x_1, ψ_2, ψ_5),

$$\alpha^{(4)} = (-0.4;\ 0;\ -0.8) \in \Omega,$$

so that $\alpha^{(4)} = x^{(5)}$ is a stationary point.

Since $\nu = 1$, we have $x^{(5)} = (-0.4;\ 0;\ -0.8)$ or, in the old coordinates, (-0.4; 0, 4.2), which is the desired solution.

6. APPLICATION TO LINEAR PROGRAMMING

1. Preliminary Remarks

The convex programming algorithm can clearly be applied to solution of the general linear programming problem discussed in detail in Chapter 2:

Minimize the function

$$z = p_1x_1 + \dots + p_nx_n$$

under the constraints

$$\psi_j(x) \equiv a_{j1}x_1 + \ldots + a_{jn}x_n + a_j \leqslant 0 \qquad (j = 1, \ldots, m),$$

which define Ω.

In contrast to the simplex method, in which motion proceeds along 1-dimensional edges from vertex to vertex of the polyhedron Ω, the algorithm considered below uses motion in higher-dimensional manifolds, which usually accelerates the solution process.

2. Algorithm

Preliminary step. To find an initial feasible approximation $x^{(0)}$, we choose an arbitrary sufficiently small $\delta_1 > 0$ and apply the algorithm discussed below to the problem of minimizing the function

$$v = \xi$$

under the constraints

$$a_{j1}x_1 + \ldots + a_{jn}x_n + a_j \leqslant \xi \qquad (j = 1, \ldots, m)$$

until we obtain an approximation $\xi_k \leqslant 0$.

Iterated step. Assume that we have chosen a sufficiently small $\delta_1 > 0$ and a point $x^{(0)} \in \Omega$.

We determine the deviations $\psi_j(x^{(0)})$ $(j = 1, \ldots, m)$ and let

$$-\delta_1 < \psi_{j_\nu}(x^{(0)}) \leqslant 0 \qquad (\nu = 1, \ldots, \nu_1),$$

$$\psi_j(x^{(0)}) \leqslant -\delta_1 \qquad (j \neq j_1, \ldots, j_{\nu_1}).$$

To find the direction of steepest descent, we solve the following, generally simpler linear programming problem:

Minimize the function

$$u = p_1\zeta_1 + \ldots + p_n\zeta_n$$

under the constraints

$$a_{j_\nu 1}\zeta_1 + \ldots + a_{j_\nu n}\zeta_n \leqslant 0 \qquad (\nu = 1, \ldots, \nu_1),$$

$$|\zeta_i| \leqslant 1 \qquad (i = 1, \ldots, n).$$

There are generally fewer constraints in this problem than in the initial problem.

Assume that we have found the direction of steepest descent $\zeta^{(1)} \equiv (\zeta_1^{(1)}, \ldots, \zeta_n^{(1)})$ and $\min u = u_1 < -\delta_1$. We then move in this direction, i.e., we increase t in the formula $x = x^{(0)} + t\zeta^{(1)}$ until we reach a value t_1 equal to the smallest positive number in the set

$$\frac{-\psi_1(x^{(0)})}{\sum_{i=1}^{n} a_{1i}\zeta_i^{(1)}}, \ldots, \frac{-\psi_m(x^{(0)})}{\sum_{i=1}^{n} a_{mi}\zeta_i^{(1)}}.$$

The point $x^{(1)} = x^{(0)} + t_1\zeta^{(1)}$ is used as the new approximation.

We now continue the process until $u = u_k > -\delta_k$ for some $x^{(k-1)}$. We now change the value of δ_k as in Section 2 and continue the process by using the new value of the parameter.

3. Example

Minimize the form

$$z = 3x_1 - 2x_2 + x_3$$

under the constraints

$$\begin{aligned}
\psi_1(x) &\equiv -x_1 + x_2 - 3x_3 \leqslant 0,\\
\psi_2(x) &\equiv -3x_1 + 4x_2 - 3x_3 - 2 \leqslant 0,\\
\psi_3(x) &\equiv x_2 - x_3 - 1 \leqslant 0,\\
\psi_4(x) &\equiv -2x_1 + 3x_3 + 2 \leqslant 0,\\
\psi_5(x) &\equiv x_1 + x_2 + x_3 - 3 \leqslant 0,\\
\psi_6(x) &\equiv 2x_1 - 3x_2 - x_3 - 2 \leqslant 0.
\end{aligned}$$

For the initial approximation we take the point $x^{(0)} = (1, 0, 0)$ and set $\delta_1 = 0.5$. We have

$$\psi_4(x^{(0)}) = 0;\ \psi_6(x^{(0)}) = 0;\ \psi_j(x^{(0)}) < -\delta_1 \quad (j = 1, 2, 3, 5).$$

First step. 1) Determination of $\zeta^{(1)}$. To find $\zeta^{(1)}$, we must solve the following linear programming problem: Minimize the form

$$u = 3\zeta_1 - 2\zeta_2 + \zeta_3$$

under the constraints

$$\begin{aligned}
-2\zeta_1 + 3\zeta_3 &\leqslant 0,\\
2\zeta_1 - 3\zeta_2 - \zeta_3 &\leqslant 0,\\
|\zeta_i| \leqslant 1 \quad (i &= 1, 2, 3).
\end{aligned}$$

By solving this problem, we find that

$$\zeta^{(1)} = (-1, 1, -1).$$

2) Computation of δ_2. We have min u = $-6 < -\delta_1$, so that $\delta_2 = \delta_1 = 0.05$.

3) Determination of t_1. The motion must be along the ray

$$x_1 = 1 - t; \quad x_2 = t; \quad x_3 = -t; \quad t > 0.$$

We find

$$t_1 = \frac{1}{5}.$$

4) Determination of a new point and new deviations.

$$x^{(1)} = \left(\frac{4}{5}, \frac{1}{5}, -\frac{1}{5}\right),$$

$$-\delta_2 < \psi_1(x^{(1)}) = 0; \quad -\delta_2 < \psi_4(x^{(1)}) < 0;$$

$$\psi_j(x^{(1)}) < -\delta_2 \qquad (j = 2, 3, 5, 6).$$

Second step. 1) Determination of $\zeta^{(2)}$. We minimize the form

$$u = 3\zeta_1 - 2\zeta_2 + \zeta_3$$

under the constraints

$$\begin{aligned} -\zeta_1 + \zeta_2 - 3\zeta_3 &\leqslant 0, \\ -2\zeta_1 \qquad + 3\zeta_3 &\leqslant 0, \\ |\zeta_i| \leqslant 1 \qquad (i &= 1, 2, 3), \end{aligned}$$

which yields

$$\zeta^{(2)} = \left(\frac{1}{3}, 1, \frac{2}{9}\right).$$

2) Computation of δ_3. We have min $u = -\frac{7}{9} < -\delta_2$, so that $\delta_3 = \delta_2$.

3) Determination of t_2. The motion must be along the ray

$$x_1 = \frac{4}{5} + \frac{1}{3}t; \quad x_2 = \frac{1}{5} + t; \quad x_3 = -\frac{1}{5} + \frac{2}{9}t; \quad t > 0.$$

We find that

$$t_2 = \frac{27}{35}.$$

4) Determination of a new point and new deviations.

$$x^{(2)} = \left(\frac{37}{35}, \frac{34}{35}, -\frac{1}{35} \right),$$

$$-\delta_3 < \psi_1(x^{(2)}) = 0; \quad -\delta_3 < \psi_3(x^{(2)}) = 0;$$

$$-\delta_3 < \psi_4(x^{(2)}) < 0;$$

$$\psi_j(x^{(2)}) < -\delta_3 \qquad (j = 2, 5, 6).$$

5) It is easy to show that the point $x^* = (1, 1, 0)$ is a solution.

References

1. A. S. Barsov, What is Linear Programming? [in Russian], Fizmatgiz, 1959.
2. S. Gass, Linear Programming, McGraw-Hill, N. Y., 1964.
3. Ye. G. Gol'shteyn, "One class of nonlinear extremal problems," Dokl. Akad. Nauk SSSR, Vol. 133, No. 3, 1960, pp. 507-510.

4a. S. I. Zukhovitskiy, "A new numerical algorithm for Chebyshev approximation of an inconsistent system of linear equations," Dokl. Akad. Nauk SSSR, Vol. 139, No. 3, 1961, pp. 534-537 (see also Dokl. Akad. Nauk SSSR, Vol. 79, No. 4, 1951, pp. 561-564).

4b. S. I. Zukhovitskiy, "Approximating inconsistent systems of linear equations by minimizing the sum of the absolute values of all deviations," Dokl. Akad. Nauk SSSR, Vol. 143, No. 5, 1962, pp. 1030-1033 (see also Zhurnal Vych. Matem, i matem. fiziki, Vol. 3, No. 3, pp. 599-605).

4c. S. I. Zukhovitskiy, "Algorithm for finding a point exhibiting the least deviation (in the Chebyshev sense) from a given system of m points", Dokl. Akad. Nauk Ukr. SSR, No. 6, 1961, pp. 404-407. (see also Nauk. Zapiski Lutsk Pedag. Inst. Vol. 1, 1953, p. 3-23).

5a. S. I. Zukhovitskiy and L. Ya. Leyfman, "A computational scheme for a convex quadratic programming algorithm," [in Russian], Siber. Ot. Akad. Nauk SSSR, Novosibirsk, 1962.

5b. S. I. Zukhovitskiy, R. A. Polyak, and M. Ye. Primak, "An algorithm for solution of problems on convex Chebyshev approximation," Dokl. Akad. Nauk SSSR, Vol. 151, No. 1, 1963, pp. 27-30.

5c. S. I. Zukhovitskiy, R. A. Polyak, and M. Ye. Primak, "An algorithm for solution of convex programming problems," Dokl. Akad. Nauk SSSR, Vol. 153, No. 5, 1963, pp. 991-994.

6. L. V. Kantorovich, Mathematical Methods for Industrial Application [in Russian], Izd-vo LGU, 1939.
7. L. V. Kantorovich, "An effective method for solving certain classes of extremal problems," Dokl. Akad. Nauk SSSR, Vol. 28, No. 3, 1940, pp. 212-215.

8. L. V. Kantorovich and M. K. Gavurin, "Application of mathematical methods to analysis of routing problems," collection: Problems on Increasing the Effectiveness of Transport Operations [in Russian], Izd-vo Akad. Nauk SSSR, 1949, pp. 110-138.
9. L. V. Kantorovich, Economical Planning of Best Distribution of Resources [in Russian], Izd-vo Akad. Nauk SSSR, 1959.
10. J. McKinsey, Introduction to the Theory of Games, McGraw-Hill, N. Y., 1952.
11. V. A. Markov, "On functions with least deviation from zero in a given interval," Collected Works [in Russian], 1892.
12. R. K. Prim, "Shortest links and generalizations," Kiberneticheskii Sbornik, Vol. 2, 1961.
13. N. Reinfeld and W. Vogel, Mathematical Programming, Prentice-Hall, 1958.
14. D. B. Yudin and Ye. G. Gol'shteyn, Linear Programming Problems and Methods [in Russian], Sovetskoye Radio, 1961.
15. H. W. Kuhn and A. W. Tucker (Eds.), Linear Inequalities and Related Systems, Princeton Univ. Press, 1956.
16. A. Charnes, "Optimality and degeneration in linear programming," Econometrica, Vol. 20, 1952, pp. 160-170.
17. G. B. Dantzig, "Programming of interdependent activities, Mathematical model." Econometrica, Vol. 17, 1949, pp. 200-211.
18. G. B. Dantizig, "Maximization of a linear function of variables subject to linear inequalities," Activity Analysis of Production and Allociation, Ed. by T. C. Koopmans, Cowles Commission Monograph 13, Wiley, New York, 1951, pp. 339-347.
19. G. B. Dantzig, "Application of the simplex method to a transportation problem," Activity Analysis of Production and Allocation, Ed. by T. C. Koopmans, Cowles Commission Monograph 13, Wiley, New York, 1951, pp. 359-373.
20. G. B. Dantzig, "A proof of the equivalence fo the programming problem and the Game problem," Activity Analysis of Production and Allocation, Ed. by T. C. Koopmans, Cowles Commission Monograph 13, Wiley, New York, 1951, pp. 330-335.
21. G. B. Dantzig, A. Orden, "Duality theorems," RAND Report RM-1265, The RAND Corporation, Santa Monica, Calif., October 1953.
22. G. B. Dantzig, A. Orden, P. Wolfe, "Generalized simplex method for minimizing a linear form under linear inequality restraints," Pacific J. Math. Vol. 5, No. 2, 1955, pp. 183-195.
23. G. B. Dantzig, W. Orchard-Hays, "The product form for the inverse in the simplex method," Math., Tables Aids Comp. Vol. 8, 1954, pp. 64-67.
24. G. B. Dantzig, "Note on solving linear programs in integers," Naval Res. Logist. Quart., 1959.
25. E. Egervary, "On combinatorial properties of matrices," Mat. Fiz. Lapok, Vol. 38, No. 28, 1931.
26. L. R. Ford, "Network flow theory," RAND Corp. paper, 1956.
26a. L. R. Ford, D. R. Fulkerson, "Maximal flow through a network," Canad. J. Math. Vol. 8, 1956, pp. 399-404.

27. R. E. Gomory, "Outline of an algorithm for integer solutions to linear problems," Bull. Amer. Math. Soc. Vol. 64, No. 5, 1958, pp. 275-278.
28. R. E. Gomory, "An algorithm for integer solutions to linear programs" (mimeographed), Princeton—IBM Math. Res. Project, Technical Report 1, 1958.
29a. R. E. Gomory, W. J. Baumol, "Integer programming and pricing," Econometrica, Vol. 28, No. 23, 1960, pp. 521-550.
29b. R. E. Gomory, A. J. Hoffman, "On the convergence of an integer-programming process," Naval Res. Logist. Quart., Vol. 10, No. 2, 1963, pp. 121-123.
30. H. W. Kuhn, "The Hungarian method for solving the assignment problem," Naval Res. Logist. Quart. Vol. 2, 1955, pp. 83-97.
31. C. E. Lemke, "The dual method of solving the linear programming problem," Naval Res. Logist. Quart., Vol. 1, 1954, pp. 36-47.
32. J. Munkres, "Algorithms for the assignment and transportation problems," J. Soc. Industr. Appl. Math. Vol. 5, 1957, pp. 32-38.
33. J. von Neumann, "A certain zero-sum two person game equivalent to the optimal assignment problem," Annals of Math. Studies, Vol. 28, 1953, pp. 5-12.
34. J. B. Rosen, "The gradient projection method for nonlinear programming, Part I, Linear constants," J. Soc. Indust. Appl. Math., Vol. 8, No. 1, 1960. "Part II, Nonlinear constants," J. Soc. Indust. Appl. Math., Vol. 9, No. 4, 1961.
35. E. Stiefel, "Note on Jordan elimination, linear programming and Chebyshev approximation," Numerische Mathematik, Vol. 2, 1960, pp. 1-17.
36. G. Zoutendijk, Methods of Feasible Directions, 1960.

Index